# THE COMPLETE DOCTOR STORIES:

## THE RIDICULOUS MOUNTAINS

## NOTHING SO SIMPLE AS CLIMBING

THE COMPLETE
DOCTOR STORIES
*combining*

# THE RIDICULOUS MOUNTAINS

*and*

# NOTHING SO SIMPLE AS CLIMBING

*The hilarious adventures of the Doctor and his hapless
companions climbing and walking in the Scottish Highlands*

G. J. F. DUTTON

with illustrations by Albert Rusling

BÂTON WICKS · LONDON

Published in 1997 by Bâton Wicks Publications, London.

All trade enquiries to:
Cordee, 3a De Montfort Street, Leicester LE1 7HD

Copyright © 1997 by G.J.F.Dutton

*British Cataloguing-in-Publication Data*
ISBN 1-898573-21-2
A catalogue record for this book is available from the British Library.

Printed and bound in Great Britain by:
T.J.International Ltd., Padstow

The original books were published individually as follows:
*The Ridiculous Mountains*
Diadem, 1984 (0-906371-61-9); 1990 (0-906371-38-4).
*Nothing So Simple As Climbing*
Diadem, 1993 (cased – 0-906371-12-0; tradepaperback – 0-906371-17-1)

# PREFACE

This is a Collected Edition of the two books of Doctor stories. The Publisher has decided that, to meet the continuing – and, it seems, increasing – demand, both should be bound together as one. And so he has asked for a Collected doubly-binding Preface – to introduce the stories to completely new readers, and stimulate further those who have read only one of the previous books. The gluttons for punishment who have read both will presumably have bought this volume after selling their first (or second) editions on the current Bull market and require no additional prospectus – or Bull – from me.

I myself am just a kind of Editor, having merely selected the tales here with the help of their exhausted Narrator. They recount his adventures among the hills with his equally hapless companion the Apprentice, in the company of the invariably optimistic and unpredictable Doctor. From the depths of his sleeping-bag, he implores me to introduce them. Very well; but these are my remarks, not his.

This Trio, with the bizarre train of characters accompanying and afflicting them, have become fairly well known in climbing and other outdoor journals, magazines and anthologies. The scene of their disasters and delights is usually Scotland, where they first gnawed the global crust. This is no disadvantage, mountain problems and protagonists being everywhere similar. An advantage, rather, for the Scottish hills are close enough together to multiply the echoes of even a minor episode, and yet large enough to display the full horrendous spectrum of today's mountain activity and anti-activity.

So in these pages we wander green-backed over whales in leisurely pursuit of pimples; feast and snore in tent, howff or igloo; and clutch the fiercest *brutissimo grado* of rock, gravel or ice. We encounter such auxiliary occupations as caving, birdwatching, angling, skiing, sailing, canoeing, deerstalking, paragliding, moss-gathering and mountain rescue. Dogs, flies, archaeologists, midges, gamekeepers, poltergeists and police assail us. Landowners, coalminers, romantic executives and the Armed forces of the United States of America welcome us to their tables. We could, with due regard for climate and custom, be in the Alps, Wales, the Lakes, Rockies, Nepal, New Zealand, the Caucasus: anywhere among mountains. The oromaniacal quest, as Norman Collie termed it a century ago, takes the same sanely irrational course, whatever militant industrialists or industrious militarists surround it. And it engenders the same mutually exclusive clubs in all places. We meet many below. To set off our pleasant illusion of Progress in Mountaineering, all are necessary; their careful friction warms the heart.

Arrangement of these tales is not strictly chronological. As evident, adventures often occurred in different order to their presentation. Some authorities imply they never occurred at all. Against that, I myself climbed sufficiently near to several of them to confirm the Narrator's testimony. And we have all met with experiences similar enough to support the authenticity of the rest. There should be no doubt. However, now and again, as a matter of simple discourtesy, names have been exchanged. And one fringe participant has, on personal demand, been largely expunged: the Doctor's wife. She appears only as a (presumably willing) supplier of curtain material in one tale, and a kind of avenging Goddess Mother of the Snows in another. But we did employ two of her unerringly pungent remarks as titles of the books collected here. The dishevelled Sunday evening return of her errant spouse was invariably greeted by: 'Well, and what have you been doing today, on your ridiculous mountains?'.

Subsequently, she objected to the inference of considering mountains ridiculous. 'I have been misunderstood. You can't blame the hills. It's what you people do on them that is absurd. Such elaborate equipment, such endless argument. Surely quite unnecessary. After all, you only have to go up – to 3000 feet, or whatever it is – and come down. Why all the fuss? I should have thought there was nothing so simple as climbing....'

So did we all.

G.J.F.D.
1997

# THE RIDICULOUS MOUNTAINS

### G. J. F. DUTTON

Illustrations by Albert Rusling

First published in 1984 by Diadem Books Limited, London.
Reprinted (with illustrations added) in 1990.

'You may have an Occasion to meet me' (p.95).

# CONTENTS

\* First published in *The Scottish Mountaineering Club Journal* (1968 – 1973)

• First published in *The Climber and Rambler* (May, 1982)

§ First Published in *Cold Climbs* (Diadem, 1983)

All other stories were previously unpublished.

# A GOOD CLEAN BREAK

We coiled the rope. It had been a good route. Warm eastern granite, and now sunburnt heather. The Doctor arranged himself elaborately at full length, head pillowed on arms.

'It *is* a shout,' confirmed the Apprentice, looking up from his last coils.

We listened. A feeble cry, which might once have been 'Help', wandered up from the other, easier, side of the crag. I peered, but saw nothing.

The Doctor reassembled his full height, climbed a convenient protuberance, and inspected the heathery hollow below.

'There! It *is* somebody. Chap lying on a ledge. Some ass fallen off.'

This was one of the Apprentice's best days. He was in excellent form, and swiftly led me down a steep series of slabs to the victim. The Doctor, irritatingly, arrived first, having walked down a heathery rake neither of us had seen.

'Well, and who are you?' asked the Doctor pleasantly, as he took off his jacket, knelt, and rolled up his sleeves.

'I'm the Casualty,' announced the figure, not altogether surprisingly.

'So it seems. Now,' said the Doctor, frisking him professionally, 'have you any pain? Back or limbs?'

'I'm bloody stiff,' remarked the Casualty. 'Been here hours.'

'Of course you'll be stiff. But have you any pain?'

'Only when you poke me like that. Who are *you* anyway?'

We all raised eyebrows. The Doctor adopted his blandest bedside approach, suitable for dealing with irate landowners, lunatics, or the concussed.

'Never mind, laddie. We're here to help. We'll soon get you down.'

'Get *me* down?' remarked the Casualty sarcastically. 'I think you'd better get *them* down.' And he stood up, yawned, hobbled stiffly to one side and, most disconcertingly, proceeded to empty his bladder over the edge of the cliff.

The Doctor was as near nonplussed as I have seen him. His fingers stroked the air; his cuffs – now loose again – fluttered uncertainly. '*Them*? Who are *they*?'

'The Rescue Team,' remarked the Casualty, turning and adjusting his dress. 'They're all stuck. Up there,' he added, jerking his head towards the cliff behind us.

We turned. Some eighty feet up, a collection of cagouled figures fluoresced ashamedly from various unlikely positions. One was clearly upside down, resting on his elbows. All (fortunately) were tied together by a welter of ropes. In reply to our gaze, they mewed in chorus a feeble and obviously highly embarrassed 'Aaa... help.'

The Casualty sat on an outcrop and lit a fag. 'I suppose we'll have to go and sort 'em out,' he said. When pressed to describe the nature of his accident, he explained that it was no accident, but just his turn to be Casualty. It was, he further explained, and somewhat belatedly, an Exercise. Training. This was the Pitfoulie Mountain Rescue Team. They came out every weekend, if the weather was fine. A sort of a club. Good fun, and useful.

The Doctor, cheated of his prey, was reluctant to believe all this. 'Concussion,' he confided to us, 'has curious effects. Now I've – '

'Concussion?' broke in the Casualty. 'He got that all right. Same as last time. Always gets it. That's why they're in that mess.' He jerked his fag towards the now silent tableau.

'So there is a real casualty, after all! 'exclaimed the Doctor, brightening and rising to his feet. He brushed down his breeches and slipped on his jacket. 'The sooner we fix him up the better.'

'Och, he's all right now, Eck is,' said the casualty, inhaling and blowing the smoke out again in neat little rings. 'We just drove him back to town. He'll get home in a day or two, like last time. They usually do, with mild concussion,' he informed the Doctor.

Eck, it turned out, was Leader of the Pitfoulie team. He had started it, having apparently discovered a passion for Rescue when a mere boy. His absence accounted for the failure of this particular exercise. The rest of the team – apart from the Casualty, who was experienced enough but, as he explained, had to take his turn as Casualty like anyone else – the rest were not too familiar with complex rope manoeuvres and had gradually fankled themselves into complete stasis.

'But how did Eck get concussion?' demanded the Doctor, still obsessed.

'He fell out of our Land Rover. He always does. He's that eager.

He leans out, directing us, as soon as we drive on to the hill. It holds things up. We didn't get started again till 11 o'clock – though we were quicker this time than last.'

So the question resolved itself simply into the four of us releasing the rescue team. We turned ourselves towards the cliff, the Casualty nipping out his fag-end with some regret. Just as we were about to plunge down the heather to the foot of the crag, a line of figures appeared above our bowl, twittering.

'Careful, now! It's an EDGE!' boomed out a rich contralto voice, with more than a brush of five o'clock shadow on it. 'Stop where you are!'

One figure, that of a long thin man in a flapping raincoat, did not stop. He slipped, sat down on his raincoat and began, inexorably, to slither towards the edge of the crag. Our eyes popped. The Doctor smelt game.

'I said STOP, Mr. Pilchard! I SAID STOP!'

Mr. Pilchard slowed down and, obediently, stopped. A large female figure made towards him and plucked him, raincoat fluttering, back to safety. The excited buzz of conversation resumed.

'It's Mrs Cairnwhapple, said the Doctor. 'Ursula Major. And that's her ornithological party. A breeding pair was reported here last week.'

Mrs Cairnwhapple, no mean woman, took in the scene at a glance. 'Just as well we STOPPED, friends. There are four foolish people down there who did not stop and who are now In Trouble. They are waiting to be rescued by the experienced mountaineers you see below you.' (Agonised twitchings from the web.) 'A real Rescue Team. We must sit and watch, and pick up some Useful Hints.' She plumped herself down in the heather, her chicks snuggling likewise. She kept a sharp eye on Mr Pilchard, who still exhibited suicidal tendencies.

We may imagine the next hour or so. Sufficient to say that by the time we disentangled the rescue team and took them down to the foot of the crag, a late June sun had mellowed into early evening. And Mrs Cairnwhapple, with a bittern-like boom of delight, had recognised the Doctor and had trodden heavily and decisively down heather and ledge to join us. Her wheepling brood accompanied her, Pilchard suffering minor mishaps on the way. The Apprentice, who had performed daring deeds over the past two hours, was particularly helpful to one admiring and attractive young lady ornithologist. 'That's Ann Scarsoch,' said the Doctor, rejoining me after wearily separating once again two entwined and fluorescent rope-coilers. 'Old Poltivet's daughter. Only yellow plastic soles on her shoes. Flighty piece.'

Mrs Cairnwhapple had caused baskets to be produced and opened; we munched in satisfaction. The Pitfoulie team, though still somewhat subdued, finished first and, with a commendable sense of duty, stretched out their casualty once more and began trussing him up for the carry-down. The Doctor was suggesting we should examine their knots. 'After all, they're doing it on purpose this time.' Behind us in the heather, the Apprentice was teaching La Scarsoch the technique of pressure grips.

Suddenly we froze. Beneath us, up the long slopes of the evening glen, the sunlight heaved with an army of people. Crowd after crowd. The Doctor snatched up his binoculars.

He paled. 'Rescue Teams. Walkie-talkies. Army. Air Force. Police. Navy. Shepherds. Civilians. Dogs. Schoolboys.' We listened. Yes... and helicopters.

We hurried over to the Casualty. (The Apprentice was too much engaged to notice.) We asked him what he knew of this invasion. Was it another, but mammoth, Exercise?

The Casualty, with disarming ease, freed his left elbow from a splint, and pulled the bandages from his mouth. He sat up and grinned.

'No, it'll be a real one this time. We'll have to join it. They *still* mustn't have come back to that car. Two whole days away, no notification, no sketch of route taken. Must be lost. That lot'll find 'em. Not that they'll want to be found, when they tot up the cost of this little trip.' He complacently stripped off his dressings, rose, and assumed command.

The Doctor and I felt the earth wither. Why, oh why *had* he parked in that car park? Why *had* he bought a parking ticket? Against all our rules. Yet there was still hope.... What sort of car was it, what number? Did anyone know?

The Casualty frowned. The occasion was rather too important for trivial curiosity. 'A big old German crate. Yes, a Merc.' Number? He had, of course, noted that. He pulled out a grubby bit of paper and read off the Doctor's registration number....

That was that. We would share his costs certainly, despite his protestations, but nothing could lessen the blow from the Accident Report in the next *Journal*. Hummel Doddie wrote these Accident Reports, it was rumoured (by all except Hummel Doddie); Hummel Doddie, whose active pen flayed the tomfools that caused unnecessary searches, that caused vast and growing inconvenience to vast and growing mountainfuls of rescuers (the helicopters nosed above us, attracted by the carrion-beetle orange of the Pitfoulie cagoules).

Hummel Doddie would certainly not spare – and rightly not spare – the Doctor, whose views (like those of the Apprentice) on these matters were not the views of the establishment....

'Blast it,' said the Doctor. He bravely stood and watched the attackers close in. His pipe remained unlit.

At that moment there was a crack, followed by a scream.

We all sprang round. Miss Scarsoch sat up in the heather, white and holding her wrist. The Apprentice stood beside her, rumpled and red. He had been trying to teach the Layback, but clumsy-like....

With a glad cry, the Doctor leapt forward and knelt down. He felt the wrist nimbly. He looked up. His eyes brimmed with happiness.

'A Colles, by the Lord. We're saved. A good clean break!'

He issued orders in all directions. The Pitfoulie team, led by their casualty, marched towards him. Behind them rose the dust of advancing myriads, the barking of dogs. The air grew thick with engines and whirring metal, with cries and commands. Miss Scarsoch would doubtless have fainted, had not Mrs Cairnwhapple bellowed encouragement in her ear.

'Stick it, Ann!  A little thing like that!'

As the impis approached, their aerials glittering in the setting sun, the Apprentice gloomily held Miss Scarsoch's other hand and thought, like me, of our small brown tents alone in the Upper Corrie. The Doctor thought of them, too, but also of a large empty Mercedes surrounded by cameramen and police officers; and blessed the animal spirits of the young human male.

I could imagine his conversation when he at last got back to his car. The saluting police officers. Himself breezily nonchalant. 'Aye, a nasty business officer, but could have been worse, could have been worse.' 'Verra fortunate you were up there, Doctor.' 'Aye, we're often called upon to render assistance wherever we may be. Inconvenient, but must be done. The Oath, you know, officer, the Oath.' 'Aye, sir, the Oath.' 'Inconvenient to you, too, officer – I expect, ah, I expect you thought I'd got lost or something, with my car here so long?' 'Och, no, sir, no, (deprecatingly).' 'One never knows when one may be delayed on this sort of business. One always has to be ready.' 'Oo aye, sir, ye cannae tell, ye cannae tell.' 'Why, I've still some Glen Houlet... I'll not risk any more, driving. But yourself – must be fairly tired and cold, officer... eh?' 'Och....' Mutual exchange of understanding. We would be saved.

That night, as we packed up our tents, the Doctor showed us the piece of paper he had been scribbling on by torchlight. 'I'm sending it to Hummel Doddie,' he said 'Old Doddie likes his reports in early, and from those first on the scene. Later on, you know, there could be all sorts of confusion.' His eyes gleamed beneath the midnight sun.

The paper read:

perienced, practising layback with more experienced companion at foot of corrie below Grouse Shoot, Lochnagar, fell her length. Fractured wrist, shock, some exposure. Found and brought down by Pitfoulie M.R. team (acting leader Alec Sprachle). Injuries dressed on spot by doctor climbing nearby. Invaluable assistance given by Army, R.A.F. and R.N. teams, shepherds, police and civilians. Dogs used. Large bodies out, including Mrs Ursula Cairnwhapple, M.B.O.U. Two helicopters broke down but crews rescued by Army, R.A.F. and R.N. teams, shepherds, police and civilians; dogs used. One policeman bitten by dog; injuries dressed on spot by doctor climbing nearby. One civilian, T. Pilchard (41), English, lost on way down; found in hotel bar later.

A considerably shortened version appeared in the subsequent *Journal*.

# THE CRAGGIE

Just on the corner, the wheel came off. Fortunately, it was a right-hand corner and an off-side wheel. I was sitting in the front and saw it appear in the headlamp beams, skipping joyfully in its new freedom. Speechless, I grabbed the Doctor's shoulder, and pointed.

'Ah, a wheel,' he said.

I curled myself up in the old nylon sling which served as safety belt, and watched fascinatedly through the fingers shielding my face.

Imperturbably, we slowed down, bumped along the grass verge and clomped to a halt. The wheel waved us goodbye and leapt into a sitka plantation. The Doctor opened his door and got out.

'Extraordinary. Rear wheel. Never happened before. Handled very well, considering it's i.r.s.' He rummaged in a door pocket, then he went off by torchlight to retrieve the errant accessory.

In grateful obscenity from the back seat the Apprentice voiced his admiration. We both agreed the Doctor was no more nerve-wracking to his passengers on three wheels than on four.

Before he returned, bowling his wheel, we had confirmed that the threads had stripped. We were stuck on a wet Saturday night in late October, halfway to our goal.

Our goal was a kindred club hut below a well-known and easy ridge. We were to scramble up the ridge and down again; a mere excuse for a spirituous weekend to celebrate the Doctor's achievement and our own survival – for the previous weekend we had taken him up his first VS, the notorious *Constipation*. An experience cathartic for us – even for the iron-nerved Apprentice, who as usual led – but apparently much enjoyed by our medical companion. I need not describe it here.

We were stuck. We had no tent, and even the Doctor's old Mercedes could not sleep three when one of them was his own six feet two. We inspected the map.

'Here's the road, the plantation. Ah!' He gave a glad cry, thumped his thigh with the torch. The light went out. 'We're just by Kindraiglet! What luck!'

The luck turned out to be that Kindraiglet was a cottage on his brother-in-law's estate. It was occupied by his brother-in-law's shepherd. 'An excellent man, MacPhedran. He'll be delighted to put us up. Remarkable luck. And – yes – I'll give you a treat tomorrow.' He chuckled ominously as he wrestled out his rucksack.

Two hours later we were admitted by a jovial MacPhedran. 'Car broke down, just on the road below,' explained the Doctor, dismissing our purgatorial sojourn in drenching 20-foot sitka spruce – the prickliest stage of growth – looking for the Kindraiglet track. ('Can't be far off; know it well; pity these trees are so high; otherwise my torch would easily pick it out.')

We dried, feasted, drank and sang. MacPhedran fiddled with gusto. When I fell asleep the Doctor and he were trying to explain to each other what went wrong with Scott Skinner.

The morning was fine, though cold and dripping. After cooking a late breakfast (MacPhedran was long before on the hill) the Doctor referred again to his Treat.

'It was damn good of you to take me up *Constipation* last weekend. I'd never have cared to go alone. Wouldn't have missed it for the world. Remarkable how straightforward those routes are when you rub noses on 'em. Well, here's one for you two. Used to stay here years ago. Always went on The Craggie, as we called it. A jolly nice little climb, quite different from *Constipation*. You'll like the change.'

So it was to be The Craggie. We had brought the minimum of equipment – only a 60-foot line and the odd assortment of ironware inseparable from the Apprentice (he clinked perceptibly even in Daddy McKay's). But we were assured The Craggie would require none of it. 'Used to go on The Craggie by myself – just boots. Balance is all you need – and an eye for a good line.'

He led out of the door. The Apprentice and I, heavy-headed, tried to imagine the amorous rugosities of warm gabbro. We splashed up through the birches.

Disconcertingly soon, he stopped. 'There she is!' he announced. We peered past him at a clearing in the scrub. Out there, moss and slime, so long beneath our feet, reared themselves up to a sheer three hundred evil feet. The upper rim was fanged in black; and black rock gleamed hungrily at us through a thousand green and dripping moustachios.

'Wonderful view from the top,' he said. Then: 'Good Lord, there *she* is!'

'Who now?' asked the Apprentice, sourly. His pallor, I noted, was not all attributable to the night before.

'Why, Aggie. Aggie McHattie. Up there, on the left. The old girl in tweeds. See her? Just by that big wet slab. I *thought* I heard a car early on.'

I found the Apprentice's expression interesting. Then I turned again to the extraordinary sight. The Doctor lowered his Leitz Trinovids and lent them to me. I saw, bang in the middle of the face a square figure in tweed jacket and skirt, thick socks, nailed shoes, frizzy grey hair and gold spectacles. I saw it standing on a line of slime prising out something from the oozing slab. I saw it lift up the something, examine it, and throw it away. I swore I could hear the 'Pshaw!'

'Hallo,' roared the Doctor. 'Allo, allo, allo,' roared back The Craggie, moistly and throatily. The figure looked round, surveyed us. A clear precise voice.

'Good morning, Doctor. I shan't be long. There's not very much here.' Then it returned to its prising, further along the line of slime.

'Miss Agnes McHattie,' explained the Doctor. 'Remarkable woman. Famous lichenologist and moss-classifier; not really Ferns, but does take a look or two at the *Ophioglossaceæ*. Used to be my leader on lots of expeditions.'

The Apprentice declined the binoculars. Also, he seemed to be having difficulty in swallowing.

We squelched up to the foot of The Craggie. We stopped below a vertical pillar of green treacle. It wet my elbow.

'*Central Buttress Direct*' said the Doctor. 'A good line on to the Main Face. I'll lead and show you the way at first; although it's obvious enough. Glad I brought trikes; there's a slippery bit near the top.'

He crouched, adopted a curious kind of dog-paddle, and levitated uncannily. He paused and settled on a heap of watercress or similar vegetation twenty feet up. 'Great to be back again. Lost youth and all that. Come on up, there's acres on this stance.' As he spoke, a large plateful of cress smacked down wetly at my feet. Politely, the Apprentice waved me on. Kindly, he gave me the rope.

'Yes, we may need the rope later on,' the Doctor advised. 'It gets harder in places if you're in vibrams. They're jolly treacherous anywhere off those Trade Routes of yours.'

I agreed. It was impossible even to leave the ground with them. I only succeeded by locking each knee alternately in the soaking groove and spooning heaps of green porridge with both hands to keep me upright. I was not ashamed to take the Doctor's bony grip. I was dragged up, and thankfully clutched a long green stem.

'Ho! Watch that! It's *Lycopodium inundatum*, a mere clubmoss. No root. Dangerous. *Cryptogamma crispa's* a good handhold. Here's one. Ah, there's *Luzula* – even better. You've got to know your mountains, in a place like this!'

I was in terror lest I should have to offer the Apprentice the rope. But up he came, seaweed in his hair.

The watercress was definitely crowded, and raring to go. So the Doctor continued. I instructed my companion in the deficiencies of *Lycopodium* and the relative security of *Cryptogamma*. He muttered darkly, still clutching the piton with which he had clawed his way up.

The cress hiccupped vertiginously. I grabbed several stems, pressed kneecaps into a Gorgon's head of bryophytes. The Apprentice said he was getting the hell out of here and boldly struck off leftward into a succession of roofs, mere vertical or overhanging rock relatively free of photosynthetic organisms and their less ambitious brethren. He panted and swore. Roots and fragments fell. I patted and reassured my cress.

A clear voice rang out from below and further left.

'What's that boy *doing* up there? He'll fall off. Quite pointless. There's nothing but *Hylocomium squarrosum* in that groove. I looked very carefully this morning.'

The Doctor was above me. I glimpsed his toothed toes projecting from an upper moustache. They dripped past my face.

'It's all right, Aggie,' he said. 'We're just up enjoying ourselves. But can we help *you* at all?'

Silence. Then: 'Ah, Doctor, if you would be good enough to send your Boy down here' (mercifully inarticulate splutters from the left) 'I could use him very well just now.'

My companions are both gentlemen. The Doctor continued gazing at the view. The Apprentice clambered and slithered down to Miss McHattie's line of slime.

She nodded, and beckoned him. 'Carefully, now. Just stand here.

Oh, you've got boots. *Rubber* boots. How foolish. Should be nailed. And should be *shoes* – for proper flexion on small ledges. But I expect you've Weak Ankles. That's why most people have to wear boots. You should walk more. Now stand carefully there, and hold on to this loose piece of rock here and this clump of *Cystopteris*. CYSTOPTERIS! Not *Cephalozia*! That's right. Bend a little, for I'm going to have to step on to your back, I'm afraid. We'll never reach that *Stereocaulon* otherwise. Very glad you've come. I have a meeting tonight in Edinburgh, and I really must go down after this.'

The Apprentice described graphically afterwards the weight of the old battleship, and displayed the variegated indentations of triple hobs and muggers trodden across his vertebrae.

She poked away at a shiny clump with her trowel, fretting with annoyance. The Apprentice gingerly let go *Cystopteris*, tapped her shoe and offered up his piton. She tried it. Her comments were punctuated by chipping.

'H'm, useful tool. Better than anything I've brought, for this job, I must say. Where did you get it? *Who*? A most curious name. Never heard of him. A great number of' (continuous chipping) 'odd persons have taken advantage of the recent interest in lichenology. Especially since Toshpatrick-Gilchrist cleaned up all the *Lecidea alpestris* variants on Ben A'an. Winter forms, too. *That* made headlines. Curious name Fifo. An immigrant, no doubt. An opportunist. He won't last, poor fellow. I get all my ironware from Pflanzhanger of Munich. Still, it's very useful' (renewed chipping) 'I particularly like the hole in the handle; one could string them on to one's belt. Very handy, indeed. I'll write old Pflanzhanger himself about it. Quite time these continentals caught up on Edinburgh firms.'

Miss McHattie scraped down her spoil, lifted her spectacles, examined it, and nodded approvingly. She handed the Apprentice a mucilaginous clot. 'Hold this, young fellow,' she said '*Stereocaulon* AND *Cerania vermicularis*, an aberrant type.' She hauled at a cord, and a haversack rose from the depths behind her. The Apprentice backed in astonishment. She eyed him severely. 'Be careful, or you'll slip. That would never do. It's the first record west of Clova at this height.' She stuffed the desirable morsels into a small tube, clapped it into her haversack, and began to shuffle rapidly towards a grassy rake. Then she stopped, smiled meaningly, pulled a small flask from a voluminous pocket, poured out a generous capful of spirit and bade the Apprentice quaff. He quaffed, appreciatively. He rubbed his eyes. She screwed the flask back into her tweeds.

'Well, thank you. I expect the Doctor is teaching you to climb. A dangerous pastime, I always think. But the Doctor is an incurable Romantic. He indulges a veritable passion for the more vascular plants. I confess I outgrew the Angiosperms when I was a mere girl; we were positively stuffed with them at school. The Doctor, I fear, is more Byzantine. However, mind you listen to what he tells you, and don't fall off. Goodbye.' And rapidly she handed herself downwards out of sight. Before vanishing, she paused and looked up. 'Goodbye Doctor,' she roared; and the cress trembled.

'Remarkable woman,' mused the Doctor, turning again to the wall. 'Had an entire liverwort subspecies named after her – *Dicronodontium uncinatum McHattiæ*; should have been a genus – *Agnesia*'. He appeared greatly amused by this, and chucklings punctuated the falling moss.

We assembled beneath the final pitch, a quite vertical water-meadow. Our stance was the usual loose-stoppered and quavering cold-water bottle. 'This is tricky. We *could* go down, if you like.' Below us the cliff dropped its 250 feet to the bottom boulders – which, characteristically, were the only bare rocks at The Craggie. They leered knowingly. Chorally, we shuddered and said no. 'The rock's quite smooth underneath, but the vegetation's sound as a bell, provided you use the insides of your arms and legs. Don't of course use your feet, or try to kick. A pity you don't wear tweed. Nylon slides off everything. Most unsatisfactory.'

He smiled paternally, dived upwards and swam rapidly out of sight. We had persuaded him to take the 60-foot line, just in case. When it was my turn I got no further than halfway. I trod water breathlessly. Below me a great sodden wig of *Plagiothecium* peeled off and smacked onto the anxious upturned face of the Apprentice. He reappeared, spluttering, but still adherent.

'Ha, I told you it was safer than *Constipation*,' cried the Doctor encouragingly, as from a boat, 'if that had been rock, all your helmets wouldn't have stopped it!'

Meanwhile, the current was washing me backwards. Towards the new black shiny rock. I called, almost for help. The Doctor swiftly knotted the line to a stem and threw me down the loose end.

'Might need a fixed rope, first time up,' he agreed.

By grabbing and changing from crawl to butterfly, I reached him on his mouldering rugosity. As I looked up, a wet jelly licked my face. I spat it out.

'Ha, *Hirneola auricula judae* – Jew's-ear fungus.' It encircled my stem. The Doctor calmed me.

'No, it doesn't attack the roots. The stem's quite sound low down where the rope is. It's rowan – fine strong safe rooting system – pliable cortex. Now if it had been ash – ' he shook his head expressively. 'Many a good climber's been let down badly by young ash. Fine in an ice-axe. But not on the hoof.'

Above us a fairly dry ten feet led to the top. It was bulging with good holds such as wild rose, broom and birch seedlings. 'Never trust heather,' admonished the Doctor, as we turned to go, 'all right in ropes, but – '

'Hi!' from below. We had forgotten the Apprentice. The Doctor gave me a pebble. I placed it under my boot as support, leaned out from my root and looked down.

The Apprentice was in trouble. My last swim had kicked away every hypnaceous deception. Between us lay a black slab, wrinkling only with water.

The Doctor looked. 'No go in vibrams,' he said. 'Try it in socks. One pair only, mind. Tie your boots round your neck, out of the way. Or to the end of the rope; but they'll get wet there.'

Bitterly, the Apprentice, on his foot-square bath-mat, removed his boots and socks. Foolishly, he slung them round his neck (he always loathed walking down in wet boots). He hauled, unashamedly upon the line. The Doctor, myself, and the root, resisted manfully.

I need not recount the inevitable. The slip on one sodden toe, the twist, the grab on the line with both hands, the clatter of falling boots, the flutter of socks. The appalling and – considering his uncertain position – imprudently blasphemous oaths from the sufferer. We landed him at last. The Doctor, in some ways quite sensitive, moved up to let him on. I inculcated the botanical rudiments necessary for the last few feet.

The Doctor sat on the cliff top, smoking his pipe.

'Pity about the boots,' he said. 'Rather a lot of scree on the way down to them – damned uncomfortable. Could go back the same way, but I don't like taking *two* inexperienced chaps down, and we'd

better stick together. It's not hard, but it's not easy. Although I grant you it's not a stiff climb like *Constipation*. Just as well, when you go losing your boots. Bad technique that; hope Aggie didn't see us.'

His soliloquy was interrupted by the Apprentice vividly explaining why, in his judgment, our present route should be termed *Diarrhoea*.

'No, it's *Central Buttress Direct*,' said the Doctor. 'A good classical name. Not in the least subjective. And look at that view. There's Schiehallion – unusual from this side. We'll get you down all right. Piggyback, if necessary. Might even meet with old MacPhedran. He humphs yowes about all day. Remarkably tough. He's docked and castrated three hundred lambs in a morning. He'll take care of you all right. And there – look over there – there's Lancet Edge. Wonderful in the sun.'

# FLIES

'Damn these blasted flies!' roared the Doctor, the hundredth time that day. The Apprentice, beginning a similar though more virile malediction, inhaled too great a horde of *Muscidae* and fell back speechless. For each of us, like an island peak, carried his own cloud. Dodging or ducking could never escape it. Bracken and branches beat in vain. Hands were blistered, arms ached. Chitinous and insistent, it clung. And it buzzed and crawled abominably. At times one of us would creep up to unload his cloud on to a companion; and then try to run free. But the companion, unencumbered – in fact, spurred – by the additional burden, would race to repay him. Heads were thrust under water: but on emergence proved even more attractive.

Walking up and walking down that year were enlivened by such performances, and we grew desperate. Camping was intolerable until darkness brought its relief and its midges – at least a familiar, almost hereditary, malady, benign by comparison. And even then the odd nocturnal fly padded damply across our faces. Driven by the horrors of reverberating sleeping bags and ham-and-fly suppers, we carried a tent – translucent with fly-squash and rustling with old wings – to the top of Ladhar Bheinn; but we left one pole in the Doctor's car, and it rained. Another weekend I gasped in a fly at an unpleasant move above The Chasm, and spat us both into space. Later that day the Doctor also came to grief, claiming he had slipped on a handful of the brutes – 'like ball-bearings on a slab'. At the top, the Apprentice solemnly declared he'd been forced to roll a cloud of them up into a convenient chockstone; it had brought the two of us over the crux before dispersing and flying away. They had in fact become part of the climbing scene. But we never got used to them. We would plot, plot in our downhill cursing. How *could* they be defeated?

Sundew, environmentally preferable, was too slow. We had tried flypaper. We hung three flypapers in the sleeve entrance of the Doctor's Mummery tent, and gloated on the speedy arrest of incomers. But we celebrated unwisely, because that night the Apprentice, wriggling out at the call of nature, forgot about the flypapers. His retreat into the alarmed and pitchblack tent, trailing flypapers and sleeve entrance, needs no elaboration. Fly-sprays were expensive, amused the flies and, according to the Doctor, ours (though not his) were dangerous to health. Nylon net bags did not fulfil their promise. They let feet through and leaked at the neck; and in driving one devil out we allowed seven more in. Ointments and suchlike merely provided the creatures with refreshment and an opportunity to linger.

We sat in despair that evening. Each spoke to the other out of his cloud. One learnt to communicate in this Jove-like fashion, through compressed and fly-denying lips.

'I got most of mine from that dead hind on the bealach,' hissed the Doctor. This provoked unkind comparisons. The Apprentice observed, sideways, that next time he'd bring up some bad meat and lose all his flies on to that.

The Doctor sprang up. His cloud re-adjusted itself nimbly.

'Of course! Of course! What about that new chemical they've made? Better than anything so far known for attracting flies – they used it as bait to clear 'em out of Egyptian hospitals. Has a fearful pong. An improvement on some amine or other from a decomposing mushroom. I know a chemist at the University. I'll get him to try for some. Bound to work!' And he fell back contented into his flies.

That Thursday in Daddy McKay's his eyes were alight.

'Astonishing luck. Chemist chap knew all about it. Had some in the next lab. Musc-a-something or other. Highly poisonous but a dead cert.' He produced a glass tube containing a small evil-looking brown bottle. 'Next weekend we'll try it....'

Next weekend was hot and sticky as usual that summer. We entered a pinewood, roaring and metallescent as Kennedy Field. We stopped. The Doctor went ahead. He selected a long pole from the thinnings. He donned surgical gloves, then extracted his tube from the rucksack, very carefully slid out the bottle, and loosened its stopper. Throttles were opened. He disappeared behind a hurricane of wings, became a pillar of buzz. Then slowly, miraculously, the pillar condensed into a ball and the ball raised itself above him, far above, clustering on the end of the pole. He signalled us to replace the bottle and its tube into his rucksack then strode on ahead, bearing the cloud of flies aloft. So we progressed, taking turns to hold the pole, bringing its end cautiously near any head visited by less perceptive Diptera. No vacuum cleaner could have done the job better.

Indeed miraculous; if somewhat odd in appearance. We mounted the plateau (it was the Gorms that weekend), and the air cleared. We gingerly laid down the pole and bolted a hundred yards or so. Only a distant revelling. We were safe.

'Marvellous stuff. Pity it's so poisonous. He only let it out because I'm a quack. Seems it's a sure thing for the Third World when the molecule's been tidied up a bit. Should get some here after Devolution.'

Coming down that evening, along the other edge of the corrie, was more difficult. No forest, no poles. We did not risk a long grass stem. Suppose it bent.... Instead, whenever our individual clouds became too irritating, the Doctor stopped and dabbed a boulder. Then we each went and, holding our noses, laid heads as close to it as possible, and so decanted our flies. Behind us, a powerful telescope would have revealed a succession of curiously-vibrating tumuli.

Peace, peace. Sheer luxury of seeing and hearing again. Of owning one's hair.

Then, just before entering the wood – and its convenience of poles – disaster struck. The Doctor had been the last to exchange flies with the local granite. In completing this transaction he had knelt – on the bottle....

A terrible cry. We looked round. An immense cloud, and out of it the Doctor running as if for life. Without his breeches or his rucksack.

When we had all run half a mile, he stopped.

'Damned good job I had on the old linen ones. Just ripped em off, pants and all, and legged it. Stuff hadn't soaked through.'

The rucksack had dropped on to the contaminated garments and, like them, would be unapproachable until wind and weather had done their work. The rucksack contained our few spare clothes, and the Doctor would have to remain breekless. He was fortunate in wearing a long tartan shirt. We made him wash thoroughly in the burn and the Apprentice lent him his belt. Tucked in suitably, the sark now resembled a kilt; on the short side, but adequate. The Doctor chose a comfortable stump, after inspecting it for ants. We munched the Apprentice's emergency rations, moist from his pocket.

'I'll come back for the things tomorrow night. No-one'll nick 'em in that state. We'll just have to go cannily down to the car. Don't want to be picked up like this... O damn these flies.'

Our descent became hilarious. Peering through my nimbus I saw the Doctor leaping hairily and bonily ahead, a swashbuckling figure fresh from Killiecrankie or, less improbably, Mons Graupius. We spurred him with Hampden cries. He responded with bursts of *Nicky Tams*.

The path passed Glendrumly Castle. We took that stretch cautiously. Young Glendrumly was a keen ornithologist and possessed a troop of bird-feeding aunts who regularly crumbed the turrets. Also he had an uncle who was a part-time lunatic and occasionally cantered about garbed as the Doctor was now. Every window might have been manned. The Doctor was so intent on watching the Castle that he failed to notice a litter of tourists lying exhausted on his right. They sat up in alarm as he fled. We explained we were from the Castle and hurried on.

Though unsettled by this episode and by the unexpectedly warm driving seat, the Doctor relaxed when his hands were on the wheel.

'We'll go through Balqueenie. Some shops might still be open. Souvenirs and stuff. Might get shorts. Bathing trunks.' He brushed flies from the windscreen, and we drove away.

Balqueenie was crowded. The road before us vanished into heaving tweed. Of course, the Highland Games. Balqueenie, if not artistically the summit of such gatherings, is certainly the social peak. We sniffed. We were snobs. We each had our favourite Meeting, and it was not Balqueenie. The Apprentice had lost his voice for Bill Anderson the week before at the *aficionado's* gathering at Brig o Dinnie. The Doctor, when subjecting us to an approximate *piobaireachd* outside his tent, was likely to explain he had just heard that particular interpretation at Lochboisdale or Portree. I myself had come second out of three in a race up the local ben at Strath Warsle – a race, it is true, disorganised at an early stage by the landing amongst the original leaders of a hammer, thrown somewhat inexpertly from elsewhere in the programme. Obviously, we were not Balqueenie men; and we enjoyed the Apprentice's graphic suppositions of the ancestry and habits of the more outrageously decorated members of its ecosystem – a regular *Tartanetum*. The gilt-edge of the crowd, in dreepy kilts and clutching equally unconvincing seven-foot-long polished cromags which kept banging into and interlocking with each other, was being

continuously photographed – no doubt as Real Jocks – by the more jovial fraternity in T-shirts and paper streamers. Watching good-humouredly were the whiskied red-faced possessors of the more indigenous genes. Aye, bonnie Balqueenie.

The road cleared. The Main Square. We wound down the window a little. At one end stood a group whose prolonged massacre of the accepted European phonetic values reduced even the Apprentice to silence. They, the really Top People, were accompanied by spectacled gentlemen of eastern appearance, heavily decked in smiles and telescopic lenses. About them stood brow-mopping men whose minds had obviously recently been relieved – the organisers. One of the organisers appeared familiar; he occupied a gratifyingly lived-in kilt. His eye brightened when he saw us. The Club Treasurer, in fact.

'Jamieson!' exclaimed the Doctor. 'That's him. Just the man I had to see. I never sent him those subscriptions – after all I promised.'

We drew into the kerb.

'I must apologise. Won't take a minute. Frightful lapse.'

The Doctor seized the door handle and sprang out of the car. He remained – for a split-second – springing, hairy legs Nijinsky-like, horror on his face. He was of course still clad only in his shirt.

Before he touched ground the Apprentice's splitter-second reflex, so welcome to us on many another crux, had whipped a travelling rug out of the back seat and over his descending frame. The Doctor, no less quick on the uptake, swept it round him in an instant, straightened, and then strode majestically forward across the Forum, attired in a somewhat dusty but nevertheless imposing toga of Ancient MacQuarrie. Before he reached Jamieson's group, which had been struck to unaccustomed silence, he had rustled up an almost believable Inverness cape. His breezy address prevailed and we watched fascinated, as the eyes of Jamieson's companions slowly rose from the long folds of MacQuarrie to the animated bony countenance. Jamieson himself supported the Doctor manfully, though his bonhomie appeared of the anxious kind. The Doctor had no such inhibitions and seemed in great form, the Gentry rapidly responding with shouts of laughter and high whinnying diphthongs. We trusted that our companion would remember to keep gesticulating with his right hand and not with the left, which was required for his rug.

The driver's window was darkened. Inspector McHaig. He appeared subdued. He leaned heavily. We expected a cheerier greeting. Perhaps he thought the Doctor had gone a little too far. Drink and driving.

'Had a good day, lads?'

'Great. And how were the Games?'

'O fine, fine. Mr Jamieson's very pleased. And Royalty was fair chuffed.'

'You look worried, Inspector. Don't mind the Doctor, he's....'

'Aye, aye; but I'm afraid we've just had bad news... there's a body on the hill, lads.'

'Can we...?'

'No, no. My lads are away up to bring it down.'

We'd thought we'd seen the Pitfoulie Land Rover trumpeting and tusking its way through the throng earlier. 'Pitfoulie there as well?'

McHaig darkened further. 'They've just rammed one of my patrol cars. We've filled the ambulance already.'

'Helicopter?'

'Busy with the traffic. Anyway the poor felly'll no be needing us to hurry, by all accounts.'

He looked meaningly at us. 'It's Captain Rawlings for sure, I'm thinking.'

Captain Rawlings. That gentleman had provided the Pitfoulie Mountain Rescue Team and its exuberant competitors with three weeks' invaluable heather-thrashing in the spring, before being entered up finally as 'Not Found'. We had remained unsurprised at this sad verdict. Captain Rawlings had been, it seemed, an English visitor at the Inverfyvie Arms. He stayed a week. He was popular with staff and guests. He was a willing, and successful, hand at the cards. He stood generous drinks on account. And on the Friday morning he had gone out – 'for a walk on the hill'. He would be back late that night.

He was not back late that night. Nor ever. *Cha till e tuille.* And such a fine gentleman. Of course, very much a novice on the hill. He had town shoes. Very inexperienced – why, he'd even carried his suitcase, it seemed; for that, with his spare clothes, was missing as well. And he'd made a careless mistake about his address, so his next-of-kin – abroad he had said – could not be traced. Tragic indeed.

'Who told you it was Captain Rawlings?' we demanded. The Inspector looked a little uncomfortable.

'Miss Threadweaver,' he said.

'Miss – ?'

'She's staying at Glendrumly, helping with the junior birdwatching courses. It's Fledgling Week.'

'Did she *recognise* Captain Rawlings?'

The Inspector looked even more uncomfortable.

'Hout, no, man. Who could recognise him after all this time? And this hot weather. But she saw – A Heap, ye ken. Off the Creag Liath path.'

'But we've just come down the Creag Liath path and we've seen no Heap.'

'Well, she *did*,' said McHaig irritably, 'and she rang us up not ten minutes ago and I've sent men out there. She was all upset. Crying. She'd only bairns with her and darena get closer. "O, it's Captain Rawlings, Inspector," she said "I know it is." '

'How *could* she know a heap was Captain Rawlings?' we persisted.

McHaig hemmed, and tapped the rim of the window. He gazed at the loquacious group across the Square, from which shrieks of well-dividended laughter could be heard. The Doctor's left hand was still firmly in place.

'There was claes and a rucksack.'

'But Captain Rawlings had a suitcase, not a rucksack.'

'He could have had a rucksack inside the suitcase and put it on when he got to the hill. Ye're better with a rucksack than a suitcase on a hill, are ye not?'

The logic was indisputable.

'Besides...' A pause. 'It was no an ordinary heap o claes. There was an awful-like smell coming from it on the wind, if you understand me. And a great cloud of flies. Terrible lot of flies, she said.' He smacked the Triplex decisively. 'It'll be him right enough. Three months, and weather like this. Poor felly. Anyway, my boys are up there, to bring him down, whoever he is. We've got to do it decent and quickly-like, with the Games on.'

The Apprentice and I looked at each other and swallowed hard. We leant over. We wound down the window to its fullest extent.

We began to explain.

# FINISHING OFF A TOP

It was impossible to see anything. Mist pressed about me, determined to stay. There was no hint of wind. Undressed for late July, I was extremely cold. Droplets explored the tail of my shirt. I stood, cursing, as for the last fifty minutes. It was a small comfort to know that within a two-mile radius of this mist, almost certainly *in* this mist, the Apprentice and – more satisfyingly – the Doctor were likewise standing; and likewise at their own particular spots, and likewise for the last fifty minutes. On this Godforsaken bald-headed hag-ridden heap, three thousand feet up.

Why were we thus enchanted? Could we not sit down? There was nowhere to sit but weeping heather. One could keep drier, or less wet, by remaining upright. Drops gathered and crept down back and knees, but to sit invited cold, prolonged and intimate embrace. Then why not move about? Why not indeed, but for an unaccountable loyalty to the Doctor; a loyalty, I discovered later, shared equally, equally unaccountably, by the Apprentice – whose displeasure in such circumstances is even greater than mine, and whose experience of the Doctor is no less. It only remains to add that at the feet of each of us lay a flag on a long pole.

It was, as I said, late July. It was the weekend after that memorable Sunday the Doctor took us up the 'rock climb' behind his brother-in-law's shepherd's cottage; a fortnight, therefore, after we – or rather the Apprentice – had taken him up his first V.S. Those episodes are recounted elsewhere. Sufficient to record that we – the Apprentice and I – had been sorely-wrought men all that previous week: starting violently at hoot of horn, crossing Princes Street only when repeatedly – at length angrily – beckoned by policemen; peering each morning at a doubtful world through a myriad of entangled and imaginary ropes. So that when on the next Thursday night in Daddy McKay's, the Doctor asked us out yet again, we both cringed involuntarily and the Apprentice in anguish slopped his Glen Riddance over the table.

'No, never mind,' said the Doctor, flashing out his handkerchief and wiping the Guidebook page rapidly dry, 'I'll get you another – same as before, eh? Fine. Another Glen Riddance, Geordie – ach, make it three more – yes of course, doubles....'

To cut the story short, he won us over. It was to be a Very Relaxing Day. We had all had enough of Difficult Routes (here the Apprentice swelled visibly; I kicked him accurately, beneath the table) and this Sunday – we could leave late Saturday, he would pick us up as usual – this Sunday would merely be to Finish Off a Top.

'Not bloody Munros – ' began the Apprentice.

'No, no, not at all,' said the Doctor.

'A Corbett – or a Donald,' I suggested, maliciously.

'If you think – ' roared the youth, gripping his Glen Riddance tighter this time –

'Certainly not,' said the Doctor placidly, gazing down his beak, 'not Munro-bashing. I did all the Munros in that section thirty years ago; in one weekend, as it happened. Not Munro-bashing. It's Tops.'

'Tops?!!!'

'Much more skilful, much more interesting. You see different country. Some of them are damned difficult to find. Not all properly measured, you know. There's one I'm still not sure of. Here it is in the List, d'you see? (Of course they've missed out the initial aspiration – they always spell these names wrong.) We'll go up there just for a stroll. I'm still quite stiff myself, so you two must be really feeling it; one never gets much exercise up and down those artificial routes of yours. We'll go for a leisurely walk, and I'll nip off and collect that little chap. The weather'll be dead clear all weekend – fine and warm and quite settled, the forecast says. You'll just lie and relax. I'll do all the running about. Tops really test a fellow. Munros! I did most of *them* when I was a student.'

'How... many... have... you... done...?' muttered the Apprentice, in morbid fascination.

'Two hundred and twenty-eight – or two hundred and twenty-nine if you include Beinn Tarsuinn. But I've hardly bagged a new Munro for years. Been after all the confounded Tops I left out before. And I haven't even done one of those since last Easter Meet.' He closed the Guidebook, put away his spectacles and smiled disarmingly. My round.

We crawled out of the tent into a dawn of lemon and blue. An early start, the Doctor insisted, would miss the Heat of the Day and ensure us time to relax among the summit heather while he rattled off in pursuit of the errant Top. Halfway up sweatily endless slopes, peopled by that detestable species, the 7 a.m. midge, we stopped for a second breakfast of warm ham sandwiches. The view was excellent. Probably even the Apprentice did not miss his rocks.

'I've brought something rather interesting,' mumbled the Doctor through his ham, rummaging in his rucksack – the only one with us, and already stuffed with the Apprentice's shirt and my cagoule. He held up triumphantly a small shining cannon-like object.

'You've probably never seen one' – this to the Apprentice. Then to me, 'Pretty good, eh?'

'Looks like a Dumpy level,' remarked the Apprentice, sourly. The Doctor, somewhat crestfallen, confirmed that it was. However, it had belonged to a Father of the Club.... After further karabiner-like janglings, he produced a diminutive brass alarm clock.

'Aneroid. Sir Hugh's very own. Patient of mine picked it up at a Kirriemuir roup.'

The Apprentice steadfastly chewed at the view. We awaited a clinometer. But it must have remained inside.

By ten o'clock we had traversed sufficient miles of peat hag to be rewarded by the cairn, beaming pyramidally from the desert horizon. The Doctor had unerringly smelt it out.

'This is the top,' he announced.

'The one you were after?' enquired the Apprentice, hopefully rubbing sweat off his shoulderblades.

'No, of course not. Not the Top, but the top. The Munro. It's the fifth time I've been here,' he added. 'Second in summer.'

He poked a boot reminiscently among burnt stems. Sun gleamed on his polished clinkers. He looked suspiciously innocent. Statistics will out.

He knelt and spread the maps. Two maps because, naturally, the elusive Top could be cornered only at the junction of two sheets. It was not named on the maps. It did not even aspire to a contour ring of its own.

'It's a very doubtful Top,' he explained. 'Phillip and Burn – and Gall Inglis as well – thought it *was* one, but they could never get decent sightings. Today's perfect. Absolutely clear. But you see the ground's so flat about there' – digging a long forefinger into a blank area of map – 'that I can't take sightings on these other two points'

– prodding at two bald unpronounceable shoulders – 'unless somebody stands up on each of them with, say, a flag.'

The Apprentice and I began to feel a familiar feeling. We avoided each other's eyes.

'Now if you two chaps would be good enough just to pop over to those two points – see them over there – and stand on them and wave a flag when you see me wave mine: then I can get accurate sightings and we'll soon know the Real Height of this top... Phillip and Burn could never do it. Nor Gall Inglis. Make a good Note for the *Journal.'*

'What about... a Flag?' I asked, mechanically.

He rooted again in his rucksack. From its lower leathern recesses, Dent-Blanche-battered, he produced a cluster of mahogany brass-ringed rods. He fitted them together.

'From Lamond Howie's tripod. Just the thing. And here's the cloth – bits of the wife's old curtains. Shove the spike through 'em. There's your flag.'

He handed us each our pole and flag, and dismissed us cheerily. We had not the heart to protest.

That had been two hours before. Flag in hand, I reached my imperceptible prominence. Across a deep corrie dozed an identical whale, surmounted by a tiny figure. Another figure, equally remote but recognisable by its bony stride, denoted the Doctor, scaling his debatable contour. His flag danced, a speck of colour, as he climbed. At the top he would wave it. I prepared to stretch out in the sun.

Then out of that blue-eyed sky the mist appeared. Suddenly. Wet, white, annihilating.

Of course, it would lift. It was bound to lift. A mere midday aberration. A casual stray. Rising air would shift it.

It stayed. Fifty minutes, as I said. An hour and a quarter.

Enough. I sighed; I gazed at the pole, I bent down and gripped it. I would go, Doctor or no Doctor. The mahogany and brass gleamed. Sun. Sun....

I looked up. Blue indecision, but blue.

Across the corrie, the whale oozed into view. Upon it a faithful figure. I waved my flag. He lifted his, not with enthusiasm. I guessed his feelings. And the Doctor? Smoke lay thick on Sinai; but it was clearing, clearing. Then – hell and damnation. Clamminess hugged again, and all was lost.

Twice this happened. At intervals of half an hour.

Then it became darker, and drizzled. Low cloud had joined us. So I bent down, gripped the pole firmly, and strode off.

But where to...? This way, keeping the corrie on the right. But where was the corrie? That would be the edge? Peat hag? No... Yes? Yes.

I halted, embarrassed. I was about to become lost on this hopeless plateau, *sans* food, *sans* map, *sans* compass, *sans* torch, in shirt and breeks and carrying a mahogany pole with a piece of curtain material on it. And doubtless over there, on his invisible whale, the Apprentice faced the same fate, but without even a shirt....

The weather being Settled, this cloud could last for days. I must obviously descend into the corrie. Forty-eight hours' circling on the plateau could never be lived down. Think of the Accident Report. Think of Daddy McKay's. Think of the shrill glee of The Weasels....

The corrie revealed itself bleakly and blackly as I went lower. Six miles down the glen, a shooting lodge. Then four miles to a public road. After that, twenty odd more round to the Doctor's car on the other side of the hill....

Two peat-haggard hours later I overtook the Apprentice pulling his feet out of a bog. He had passed the savage state, and the weeping state. He was impervious to all, and merely nodded. A dark green stain down his neck indicated where at one time in his vigil he had tried to clothe himself in his flag. (My own was red.)

We reached a puddled track and trudged on silently, in thin sheets of sweeping rain. Wind had arrived, and chased hungrily over vanishing slopes. We half-hoped the Doctor might still be up there, checking his watch. But of course, with map and compass, he would be down at his car. Or perhaps – we must both have thought of this together, for we stopped and looked at each other – perhaps he had backtracked on bearings to each of our lonely stances, to collect us....

No help, we were down. If he was up, looking for us, hard luck.

The Lodge came into view. Large shiny limousine. Early shooters, awaiting August; or landlord inspecting before the let. Probably the latter. A sniffy-looking cove in tweeds emerged from the door, said 'Aah....'

Before the Apprentice could reply suitably, I got in with a cordial 'Good afternoon'. Four miles to the public road. You never knew.

'Aah... your friend rang up. He'll be round by car presently. Do come in, woncha?'

We stopped, breathed deeply, and turned into the porchway.

'Aah... by the way... perhaps you could leave those things... out here, eh?'

We were still carrying our poles with pieces of curtain on them. We leant them carefully against the ox-blood pine door posts and went inside.

An hour later, a car scritched on the gravel and the Doctor appeared in the room. From our armchairs, we saw him vaguely across the roar of fire, the shine of plates and glasses. The Apprentice, much moved, extended a wavering hairy arm from beneath his thick wool travelling rug.

'Ha,' said the Doctor. 'Knew where you'd skedaddle to when you deserted your posts. Rang up Charlie here – you look fine, Charlie, no more trouble, eh?' (another of his patients, no doubt...) – 'rang up Charlie here – yes, thanks, I'll have a Strath Grapple – told him to look after you. Good thing, keeping the flags. Kept mine, too. We'll have another shot next weekend, eh? Settled weather – this is just a local front. Then we'll finish it off, and get back to some real stuff. I'm sure it's a Top all right. The aneroid made it three thousand and two – can I check with your barometer, Charlie?'

# CHALKING IT UP

'Come along now, gentlemen, PLEASE,' repeated Daddy McKay almost testily, shepherding glasses on to his impatient tray and flicking his napkin through our animated discussion. But we were slow to leave the back bar that night and the Doctor was still defiant as he struggled into his raincoat at the door, Daddy McKay determinedly freeing a sleeve. 'It's the old days again; the end of your artificial aids.'

He had been lent some Hard Men's Glossies, and his imagination billowed chalk dust and waves of golden Apollos swarming effortlessly up the impossible, ropeless and shirtless (it was the Fawcett era). Climbing was free again, chalk was scarcely an Aid, no more than boots, and quite invisible if tinted to match the rock ('Torridonian would need, let me see, BS 04D43: say, Manders' *Copper Rose* or something like that...'). But Scottish orogeny is diverse and contorted, and it seemed a whole palette might be required to satisfy the hues encountered on a single route. The Apprentice, veteran of countless gritted hours with fellow Weasels on rain-battered rugosities, dissolved these calciferous enthusiasms as best he could; he preferred a rope. I, as so often on the hill, followed his lead; for the prospect of trails of polychromatic guano – however tastefully selected – lengthening with the weather down our favourite buttresses, was not attractive. Also, although we appreciated the Doctor's company, and his transport, for frequent escalades of the earlier Scottish classics, we were doubtful of his ability, powdered or plain, to adhere sufficiently to much above Severe (Winter was a different matter). His easy denunciations stung us. So, unwisely, before we parted at the Mound the Apprentice invited him to join us that weekend at the Ben, on a new HVS – just to see what it was like. And equally unwisely, the Doctor agreed.

'Ha, *Constipation*, is it? Yes, I've heard of that. Pretty stiff, by all accounts. But an experience. Even if a limited one: you chaps – ' We choked off another tirade, and pushed him homeward. 'Now mind you mug up your ropework. And no bloody chalk...' was the Apprentice's parting shot. The vision of the Doctor leaping heroically ahead, in dust and bathing trunks, up two hundred leering metres of vertical Lochaber was, that night, most amusing.

It grew less amusing as the weekend approached, and we were strangely silent during the Saturday journey north. The Doctor's old Mercedes lumbered more thoughtfully round the bends in Glencoe, its usual elephantine squeals reined in. After lunch on the shore beyond Ballachulish the Apprentice whistled tunelessly, I plucked grassheads, and the Doctor poked about among seaweed on the boulders. None of us mentioned The Climb, not even by evening when we reached the hut.

We were greeted by the occupants, sundry youths of lurid and basic communicatory skills hailing from the more abrasively north of England. They had, it appeared, gained unlawful entry several days before, and generously offered us the three remaining bunks. Their leader was one Sodder, a formidable XS exponent of whose exploits on alcohol and crag the Apprentice and – since his magazine excursions – the Doctor were well informed. As a large, legitimate and uncompromisingly Glaswegian party was also booked for the hut that night, and was at this instant celebrating thirstily its arrival at the Fort, we gloomily predicted a disturbed prelude to tomorrow's epic.

In the hour or so before the engagement we heard the Englishmen had suffered no trouble from *Constipation* and had, superfluously enough, gone on to take in an adjacent shocking artificial, *Purgative*, dismantling that of aid except halfway up the crux – a quite holdless bulging slab over a horrible, truly aperient, exposure. They had removed even that peg afterwards, for the benefit of their successors.... It would be at least an XS, climbed free.

The Doctor, scenting chalk, engaged them in earnest conversation. Unfortunately, his incautious extempores in magazine lingo gave them the startled impression that he intended to climb *Constipation* without a rope. The crimson Apprentice was about to cross to the guffaws and explain, when the doorway was filled with Glaswegians; then silence; then expletives.

We managed a few hours' sleep after the battle, one of Bannockburnian intensity and conclusion; and then padded painfully to the foot of our climb. We wore E.B.'s, the Doctor his old gym shoes, bared to the canvas ('probably illegal...') and were laden with iron-mongery of all configurations and clatter – clusters and panicles of wires, hexcentrics, bongs, étriers... and ropes, ropes, ropes. The Apprentice was taking no chances. He kept instructing the Doctor on the red rope, the green rope, the fixed rope, the free rope, this rope and that rope. The Doctor nodded sagely, obviously and irritatingly wishing to understand little of it. As he strode, his coils opened and shut, disclosing a small canvas bag tied to his waistband. Chalk...? Chalk, it must be. If the English saw us.... From the disgruntled tents of the vanquished far up the Allt a'Mhuillin (whence they could, at their own convenience, pollute the hut's alleged water supply) we imagined the first faint jeers. But we said nothing.

The initial pitches were fairly uneventful: steep dry rock in early sun. The Apprentice had struck form. I followed adequately despite my burden of prophylaxis, and the Doctor rattled up behind, multijointedly competent as a harvestman crossing a flysheet. But he was troubled by the prolixity of ropes. I gathered them up before him, as one conjures the cords of a disobedient Venetian blind. He arrived and cast further superfluity at my feet. 'Most tiresome, all these unnecessary ropes. No wonder they hardly use them nowadays.' He held out his arms like one accepting wool; I wound him about suitably and turned upwards again.

There were of course minor anxieties. As when the Doctor suddenly stuck. In midswarm. He was surmounting a roof, a narrowing crack on his left. He strained and swore. No use.

'I think I'm stuck.' Then, more specifically, 'These damned things are caught somewhere below.' Further information revealed that he could not spare a single limb, and his neck (surprisingly) was not long enough to allow his teeth full play. Praying and cursing, I secured his ropes and abseiled down. The nuts on the wire slings attached to his harness had travelled beside him up the crack; when it narrowed they had fulfilled the intentions of their designer. Extrication proved lengthy. I relieved him of slings. A similar incident occurred shortly afterwards on an outward-pressing wall, to the anguish of our leader, spread on a balance stance out of sight above; it involved a mysterious loop of rope about the Doctor's rucksack and a mutual tying and re-tying in a parabiotic embrace on a halfhearted wrinkle of rock; it was complicated by a hook in his fishing hat refusing to leave my ear. Clearly he was not to be trusted with this mileage of rope. We were already garlanded grotesquely; soon he would be a cocoon. I pruned him of rucksack, ironmongery and spare coils and left him with a suitably modest bell-pulling repertoire, the bare minimum of attachment.

It is the next pitch, the pendulum pitch, that still shakes our memories. *Constipation* entails only a brief pendulum – as its name implies, it concentrates on a fairly rigid line – but the Doctor, drunk from his liberation, leapt lankily rightward from so far left he outshot the route, collided with a brutal rib on the other side, twisted, and vanished out of sight behind it. He did not come back. I pulled the red rope. No reply. The green one. It pulled back. His seventy-four inches were presumably still consecutive.

Their retrieval was less obvious. The rib cut off sight and coherent sound. Only a muffle. I roared instructions. Only a muffle. Then, a high whoop of derision. It was the English. Even farther to our right, in several parties, on fearsome lines. And much enjoying our plight. The ribaldries of Sodder were particularly displeasing to the Apprentice, who was informed from that embarrassing source of the fate of our colleague.

'Yer know were e is? E's on *Purgative*. An e's there for keeps. Right under the bloody crux!'

We froze. His return demanded a computery of rope-twiddling impossible to convey through twenty metres of indifferent andesite. And clearly the English were going to enjoy the situation as long as possible. Last night would not soon be forgotten. They began to sing. '*Will yer no come baaack again....*'

Pushing rightward on vanishing balance holds the Apprentice managed to look over an impassable gulf to our companion. He shouted down instructions to both of us. No easy task, with the Auld Enemy jamming the wavelength. ('*Boney Chaarlie's noo awaah...*'). The inevitable had to happen. The Doctor, none too clear anyway about which of the unidentifiable ropes to clip or unclip or haul or let out, and counterinstructed by the echoes booming about his vertical danknesses, let slip the only line that could have ensured his return to us – that even joined us.... The end snaked down into limbo. We heard a muffled 'Blast!'

The English, if they were sympathetic, did not show it. The singing stopped.

'E's chucked off is bloody rope like e said e would. E's goin to do *Purgative* solo! Ah, yer can't old im back, can yer? Good ole Golden Boy!' Unfeeling roars of laughter. Whistles, hoots; then *'Scotland the Brave'*, much off-key.

Although we knew the Doctor's remarkable powers of survival, we began to sweat. I struggled up slabs and roofs to the Apprentice, and crabbed out to the edge overlooking *Purgative*. The Doctor occupied its one gesture at a ledge, but seemed in good form, hat rammed firmly on, the usual sign of determination. We could not cross down to him; but would have to descend *Constipation*, peg up *Purgative*, work out runners and then somehow gather him in. A long job. He could not abseil from his present position; to climb down was unthinkable; to climb up would bring him almost alongside us, but was equally unthinkable – the crux of *Purgative* free and without protection! And now a thin mist moistened the rocks.... It might have to be helicopters, or Pitfoulie. O, the shame of it.... Comment and songs continued ('Come on Jock, straight up, that's it.' 'Yer alfway there already mate.' *'You take the igh road and I'll...'*).

The Apprentice whipped his ropes and hammered in the first abseil peg. I gazed fascinated at the Doctor.

'Lord, what's he doing now?' The Apprentice paused; and stared, too. The singing stopped. Whistles died.

He had hauled his loose end back, tied it in a loop and, after a couple of shots, miraculously lassoed an evil razor-edged spike to his right. A parapsychological belay, indeed. He looked up, saw us, grinned, and waved perilously. And then, balancing outward against all his years of Alpine anecdote, put his hand surreptitiously into his little canvas bag.

'Chalk! He's not going to try the crux on CHALK?!!!'

His hand emerged, pressed the rock in front of him firmly, patted it, and returned to the bag. Then he patted the rock a little higher up, similarly.

Chalk? The English were as dead silent as us. Sodder was poised on one toe and a finger, agape. Chalk?

A few more gropings in the bag and pattings, and he began to move up the appalling bare bulge of slab that gave *Purgative* its name.

Not true. Our mouths cracked with drought.

He groped again. More pattings. And up another metre or so. The crux is not so vertical as impossibly smooth and holdless. Yet he climbed the six metres of it as deliberately as if he were moving from invisible pimple to pimple, or pick-scratch to pick-scratch as in his tales of the moonlit Brenva; even the venomously gentle detachment of belay from spike did not disturb him. One slip....

Incredibly, falling was far from our thoughts. We were hypnotised by his proceeding up that unthinkable slab. Of course, he had a Glenmorangie reach, but....

He was suddenly just below us on the right. He had climbed the crux. He gripped, white-knuckled and thankfully enough, its final rim. He grinned. A deep breath, and he mantelshelfed on to a stance, stood up, stretched, and rubbed his arms.

'Can you chuck me a rope? Might as well use one now. The rest's a doddle, but the easy bits are always the most dangerous.... And all your tomfoolery took it out of me at the beginning.'

Our emotion was great as we lassoed his outstretched arm, and became greater with the applause from across the cliff, punctuated by only a few face-saving catcalls. The English are sportsmen yet.

The respectful spell was somewhat broken by a subsequent barrage of queries. They possessed the same tenor:

'Ow the —— —— did a daft ole —— like that get up *Purgative?*'

How indeed? When we finally all arrived at the top of *Constipation*, which gave us little trouble after our remedial dose of its neighbour, the Apprentice and I, still trembling, put the question in less generally philosophical terms.

'What the devil have you got in that bag? Plaster of Paris?'

He smiled avuncularly, and untied the canvas. He held it high and shook it upside down over the Apprentice's doubtful palm. Two or three moist conical objects dropped out.

The Apprentice drew his hand away hurriedly. The objects fell to the scree. The Doctor bent and picked them up.

'Lucky I had enough. I was just running out.'

'What *are* they, for heaven's sake?' We stared uncomprehendingly. The answer was simple. He held it out.

'Limpets. *Patella vulgata*. Got them yesterday on the shore. Not the rockpool sort, but the real knobbly high-water-mark jobs. Tough;

used to exposure. Can stand waves of 25 tons to the square yard. Thought they might come in handy. Winthrop Young recommended 'em. Of course you put your weight on 'em gradually. Give 'em time to suck. Too quick dislodges 'em. Interesting technique.

'Not really artificial: sort of Combined Tactics – after all, they *are* alive....'

We were still speechless.

'Ha, you thought they were chalk? So they are – chalk on the hoof. It's lucky the rock got damp just then and kept 'em happy; though I did bring some sea water, just in case.'

We rattled down the path. Neither the Apprentice nor I, still shaking, could face Tower Ridge, and the Doctor was not keen to descend *Purgative*. 'You know, they're chancy beasts.'

That evening Sodder came down, to see the Doctor. They had a long discussion, as between equals. Sodder went away after only half a bottle of Strath Hashie; he appeared preoccupied.

'He's going to try *Purgative* solo tomorrow.' We asked about the limpets. 'I mentioned them in passing. I don't think he took it in. You technicians are terribly limited. And it'll rain tonight. He'll never see them. They'll have moved, or been eaten, by the morning. You know, you need a fresh lot each time.'

# ONCE IN A WHILE

Skiing is a vice few of us can altogether avoid. I had succumbed to temptation several times, once even tasted a polythene-wrapped package course under sardonic Continental instruction. The Apprentice, well trained by early glissades in vibrams down Twisting Gully, took to it readily. Goggle-hats and numbers fitted in well when he felt too tired for climbing or when the particular bird-in-hand leaned agreeably towards *après-ski* complaisance. Obviously our ski-tracks did not often cross. Moreover, the Doctor's performance on boards, though darkly hinted at, remained unknown to us.

One weekend, however, we did, more or less, ski together. The Apprentice's girl friend and his mini-van had both suffered mechanical failure at the last moment. Snow was flour on marble, good for ski-ing, shocking for gullies. He came to my door on the Saturday morning, disconsolately magnificent in heliographic steel-and-plastic boots, and carrying the glittering balance of three hundred pounds sterling on his shoulder. Such splendour in distress moved me to pity, though I preferred the kind of sartorial ostentation more usually displayed by The Weasels – rusted ironware and egghardened rags. Could I, would I, join him? But I had no car that weekend either.... We thought of the Doctor, traditional transport in emergency. We rang him up.

'Where were you off to? Glen Scree? Ha, so was I. Excellent snow I believe. Jolly good idea. Like to see how you fellows ski. You can't have been at it very long....' So he met us with his old Mercedes and we strapped our planks aloft, beside a long leather canoe-like object.

At Glen Scree the fair was in full swing. We took down our skis. The Doctor unlaced the canoe and drew out a pair of huge sledge-runners, turned up fully a foot at each solid hickory toe. He laid them massively down, then extracted two long bamboo poles, ending in plate-sized wattle baskets. A large shapeless rucksack appeared on his back. As he wore his regular poacher-pocketed climbing tweeds, fishing hat, gaiters and clinkered boots he struck uncommon silence into the chromatic throng about us. Shouldering his burden and scattering lesser fry, he strode off. We had agreed to go on to the plateau, although the Apprentice, dreaming of effortless thousands of feet of Jaguar (a curiously revolting Grade II descent), remained reluctant. I followed. The Apprentice roared at us over the juke-boxes.

'You're not *climbing* up? What's the lift for?'

The Doctor smiled benignly across an open sea of mouths.

'We can't waste time on a lift. We're late already. I told you, you should have brought your skins.' He turned, causing a travelling ripple of ducking, and marched on. I hurried after him.

When the crowd had thinned sufficiently for us to see the snow beneath us, we stopped and put on skins. The Doctor produced from his rucksack two seven-foot lengths of genuine seal skin. 'Damned fine animal it must have been,' he said reverently as he buckled the harness. 'Never let me down in twenty-five years. Tore out a big chunk on a tin the first time we did the Haute Route, and lemmings ate a bit that Lapland trip; but there's always enough left for patching.' He pulled the last thong tight and stepped aboard into great hinged and bolt-headed bindings. A pause to press his pipe; then he clanked away elk-like and I shuffled after, in unyielding contemporary footgear. No wonder the Apprentice – who would be clamped irreversibly flat to aluminium and fibreglass – preferred the chairlift.

Hoots followed us from the queue where that metallescent youth was indulging in ignoble gibes.

'Can't think how he can waste good ski-ing time – never mind money – on those antiquated tattie-elevators,' remarked the Doctor, plunging upwards through a Gate. A local Beer Trophy was being run, and I scuttled alongside, ears burning.

True enough, we were quite a way up before the Apprentice reached the end of the queue. Then he whisked above us, attempting to spear the Doctor's hat with a flash of Japanese chrome steel. 'I'll get a couple of runs in while I'm waiting for you,' he shouted. Waggling his glitter in triumph, he vanished into the blue. I heaved along grimly, exiguous on icy rubble. The Doctor, well ahead, elaborated on the superior rhythm of climbing in skins. 'Now even with trikes your feet would be slipping about in a place like this. Effortless with skins.' Push. Slide. Push. Slither. Slide. Push.

We climbed higher. We stopped once to reassemble a gentleman in an ankle-length cagoule and a label. My companion felt him all over, pronounced him fit as a fiddle, slapped him on the back and returned him to his erratic and billowing descent. He did not get far.

'Carrying too much sail,' observed the Doctor. Push. Slide. Push.

Nearly there. Above us an individual appeared at great speed, bent in a stiff right-angle. We paused. Ski-sticks and expression fixed unwaveringly ahead, legs wide apart, he charged past us to the enemy below. Appropriately, he was capped with a Balaclava. Our respectful resumption was momentarily interrupted by the trajectory of his Instructor, bewailing the errant lamb – 'Benzeneez, benzeneez' – and cursing fluently in Austro-Glaswegian. The rest of the flock clutched each other on the pebble-dash wall above. We agreed the slopes were busy enough for the time of year. Slither. Push. Slide. Push.

The air rarefied and I became aware of a great silence. We had topped the corrie. The upper station of the lift lay just visible on our left. No sign of the Apprentice. 'He's probably gone down again for his run,' I remarked, not without envy.

'We can't wait all day. If he doesn't come by the time I've finished waxing, he's obviously funked it,' said the Doctor. 'Seems to admit he needs more practice. Though I'm not at all sure we haven't beaten him. Those things are so slow.'

We had in fact beaten him, as we discovered later. At that moment, and for the next three hours, the Apprentice, blue as his boots, was dangling thirty feet above icy scree in a cold iron chair, consoled by a boisterous north wind. The drive sprocket or some such appendage had jammed. The papers made a lot of it the next day.

Meanwhile, the Doctor applied a glistening tar-like concoction, smelling of Andalsnes boat-yards, to his considerable square-footage. He rubbed each hull energetically with a slab of cork, explaining the eminent practicability of this composition. 'Your plastic soles'll be ripped to pieces on any really interesting bit of ground. All I need do is give another rub – just like this – and be as smooth as ever. Sure you don't want some?' I declined, but my apprehensions, always alert in the Doctor's company, shifted uneasily.

No Apprentice. 'The lad's not coming. Playing at Sliders. Even a lift can't take as long as this. Let's go.' And the Doctor poled off bonily across diamonded whiteness.

There was an uncanny lack of orange peel. There were no other tracks. The sun shone out of a cloudless sky. Miles of glistering plateau. The Doctor was moved to song, not one of his several accomplishments. I cruised behind, lulled by the more agreeable purr of powder beneath smooth plastic. Bliss.

Yes, it was a good day, although, being early January, a short one. I steered him away from the worst stretches of dragon's teeth ('nothing like rough stuff to test your technique!'). I followed gratefully his tracks, twin country lanes, through fathoms of drift. I skidded, marvelling, above his flagship manoeuvrings on steep ice (gold would not have tempted me beneath them – nor within range of his poles, wielded with true Bannockburn fervour). I drank unashamedly his ice-cold wine and tea at our farthest point. 'Nothing like it; cools you and warms you at the same time. Just the thing for today. I bet *he's* slogging beer right now, hogging the fleshpots between runs. Must have done tens of thousands of feet – but he's young, and needs the practice. Takes a long time to learn how to ski.'

We sailed leisurely back. At times, I clattered frantically and

expensively across windsawn patches of granite and heather; the Doctor did not appear to notice them, being occupied with his pipe, which was not drawing well that day ('this damned north wind'). At times, too, I narrowly escaped engulfment by the craters his baskets left among the polished windslab.

His falls, for – mercifully – he too had falls, were collapses worthy of such imperial progress. When the powder clouds had blown away, crossed limbs and hickory stood magnificent in ruin against the landscape. A grunt, then Ozymandias himself creaked and elevated out of the depths, raising himself with impossible flexions of hinge, leather and tendon. He would dust himself down, search for his pipe, and explain at length how, given that precise conjunction of dynamics and meteorology, such a fall in such a direction in such snow was quite inevitable; almost, it seemed, praiseworthy. After which, climbing over the rim of his late demonstration, he would punt away, apparently satisfied. He was, however, notably more cautious for fully three minutes after each fall, and later in the day I detected a slight limp and a recurrent reindeer-like clang as if some weight-bearing machinery had come adrift in his bindings; but there seemed more than enough to spare and our speed remained respectably high on the Amundsen scale.

At last we returned to our starting point, not far from the top station. The Doctor cast anchor with both sticks, fiddled a chain or two and sprang lightly ashore. Puffing his pipe, he raised seven feet of hickory and examined below waterline, to the wonder of a small crash-hatted green-goggled urchin, Number 10.

'Hm, not bad. Picked up very few stones this time. Excellent wax. Pity I've almost finished the last barrel. Comes in drums now; not half so good.' Then he suddenly straightened up and dropped his timber, pinning beneath it the fluorescent ski-lets of Number 10. 'There he is! Just coming off the lift. For the *nth* time, I'd say. Look how he's staggering. Punchdrunk, these fellows.' The Apprentice indeed slid drunkenly towards us, skis crossed, eyes staring. He had in fact just been released from his three-hour dangle at minus five. He could not speak.

The Doctor picked up his skis, reassuringly patted the liberated Number 10, and climbed back into the cockpit. He put away his pipe and prodded the still speechless Apprentice with a monstrous basket

(I was fascinated by the curved iron hook beneath it). He beamed invitingly.

'Come on, now – a race down, eh? Give us ten yards' start; remember you've been practising all day, and we're stiff.'

He sculled furiously off, leaving black streaks on the snow.

A couple of wee smashers, preening nearby, tittered.

My leader of a hundred icy cruxes, the Apprentice is nothing if not game. He rumbled some improbable liquid-nitrogen oath, rolled eyes to the sky, and hurled himself stiffly down. I followed, circumspectly. It was, after all, Jaguar.

There is a small rock island near the middle of Jaguar. The Doctor, leaning back contemplatively in a shower of ice, rode his sticks like an experienced cavalry general; a tug at the reins, and he was carried off safely leftwards, out of the fray. The Apprentice, bombing down inert and frozen, remembered too late. Jaguar struck – hard. He somersaulted several yards and continued, mercifully beyond teeth and claws, on his back, head foremost. Eventually he came to rest, against a pair of spectators. The Doctor, completing his hundred-metre flourish, sallied in on one knee, bent in a pensive Telemark. He slowed gracefully to a halt; rose, and leaned, sticks beneath chin. He looked down, Wellington from his horse. The spectators held gloved hands in silence.

'Well, well. You fellows just do too much Downhill for one day. You should take time off, sit around a bit. Chair and a nice cold beer in the sun for an hour or two. That's what I'd do if I had to stay and practice here. Not race up and down like this. You get careless. Lose control. Must keep control on a mountain, you know; otherwise, even ski-ing can become dangerous.' He and the sun gleamed together, through gold-rimmed Polaroids.

The Apprentice glared up weakly. His crash hat was dented. Small blue fragments lay about him on the snow.

In the bar we grew mellow. The Apprentice was gratefully welcoming back his various joints. 'Oh, ski-ing's good fun once in a while,' said the Doctor, raising his Glen Rauchle, 'but not a patch on glissading. Glissading's straightforward. Don't need all these contraptions. But mind you, one thing you do need' – he tipped back reminiscently – 'you do need a good long axe.'

# SPORTSMANSHIP

'The sport of mountaineering ought not to be conducted so as to interfere with the sport of shooting.' The Doctor finished his quotation from the Club Guide, closed the book with a righteous snap and stuffed it back in his rucksack.

'Well then, what do we do?' asked the Apprentice irritably.

Of course, we shouldn't have been there on a late September Thursday afternoon, bang (we crouched apprehensively) in the middle of Inversightie deer forest. But coincidence of a sudden holiday, glorious sun, and a fine new route on the Upper Corrie, had overcome scruples. We had done the climb, lazed the tops and were lolloping down long heathery slopes. Then we had seen glittering beads – Range Rover, Land Rover and some hermaphroditic kind of Terrain Vehicle – parked below in the glen. We had sunk in the heather. We felt horribly exposed.

Indeed, a dilemma. To crawl away unseen would risk intercepting an accidental high-velocity rifle bullet. To rise and march brazenly down would, though satisfying the Apprentice's political views, upset the sport and possibly risk intercepting a not so accidental high-velocity rifle bullet. One never knew. Stalking was Big Money these days, and Inversightie was now in the hands of a London leisure syndicate. Their guests could include any aggressive entrepreneur.

The Doctor scanned the hill with his Trinovids. He searched for stalkers, not stalked. He found both, and worked out a route. If we were quick, we could slip between hairy hide and Harris tweed; unseen, unheard and unsmelt. The ground was peat-haggy enough to protect us from all except mortar fire.

He led away, wriggling from sopping depression to depression. We followed, groaning silently, elbows and knees soaked. The Doctor's tweeds were better than terylene for this vermicular progress; the hairs acted as *setae*; and wetness remained warm, mud invisible. Every so often he raised a tweed-clad head. We were still safe; on one side, ten points grazing; on the other, six backsides crawling; all seven intent on the day's business, not on us. Our sympathies lay with the stag, not with the plump executive doups. Through the glasses we saw the beast browse; sniff, lower, and browse again. It moved from patch to patch, a ripple of sunlit muscle. It would soon be sausages. We consoled ourselves by making merry at the guests' expense, which must already have been considerable.

We were just about to leave a large green saucer of watercress, and the Doctor had breasted the top of its heathery rim, when we heard a burst of hissing like a conflagration of snakes. Astonishment radiated down on us, together with a metallic clatter; and then loud furious whispers.

'Damnation, who the devil are *you*, sir?' breathed an unknown but tightly-buttoned court-martial voice.

'Confound it, I could ask the same of you, sir!' we heard the Doctor stoutly breathe back. We sank deeper into dank stalks, the Apprentice purple with suppressed mirth.

The Doctor and the stranger had met eye-to-eye at the top, each having crawled up, with elaborate precautions, from opposite sides. Chagrin was mutual. The stranger received such a fright he had let go his rifle; hence the clatter. With dreadful consequences.

'Damnation, damnation, you have lost me my beast!' The stag was no longer grazing. It had vanished. This was serious. But our leader was up to it.

'Confound it, man, you have lost me *mine* – dropping your rifle; dash it, *dropping your rifle!* The whole corrie echoed!' The Doctor pointed to the hillside behind the stranger. 'Look – nothing there now!' Which was true.

The stranger was clearly unsettled. He paused. He cleared his throat. He asked the Doctor over; he produced a flask, apologies, and his name. Colonel Gow-Gow. Embassies were established. As the Doctor crawled over, he divested himself of rucksack and signalled us to stay put. We glanced behind us. The other hunters continued, obviously after a different stag.

Colonel Gow-Gow was, despite his name, alone. 'My man is away down the corrie. With the other two of the party.' Sad days for Inversightie: one stalker to three gentlemen – if they were gentlemen; the Colonel's intonation suggested the others were not. We heard the Doctor intimate that *his* man (and presumably his rifle) were behind, together with a gillie. Colonel Gow-Gow paused again, disconcerted by this suggestion of a retinue. He went on, more rapidly, 'I think *my* man said some *climbers* were coming down the glen. He's gone to give 'em hell. The most stupid, selfish, devils, climbers. Always going out and getting lost and killing other people *looking* for them. I'd leave 'em to rot.' 'I'm sure' agreed the Doctor. 'Selfish swine, spoiling a whole day's sport – *one man* – ' hissed the Colonel (his voice was crimson) 'one man can spoil a *whole day's* sport for people who've had to travel hundreds of miles to get it.' 'And some have had to pay hundreds of pounds to get it, as well,' added the Doctor, genially. The Colonel stopped, and cleared his throat; he nosed to a different line. 'Changed days at the old place now. Not like when the Duke was here. *Then* we had some good times!'

Having inferred his at least previous eminence, the Colonel was moved to pour out another dram; we heard the glob-glob. Then smacking of two pairs of lips. Below stairs, we thirsted. (One pair smacked like boots on a doormat; we guessed (correctly) that the Colonel had protruding teeth and a moustache.) 'Went off jolly sudden, didn't he, the old Duke?' said the Doctor, still lip-tasting. 'Got a shock when I read about it,' agreed the Colonel. 'Happened to be at the house with him that day,' remarked the Doctor casually, 'he never recovered consciousness after dinner.' (The Doctor had indeed been at the ducal residence that day, called over from the campsite hastily in a professional capacity.) The point was taken, and Gow-Gow was noticeably more respectful. 'Errrhghm; might as well finish this dashed stuff, eh?' Glob-glob. Smack-smack. Sighs.

'Well, I'll just carry on over the hill,' said the Doctor, kindly. 'I feel we haven't lost him yet.' 'I hope you haven't, sir, I *hope* you haven't,' devoutly wished the colonel, 'shall I see you back at the – ah – house?' (he could not say 'hotel'). 'Probably not, probably not,' replied the Doctor, gazing past Cairn Toul, 'I can't *bear* to see what's going on there now. I have – more or less – ah – my own – ah – special arrangements – not, you see, ah – in a Party....' He smiled equally distantly and slithered away, beckoning us to follow well to the right. Our procession left a deflated Colonel, stagless and whiskyless. Also, mud was up his barrel.

Much amused, we wormed on. Some twenty minutes later, we elbowed on to a track; we judged it safe to get up and walk. Immediately, a ferocious blast of hot air hit us.

'What the hell are you doing here?' Most discourteous.

The stalker. A tall man, black as the landscape, with pinebark complexion and expression like a granite cliff; and with curiously shifting black eyes.

The Doctor carefully took him in.

'Andrew, Andrew, that's a fine way to greet us.'

Instantaneous effect. Huge hands clasped his. 'Man, man, it's yourself, so it is. Ah, Doctor, Doctor.'

This pleasing emotion, we learned, was due to the Doctor's having saved Andrew's life when a guest had shot him instead of a stag (another call from the campsite). The Doctor had thus performed the most valuable service in the world. Andrew, it seemed, would do anything for him.

'Now, can I help you at all, Doctor?'

This time we all sampled the flask. (Climbing was not mentioned.) We spoke of the Colonel, and how he had dropped his rifle and lost his beast. Andrew had indeed been the Colonel's 'man'.

'What, yon havering old goat? Comes here for a day and orders you about as if he were – as if he were on a Fortnight's Executive Special, Royal Introductions and all.... I left him to it.' Andrew spat. He was an emotional man; and maybe remembered other days. We asked about the rest of the Colonel's party.

'Just come up from them. Left them on the road. I'm taking the Range Rover down to pick 'em up. Now, let me give you a lift... och, there's room.' We enquired gently about the fate of the Colonel. 'Oh, damn the Colonel. I'll send a boy up for him later. His ticket runs out at six o'clock anyway: that's another full day he'll have to fork out for. Mean old sod. Never a tip. Aye on about his pension. I'd pension him.' We asked again about the remaining guests.

'One's a Dutchman; drunk. And the other's a Jap,' said Andrew, stretching his head out of the window and pulling the wheel round hard. 'Both industrialists. Both too fat. Both good sports. Just here for the hell of it.' We jolted over the ruts. Then: 'Now, here's something you can perhaps do for *me*, Doctor' – Andrew changed into second and glanced sidewise at our companion.

The Japanese gentleman was to fly home that night. He had been a week at Inversightie, his only glimpse of the British Isles, and still had not seen – a Duke. It was once the home of a Duke, the brochure had said. He would so like to see a Duke. Could Andrew not find him a Duke to see? (Here our driver looked meaningly at us all, leant back and patted his trouser pocket; he was clearly a practical man.) Now – he changed into third as the surface improved – what about the Doctor being a Duke? The Doctor would look the very part – tall, distinguished – here Andrew laid it on unhesitatingly, with sidelong shifts of his bright black eyes (to produce which his father, a dour Speysider, had eventually to marry Maureen Mary Maguire, on the old Duke's former Killarney estate).

The Doctor was entertained. 'Right, I'll be a Duke for the next few miles.' But when we reached the venue, there was no Japanese. Only the Dutchman, flat as a polder. He had been sick. Andrew jumped out and roused him ungently. He was pushed in, rubbing eyes. Apparently the Japanese had been given a lift by someone else back to the hotel; the Nederlander was too well sluiced, half Zuider Zees over, to be admitted to a car. He began, in fact, to embrace Andrew and was heaved behind the back seats, where he resumed his snores. Tight as a windmill, and in no state to be impressed by nobility. Andrew and the duke-elect therefore discussed the Japanese, who had insisted on going out to stalk in the kilt he had bought in Balqueenie. 'But the midges?' No bother; he had kept on his long cotton underpants. Andrew shook his head in admiration.

'There he is!' Outside the hotel gates, taking photographs of his late crew. When he saw us, he trundled over, lenses flashing, long-johns winking through the tartan.

'Mr Matsui, I have a great surprise for you.' 'For me, for me? Thank you, thank you.' 'I have the honour to introduce to you a gentleman who expressed a great desire to meet the President of the, of the....' 'Koriyanagishigamatsu Corporation,' gleamed Mr Matsui, arm outstretched, '...of the Corporororation,' continued Andrew ('he *is* drunk,' the Apprentice whispered, 'he *must* be') '... His Grace, His Grace the Duke, THE DUKE OF GLENLIVET....'

The Doctor lightly extended three fingers, eyes aglint... Mr Matsui seized them and bowed deeply, kilt (Ancient Matheson) sweeping the ground. The Duke nearly overbalanced, but managed to get free in time. He inclined his head, graciously. 'Excuse, my Duke; a photograph.'

Click.

And another lens.

Click.

Two steps back, and a huge lens.

'One moment, my Duke.' A tripod appeared and extended itself. Matsui pressed something, skipped and joined us, smiling up at the Duke.

Delayed action.

Click.

We all relaxed. Smiles were passed round, several circuits. The Duke, reluctantly, could not accept the so kind invitation to the hotel. He had to be back. To see, presumably, to his dukedom. More handshaking, bows, inclinations, scuttling of smiles. We left, Andrew accompanying Mr Matsui with a straight face, grim as Braeriach; invisible clouds of blarney played about him.

'A pleasing rogue in some ways, Andrew,' was the ex–duke's comment as we trudged to Balqueenie. 'Tells me he'll be head stalker soon. Never got beyond pony-man in the old boy's time; but he probably suits the new owners – or they him.'

We had a good meal in Balqueenie and were walking towards the Doctor's car when a taxi passed us. It stopped. It was Mr Matsui, returning to Japan, via Dyce. He and the Doctor, a Duke once again, chatted. The Doct... Duke... had of course visited Japan; and climbed mountains. And toured shrines. And seen castles. They were soon deep in the Katsura Imperial Villa at Kyoto. 'Such a difference the lay-out there to the warrior garden of the Shogun's – *that* was all bristles,' smiled the Duke, 'like Colonel Gow-Gow.'

'Ah, you know Go-Go! I tell him I meet a Duke. Long thin gentleman in knee-breeches. Who had been on hill. He very upset. He meet you before and he not know – you were Duke!' 'Ah, there's no point in blazoning it about nowadays,' shrugged our nobleman. Mr Matsui gazed up admiringly.

Just then a ragged unwashed crowd appeared, dangling helmets and karabiners, singing a loud improper song. Some of the Weasels. They hooted at their fellow-member, the Apprentice. They knew the Doctor, and came over to us. They slapped him on the back unceremoniously – 'Hi Doc, been sunning yer erse all day, eh?' and suchlike remarks well out of protocol. The Duke bore it, but eased himself and Mr Matsui away. The latter had clasped his hands together. (We trusted he had taken 'Doc' for 'Duke', and had inferred some linguistic relaxation.)

'So wonderful. Democracy. Now I do understand your country: all in same boat, now. Beautiful!' Then, briskly, 'One more picture, please.' He snapped the Duke, who looked less happy, among the riotous Weasels. One of them was bowing. Another held his nose.

Had that swine of an Apprentice hinted anything?

Mr Matsui popped back into the taxi. He shook hands through the window with the Duke repeatedly, as it gathered speed. The Duke trotted alongside, clutched inextricably.

'So wonderful to meet you, dear sir, so wonderful. Such experience to meet gentleman who so – ' here he let go, mercifully, and continued leaning out of the window, waving ' – so like *real* Duke in storybook....'

The Doctor rejoined us, exhausted. We never decided what Mr Matsui meant. His English was poor. But he was a very successful industrialist. The Doctor did not ask Andrew; those West Kerry eyes.... Perhaps a joke had been worth more yen than a mere introduction.

As we lay back in the car, we saw the Colonel. He paused, then hurried across. The Doctor skilfully slipped into gear, and waved briefly. The Colonel's smile died, his carefully prepared apology remained undelivered. He diminished in the rear window, tail wagging slower and slower, bone dropped.

His ex-Grace slowed, sighed, and mopped his brow. He pushed his coronet into the gloveshelf. He did not join our conversation. It had been a tiring day. Some miles later, he delivered his conclusion.

It was that, all being equal, the sport of mountaineering ought to be conducted so as not to be interfered with by the sport of shooting.

# THE LOOSENING UP

The Doctor was leading. At least, he was in front. The Apprentice was below me. We all waited. We were all, so far, on a dirty face beneath Càrn Righ. The time was a grey eastwindy November afternoon and far too late. This excursion had begun as a loosening-up for the winter and the Doctor, loose enough, had suggested a final scramble up the sputter of crags before we snuffed the day out with Càrn Righ. 'I brought a rope anyway, in case,' he said.

So here we were. Càrn Righ, tired of waiting, had turned back into mist. But the weather was becoming interested in us. Gusts sniffed, and I swore I saw snow. That east wind....

'What the hell's the matter?' I shouted again. The rope, ridiculous twins of baby nylon, twirled up round an assemblage of idle blocks, among frozen slime and the queasy comforts of the less vascular plants. It was a perfectly easy scramble but for the verglas. And the Doctor had tricounis. He loved them. Their toothless gums gnashed gallantly of his youth. 'Much more reliable than vibrams. Especially on ground like this. Now where' – fixing severely the interjecting Apprentice – 'where would crampons be on ground like this?' We agreed that, on ground like this, we did not know where crampons would be. So the Doctor had led off, scraping pointedly, impressing the moss, while we slid and clutched behind, nimble in fleeting soles. The angle had steepened, to frozen turf, enamelled slabs, and then these lounging blocks. So we had roped up, and the Doctor went on.

That was twenty minutes ago, and there had been no further medical bulletin. The Apprentice gazed about morosely, iron-less. His Rose Street hoard was at home. This was only a loosening-up, and he had come – like me – because of the Doctor's car and considerate habits at bars on the way back.

The blocks eyed us genially, winking with an occasional fleck of snow. Still silence. 'Pull the bloody rope,' suggested the Apprentice. I pulled, quite hard. Shortly after, an irate tug indicated distant displeasure.

'Go up and see,' suggested the Apprentice. I moved off.

'I'll come, too,' said the youth. 'I'll stop you if you slip,' he added generously.

We acknowledged the boulders, patted the liverworts, and progressed slowly, scolding the little ropes as they ran into holes and behind spikes. At the top of a long sleeping block we met the Doctor, folded in a niche.

'Well, you're up at last,' he said. 'Not bad, for vibrams. Now wait here and I'll go on again'

We persuaded him it would be quicker and safer to move together. Darkness and snow were approaching arm in arm, chanting on the wind. To please him we retained the twins, but whipped them into temporary obedience. If we slipped, the thoughtful blocks would sooner or later remember to stop us.

We reached the top of the heap. A few more gaping jumps, and then the greasy plates of summit scree, already well floured. And then, of course, he stuck.

'My foot!' he shouted.

It was well in, out of sight, between the last two big snoring blocks. The Apprentice and I pulled and pushed without avail. We beat thinly at tons of granite. Snow chilled our hands. Wind blew down our necks, telling us so.

Hoods up, we regarded the Doctor. He wiped slush from his eyes.

'Blast,' he remarked.

'Well, you can't stop here,' said the Apprentice. 'You'll have to get the boot off, or the bloody foot or something.'

He produced a large bowie-knife, looked enquiringly at the prisoner, who wiped away more snow, and then he poked it down, sharp end first, beside the ankle.

'Mind my foot.'

'It's the laces first, anyway.'

But he dropped the knife. It clattered irrecoverably.

'We'll have to make a sort of tent,' said the Doctor, 'anoraks weighed down with stones. And I'll be the pole.'

He was most brave. But it was nearly dark and the snow was that thick felted horizontal kind that means to get you. He had to come out. So we pulled, wrenched, back-broke him, until the startled knot peered up; fortunately the laces had been white. My penknife sawed away. A pencil worked under the tip of the tongue.

'Now pull yourself out of the boot.

He lay back, contracting intensely, remembering the correct muscles.

Astonishingly – he was out. The boot dropped hollowly within. We fumbled at various darknesses for it but it was well boxed. He hopped, cursing. We all cursed, gratefully. With oaths and a lace we bound a scarf round the outraged sock and led him off, but not before he'd scratched a mark on the impassive pedal sarcophagus, so that he could come back later with a crowbar.

We hirpled, baby nylons riding our shoulders, over the ridge on the tide of the night, and down rough soft leeward slopes to the eventual road, the blizzard singeing past into tall heather. We fell and rolled and were merry. The Apprentice found a torch in his sack, and it lit. Every flickering burn or so we tied up the scarf, wringing it out. But the foot was warm, thrilled with importance.

'A remarkable thing,' said the Doctor. 'In thirty years on the hills, it's never happened before. And they were going so well, far better than your vibrams. I suppose it was almost a Route. Do you know,' he said, 'I think we should call it The Clam.'

# A CAVE MEET

'The original Cave Meet,' explained the Doctor, 'was nothing of the sort. It was merely named after the cave Adullam, where the discontented gathered – in the twenty-second chapter of the first book of Samuel – remember? Chaps who disagreed with the Committee's Meet went to the Cave Meet, and climbed the hills they wanted to. What I'm suggesting'– he beamed round the silently-sipping table – 'is a Real Cave Meet. Speleology. Pot-holing.'

'Sort of climbing underground,' mused the Apprentice.

'Exactly. But you climb down to start off and up to come back.'

The Doctor was beginning to elaborate on the trials and rewards of the pursuit, when the bell rang for time. We resisted further attempts to raise our enthusiasm below ground level and left him at the Mound somewhat discouraged. 'But he'll be up to something soon, you bet, about these caves,' prophesied the Apprentice gloomily. 'We'll need to keep our weekends booked.'

Not until the Spring did caves rear themselves again. The Doctor drove us to the North-West for the May Holiday. We each designed one of the three days. The Apprentice forged us a new route on An Teallach for Saturday; I shepherded a Sunday marathon to Seana Bhraigh; and the Doctor had charge of Monday.

'An early start,' he warned, the night before. 'We've to drive a bit, first.'

The early start caused our first incident. The Apprentice, eager to assist, offered to move the Doctor's car back to the road while we dismantled the tent. Unfamiliar with the early morning habits of the usually goodnatured old Mercedes, he was rather rough on the rein. Also he had forgotten that reverse occupied that particular position. The Doctor and I escaped with our lives; but the tent was less nimble.

'New poles,' concluded the Doctor philosophically, amidst beetroot apologies. 'We can eat at a B & B tonight. There's one near the place. Old MacGillivray's.'

Where the 'place' was and what we would do there he did not divulge. He hummed to himself, and our hearts sank. Still, it was his day; and it had been his tent. We kept silence.

We kept silence even when he stopped beside a cottage somewhere in Assynt, miles from anywhere above 500 metres. We kept silence when, with broad smiles, he pulled an old kitbag from the boot, loosened the strings and shook out an evil-looking heap of overalls and strange equipment.

The Apprentice automatically kneeled to examine the ironware. Certain items – pitons, slings, étriers, we recognised. But the rest....

The Doctor was proud of his Surprise.

'Ha, thought you'd be interested. Kept it a secret. In England over the New Year – why I wasn't at the Meet. Stayed with a friend at Ingleborough. He's a potholer. Taught me the drill. We did some fine things. Lost John. Alum Pot. And this is the best place in Scotland for caves. Unexplored. Don't worry. I'll lead. You just do exactly as you're told. Easy, for a climber. For instance, these wires....'

And he explained – clearly, I admit – the use of the more comprehensible pieces of iron and webbing. Miners' helmets. Carbide lamps. Flints. Kitbags. Pulleys. And an assemblage of neoprene holes graphically described as a 'wet-suit.'

Some of the kit was all too familiar.

'A shovel – a bloody shovel!' exclaimed the outraged Apprentice, holding up a trenching tool. The crowbar, short, black and malevolent, reduced him to silence.

'Might need 'em,' explained the Doctor 'Unknown ground. Might have to assist Nature.'

Behind the car we changed into unyielding garb smelling of the Ordovician. The Apprentice chose the wet-suit, covering its widespread indecencies with pieces of overall. Unlike our ragged selves the Doctor looked impressive. A Stakhanovite face worker. His carbide, for example, slipped into his headlamp. We others trailed unhappy tubes from a bulging pocket. 'Yes, sometimes they do get caught.'

As he buttoned up, the Doctor began briskly extolling the caves of the neighbourhood. He was becoming intolerable.

'And there's one by Inchnadamph, lived in just after the Ice Age. Peach and Horne found lots of bones there – '

'Red deer, cave bear, reindeer-wolf-and-lynx,' intoned the Apprentice. Cruel; but effective. The Doctor nodded, and laced up his great ironclad boots. Silence.

We were ready. We became aware of prickling eyes of children. Our leader looked at his watch.

'I'll go in and arrange supper,' he said. 'They do a damned good meal.'

He emerged and beckoned us. Embarrassed, we creaked in. Low ceiling. Spread table. More children.

We could not refuse the proffered cups. It was still not nine o'clock.

Mrs MacGillivray, a large and capable body apparently related to people who had looked after the Doctor's wife when a child, doubted the pleasure our mission was supposed to afford.

'And what would you be doing, down there away from the sun and the air, on a fine day like this?' (What, indeed.)

Old MacGillivray, cleaning his gun in the corner, could not see the *use* of it at all, at all. Though it might be interesting, interesting. Down there. But *he* would not go. At all, at all.

Two of our hearts warmed to the MacGillivrays. But the Doctor, rescuing a lump of carbide from a MacGillivray child (they infested the place), enlarged upon the utility of the pursuit. It appeared necessary to investigate almost every crack in the ground, to see where it led... whether chambers, cathedrals, lakes or rivers lay hidden beneath an innocent sheep-snoring brae. Especially rivers.

'Your water will be hard, Mrs MacGillivray? I thought so. Good for thrombosis, bad for soap. And you say you sometimes run short? Well, potholers have often improved water supplies like yours – traced 'em right back, diverted other underground streams to feed 'em. Yours'll be fed by underground streams.'

The MacGillivrays' water supply, in fact, issued biblically out of a split rock just behind the house. Interest having been aroused, the Doctor dilated on the remarkable habits of underground rivers, popping into and out of holes like rabbits; even disappearing on one side of a mountain range, to reappear on the other.

We again became impatient, but old MacGillivray laid down his gun. Unfortunately, he was the ideal listener.

'And what way, Doctor, are they telling if it is the *same* water that comes out one side of a hill that goes in at the other?'

'Fluorescein, Mr MacGillivray, fluorescein. A green dye. A little lasts a long time, and goes a long way. Empty some in a burn one side of a hill – and look for green rivers on the other.'

'Then maybe they could be telling us where the Uisge Dubh comes from.'

The Uisge Dubh was the biggest river on the estate. Its salmon fishing was old Inverludie's main source of income. But it often fell very low, almost to dryness. Especially this year. Now it came out of a hole, way up in Coire Ghlas. Would we be able to trace its origin? No green dye, though – or very little. The fishing tenants might object.

'Perfectly harmless. But I see their point. Could dye the fish. Green salmon and salad....'

We brightened. The day achieved an aim. We would search for the underground source of the Uisge Dubh. McGillivray assured us the hole was big enough to squeeze through. Our clothes were old ones. And the Doctor was long, not wide. A fine opportunity, with the water so low. But it would be dangerous in rain. We would need a sharp eye in case the weather turned cloudy.

We reflected that the eye would need to be sharp to penetrate several hundred feet of Beinn a' Ghrunnda, a morose protuberance above the corrie which doubtless somewhere fathered the Uisge Dubh. Still, a touch of peril would add interest....

We trudged away, MacGillivray at the gate remarking that the weather might well hold. But he would not like to be going down there; at all, at all. But we should be doing a grand job, a grand job. The higher the Uisge Dubh the higher the fishing rent, and the higher the fishing rent the longer old Inverludie could keep The Company from buying up the estate.

The sight of the Hole silenced the Apprentice's harangue on Historical Necessity. It was indeed uninviting. Its waistcoat of grass was a poisonous emerald. It looked narrow enough, but by the end of the day we considered it well into the coach and horses category. It was, however, only three feet high, one of which feet was occupied by the Uisge Dubh.

'Light up!' cried the Doctor.

We worked our flints assiduously. At length a pallid glare appeared, flickering balefully as we soothed our tubes. The Doctor turned a knob, and immediately shone like Pharos. 'These later types are much better.'

With a sigh, the Apprentice and I knelt – Lord! – and squeezed into cold issuing darkness. The Doctor dismissed the few clouds in the west as insignificant, and followed. Why he didn't go first, I don't know. These things just happen. So we all had to back out again, cursing and bumping. Then he led in. I blinked furtively westward. Quite a few more clouds. Rushes were bending. South-west wind....

In again. I need not describe the progress. We were on all fours, straddled amongst vindictive boulders, in a foot of impatient elbowing water, kitbags clutching the roof. The Doctor's boots were just in front of my helmet, mine just in front of the Apprentice's. We suffered the basic principles of shunting. Clang. Stop. Clang. Go. Clang. Stop. Then cries from behind. The Apprentice's light had gone out. I turned my head; to be clouted back by the roof. Then mine went out. The carbide tin fell into the water.

In this emergency the light in front also disappeared. I roared. An echo. Then the Doctor's voice, booming Plutonically.

'Marvellous. Good Lord. Had no idea. Look at this!'

I bumped on towards the voice. A dim circle of light. I fell through, into a vast cavern, lit by the Doctor's headlamp. The luxury of – ah! – unfolding, standing up.

Preceded by oaths, the Apprentice appeared. He gazed up from the hole, chimpanzee-like. It really was remarkable. The air was still, warm. Only drips in the silence. Huge damp encrusted walls swam above us out of torchlight.

I wandered off across the pebbly beach, but was called back.

'Careful. Must keep together. Like a plateau in mist. Even Pitfoulie couldn't find us here.'

The Uisge Dubh itself had disappeared. Before hunting it, the Doctor took out compass, wax pencil and plastic notebook, and muttered and scribbled. We gathered it was much more difficult than back-bearings on Braeriach. He pencilled a runic symbol over the exit from our hole, then, nose down, bloodhounded the deepest centimetres of water, lifting his pencil intermittently to the nearest wall. We followed, the Apprentice occasionally adding artistic touches, for the pleasure of a future Abbé Breuil.

The cave unrolled, became narrower. At one point the Apprentice tweaked my sleeve, grinning. He extracted a huge meat bone from his kitbag (begged from Mrs MacGillivray, a woman with an iron sense of humour) and laid it by a boulder. It should interest the Doctor on the way back....

Presently we heard a thunder of splashing. The Apprentice paled beneath his acetylene. Those clouds.

'Ha, a waterfall. Thought so. Should make a good climb.'

Let us pass briefly over the next four hours. The three pitches in the waterfall (where the Apprentice's wet-suit acted like the rose on a watering can). The time the étrier stuck in the pulleys. The number of times the lights went out. The spilling of the spare carbide tin inside the Apprentice's wet kitbag, and his malodorous and potentially explosive presence thereafter. The contortions, abrasions, suffocations. The terrible thought of the sun above. The worse thought of the clouds.

Once, when we had come through a particularly trying tunnel, we were walking gratefully towards a flat clean floor and the Doctor was explaining the doubtless perinatal basis of our satisfaction ('Just like being born, you know'); when suddenly he disappeared and the floor parted in a splash.

'Should have remembered,' he spluttered. 'Still water's quite invisible.' This pleased us; until the pool ended in a blank wall. Below it the water lay black and faintly stirring. Horrible.

'Ah, a Sump. Good!'

The sump fulfilled its unattractive name. One had to go down under the oily water, along a short submerged passage (if there was one) and up to the other side (if, again, there was one). It was debatable who would fare worse – the leader seeking a way, or the last man, alone with thoughts of the Other Side.

The Doctor probed. He knelt, dipped his head and rubber torch. We watched these more veterinary procedures numbly. His head emerged.

'Looks all right. Quite short. What luck to find one. Superb cave. Now, you hold on to this string. It's tied to me. I'll tug twice when I'm through. Three times and you follow. Don't get tangled in it.' And he disappeared completely.

The water gurgled, and resumed its black ruminations. The Apprentice squatted glumly, holding his string. We counted and watched the line. A float would have helped. Ten. Twenty. No bite. Fifty. A hundred.... We looked at each other. 'Tug it,' I suggested.

He tugged. No reply. He pulled, and the string rose, length after length, from the darkness, to the very end. We laid it reverently on the muddy bank, a wet wreath. Well....

'We've *got* to find him..!' – and the Apprentice, too, slipped down and vanished into the unknown.

My feelings may be imagined. Five. Ten. Twenty....

Suddenly the water boiled and a gasping Apprentice appeared. 'He's trapped, struggling,' he choked, and vanished again. Sweat. Ages. Then another swirl, and the Apprentice emerged, dragging a convulsive figure after him. We stretched the wreckage on the bank, coughing and streaming. The Apprentice's remarkable courage had been rewarded. He smiled modestly. I gripped his hand.

When sufficiently oxygenated, the Doctor sat up. (He had violently refused the Kiss of Life.) He swore. Loudly, and for half a minute. We feared shock. But it was not shock. The explanation panted out, punctuated by fearsome hoastings and spittings.

He had got to the other side. But the string had come undone. He had waited. No follower. So he had plunged in again and gone back in search. Midway in the submerged tunnel he had encountered the Apprentice – also in search. Naturally they vigorously attempted to rescue each other. Neither won, and each retired to his corner for air. In the second round, as we had seen, the Apprentice prevailed.

After a decent interval, the Doctor led off again, *sans* string. It was bad, but soon over. The Doctor wrung my hand, adjusted my trembling helmet.

'Jolly good, eh? Don't worry' – as my shakings increased – 'I've a $CO_2$ lifejacket, in case you get cramp.'

That lifejacket nearly belied its name, as we shall see. But just then we guests were quite demoralised. The Apprentice was praying for the elevated peace of a *sestogrado*.

'Blood glucose low. Good spot for a bite.' So we ate our acetylene sandwiches, by one lamp turned down. The Doctor, munching, peered at his muddy pages, tapped his fingers mathematically. Navigation was in progress.

'We should be almost at the watershed, if the strata lie as I think. That means we *could* divert the next big stream we meet. It's through that wall, probably' – indicating a brutal million tons or so – 'and send it down the one we've come up. *That* would feed the Uisge Dubh, and buck up old Inverludie no end.'

We pointed out that despite the pleasure of old Inverludie we had to get out by the hole we came in, together with old Inverludie's increased rental.

'Of course, we first need to find a higher way out. But there are dozens of little passages up there. Shouldn't take long.'

With foreboding, we climbed after him. Three wax pencils and a ball of string later, navigation assured us we were on tapping terms with the southwest face of Beinn a' Ghrunnda. As if to confirm this improbable suggestion, a hairline of light coincided in all our imaginations at the end of a tunnel on the right. But that tunnel was even narrower than ours. We stuck. Retreat throttled us with jackets.

'No good. Have to strip off,' said the Doctor.

'Strip off?'

'Put clothes in kitbags and drag 'em behind.'

This last degradation was not eased by the Doctor's jovially clinical remarks. He led off. I followed his kitbag. Then my kitbag. Then the Apprentice. Then, presumably, his kitbag. The Doctor gripped the trenching tool. ('Might need it; but mustn't dislodge anything; could be awkward.')

After an hour and twenty feet of this horizontal crux even our leader became less sanguine. With weary humour the Apprentice suggested we call it off and get back before they missed us at roll-call. Kitbags mercifully fielded the Doctor's subsequent puns about Stalag Meit. Then he called excitedly.

'I can dig here. I'm sure there's light ahead. We're moving.' Then, 'My kitbag's jammed. Poke it along and I'll pull with my foot.'

I poked. He pulled. Badly jammed. The crowbar in it didn't help. Pull. Push. It moved a little, then hooked once more.

In despair I punched it, hard into its guts. Damn the thing.

Then a hiss. Carbide? Good Lord, not here.

Not carbide. No smell. But the bag began to bulge, expand, swell visibly, until it filled the whole width of the passage. It was quite immovable, and resilient as a football.

Communication with the Doctor became understandably even more difficult, but I gathered that I must have depressed the emergency button on the $CO_2$ lifejacket. It was now inflated, and would keep the wearer afloat for 4 weeks in a normal sea.

'Jings!' said the Apprentice, when informed. He reserved mildest oaths for the worst occasions. I agreed. We simply had to uncork the Doctor. We caterpillared back, propelling our bags. In the relative space of the outer passage we searched them for suitable instruments. Then the Apprentice – he was fresher, and this was clearly a V.S. pitch – went in, a great knife between his teeth and a hook (probably meant for some shuddering abseil) in his hand. I squatted and tried to keep warm and think of nothing. Especially not of $CO_2$ poisoning. *Grotte des Chiens.*

At last a scuffling, gasping. The operation had been successful. Breech delivery. The Doctor lay, deflated as his kitbag. But we had to get back. While we dressed he admitted that although there must be an exit along there, this perhaps was not the time to explore it. Rheumatically, we returned, ticking off the waxings, winding up the string. Before the sump, the Doctor made a half-hearted sortie; but he could not go far alone.... We others pointedly pricked our jets.

He crawled back, jubilantly. He had found two small streams. One on the right should be the Uisge Dubh; the other, its potential feeder. To gain information, he had put a little – just a little – fluorescein into the left-hand one. In a cardboard packet. So as not to get ourselves all green, if it did happen to be the Uisge Dubh. The cardboard would dissolve in a couple of hours, when we should be out.

We made good time. The sump held no terrors. We had less clothes and skin to delay us in the tunnels. The Doctor, leanest, was well ahead. Suddenly he bellowed.

'CAVE BEAR!'

Thirty thousand years of conditioning flung myself and the Apprentice high up the wall. We clung there a horrible second before contemporary sense and the Doctor returned, the latter dangling Mrs MacGillivray's bone.

'Ha!' he said.

The Apprentice, higher than I was, carefully concluded his examination of an interesting section of strata. We climbed down and continued.

Fast. Faster. We wanted sun and air. Even the Doctor claimed he smelt grass (*Molinia*). We worried about the clouds. But our leader had recorded the drips per second at various spots on the way in; as the same number dripped on the way out, he pronounced it still a fine day.

It was. Two hours later we lay on the bank, photosynthesising morale. The water showed no trace of dye, then or as we staggered down to the cottage.

'That left-hand branch will make a fine feeder. We'll come back' – he caught our eyes – 'I'll come back with that Ingleborough chap and switch the points. Then old Inverludie can enjoy his moths in

peace.' (The laird was a diligent lepidopterist; he had taken a Dotted Footman on the very slopes we were crossing.) The Uisge Dubh had more or less washed us and the sun had dried us. We changed at the car.

Weary, almost happy, certainly very relieved, we plodded up MacGillivray's path. An urchin scampered down, swinging two yellow buckets. Birds sang.

'Well, and did you enjoy your day?' Mrs MacGillivray, arms akimbo, looked quizzically down at us. We truthfully said it had been memorable. The Doctor limped over to old MacGillivray; he began to sketch and explain vigorously.

'Your supper will be a little late,' said Mrs MacGillivray. 'I've had to send the lad out for water. But there's enough for you to wash,' she added, a trifle grimly. She returned to the kitchen.

The Apprentice looked at his hands and guessed about his face. Also, he still smelt a little. He went to the bathroom. I patted a small wetnosed child.

Suddenly a roar. The Apprentice's head through the doorway. It was a horrible colour of bile. I leapt up. Acetylene poisoning....

'Green! The water's all green!'

The Doctor spun round in horror.

'Green! All green!' the Apprentice roared.

Mr MacGillivray went on talking.

'I would not like to have been down there at all, at all,' he said.

# FIXING US UP*

The forecast was frightful for the North. Gale winds, blizzards of powder snow. Gullies would be choked, faces wiped. All this after weeks of rain, and now in a final pipe-splitting frost. And the Apprentice had brand-new lobster-points to try out, cooked expensively to a gourmet's taste, and I a grinning Terrordactyl of advanced evolution, fierce from its creator; both of us fondled virgin ice-daggers fit for some sub-glacial Mafia. We had lightened our wallets for the new season, and this could have been the first run. We ached to prickle up some crisp verticality, glassy between admiring cliffs. We thought of Zero in two hours. We were bitter....

So we fell for the Doctor's jovial invitation:

'I can fix you up!'

He would take us to some southern ice. Not the Lakes – weather just as bad there. Nor even the Grey Mare's Tail – that would fairly wag in this wind. But much nearer:

'Just outside Edinburgh – edge of the Moorfoots. Perfect just now – sheltered, private, fine for a practice.'

Our forebodings, well-nourished on the past, gorged themselves as we trudged up the scabby grass of vast mounds ambling with sheep. But no: improbably, two of these heaps heaved back and exhibited, with considerable pride, an astonishingly high and apparently vertical earthen gully. On either side grazed well-belayed sheep; below lay more earth, and more sheep; but within, a sliver of ice launched dazzlingly upwards to a giddy bulge and then vanished backwards into blue sky.

The Doctor extended a long arm hospitably: 'This hill's the Corse o Whalloch, and that's – Whalloch's Dreepie. It should fix you up all right.'

Apparently the Dreepie only dreeped after heavy rain, being fed from a bog above. Some geological quirk ensured its almost vertical incision in turfy earth.

We approached gingerly and prodded. The surface was yielding but sound; inside was hard.

'It's even better higher up,' announced our host, complacently.

* Originally titled 'The Dreepie' when first published in *Cold Climbs*

We demurred a little at the grass stems, rushes and bits of turf poking through here and there.

'Ah, they give it body. Make it tough, absolutely reliable. Can't come away. Never splits. Make it like fibreglass, reinforced concrete, bricks with straw; and all that.'

We cut short the Doctor's technical explanations of Griffith cracks and buckled on our new equipment. The Doctor was faithful to long axe, fishing hat, tweeds and tricounis. 'You can hold a long axe short, but not a short one long.' And tweeds stuck better than terylene – but, he assured us, the Dreepie ice would be very adherent. It was.

He took to the proffered lead ('Might as well show the way') and bucketed up at a showering Charlet gallop. Earth and roots, as well as ice, fell around us. Unconvinced by the stems, we had agreed on a rope. We hoped only sheep were watching. Our leader hacked a platform, harrowed it, and summoned us.

The Apprentice went before me, taking the thin unbucketed edge, pointing elegantly. I followed, loops in hand. It was good stuff.  A gentle kick and a stab: delicious admittance, firm grasp. Wonderfully safe.  We mounted rapidly, calves thrilling.  Marvellous to be back on ice even if the Nordwand of a Corse o Whalloch and ten feet wide, and even if sheep did munch mildly eye to eye with you as you passed. *Maa*. We were merry, and exchanged a word with each of them in turn. *Baa*.

The Doctor, having identified for us the local Traverse of the Gods and the White Spider (the latter carrying much grass in its web), began the final stretch below the bulge.

'Time me. See how much longer you are with spikes. No need for crampons in Scotland – take all the craft out of climbing. And as for daggers – too damned emotional.'

Multi-coloured debris rocketed past: the Apprentice drove in a peg to make sure, extracted his claws with difficulty and then slammed them well home; we would cut no steps. I did likewise, some 15ft. below, and we settled to wait, muscles twanging. But it was good training for the Ben and Raven's and the rest.

The Doctor's toothy heels above us ceased to gnash: 'Come on up a bit. I'll need all the rope to get over that bulge.'

The Apprentice nodded, unclipped and heaved at his peg, cursed, bashed it, heaved and cursed again. Jammed fast.

'Ah, that's the Dreepie ice,' explained the Doctor. 'Particularly near the edge. It's the mud and stems. Plastic. Very binding. Leave it for now.'

The Apprentice cursed again, straightened up and tried to extract his left foot. Squirm.

His right foot. Squirm.

His dagger. Squirm.

He undulated on his points of attachment like a tent in a gale. But he did not take off. He was stuck.

Stuck.

Terrible oaths. Squirm.

Stuck....

I informed our consultant.

'It'll be the grass again. Same as for the peg. Still, it does make it absolutely reliable.... Pity you had to use those things. Rather spoilt a classic little climb. Shouldn't have kicked in so far; but then of course you mightn't have kicked in far enough.... Need plenty of experience, crampons. Especially in Scotland.'

We decided to abandon the Apprentice meanwhile. I was to unclip the rope, reach the Doctor, and belay him. Then he could top the bulge, gain the bog, peg in, abseil down and prise our writhing companion from his flypaper.

'You just wait there,' the Doctor called down, 'you'll be fine, you can't fall; Dreepie ice is very firm....'

It had begun to snow. I was fortunately below the really possessive stuff. I clawed up the steps. The Doctor then tackled the bulge.

The ice went *poop* under his axe. He explained how to carve such rubber. He feathered his slash ('like rowing Stroke in rough water'), then spooned each step backwards adzewise ('like serving jelly; but firmer').

Much firmer. I found my prongs tight. I kicked back in alarm. But I must have offended some monocotyledon or other, for my left foot shot free and swung me backwards out of balance. I flung up both arms and my Terrordactyl took wing. I saw the Doctor silhouetted above, tongue out, reaching his axe over the bulge. With a fearful effort I lunged forward again on my right foot and drove the dagger well home before me; and clung. Relief. Sob.

But I had stabbed the rope and buried it through the dagger point well into the solid treacle. Irretrievable....

And worse.... Groans from above indicated that I had tautened the rope just as my leader had fully extended himself and his tongue, arm over the bulge. He had been pulled down onto his tongue and his angular chin, his axe had been driven in hard somewhere up there and his grip plucked off it; so that his bony wrist now flapped weakly above, twisted firmly into the end of the axe-sling.

We were indeed in a fix; in a frozen frieze. Snow fell heavier, burying the Doctor's bitten and fragmentary oaths. The sheep were impressed. They crowded the top of The Dreepie, chewing knowledgeably. Then they scattered. They had been disturbed. We heard other voices:

'Aye, aye; ye'll be daein an ice-climb.'

'That'll be hit: they'll be daein an ice-climb!'

A miracle. Geordie and Wull. Two inveterate veteran hillbashers, cautious in all weathers. They masticated their jammy pieces above us, brushing snow off their balaclavas.

'Ye'll soon be there, lads. Hang on. There's naethin after this,' said Geordie.

'Aye, it ends here,' confirmed Wull. 'Stick tae it.'

They consulted each other for a moment, crust to crust.

'A pity ye couldna stop like yon for jist a bittie longer; for the ithers tae see ye,' suggested Geordie, through crumbs. 'If yir holds is good, mind.'

'Aye, they'd like fine tae see yese hack-hackin yir way up,' added Wull. 'Jist stay there, like, if ye can.'

It appeared that Geordie and Wull were but the van of a whole flutter of local sub-Munroists, the Pittemdoon Cairn Gatherers, who, like us, had been deterred from going north and had swooped on the Corse o Whalloch as suitable lowlevel carrion for their day.

We tried to explain, gurgles above and expletives beneath, our predicament, now truly horrendous. But Geordie and Wull were slow, and voices began to chirrup above us. O the shame, shame of it.... I glimpsed orange anoraks and peering eyes. I felt cameras being unpacked, lenses screwed on.

But Geordie was not that slow. He had his own camera in his hand, a huge mahogany box-like affair, and fixed his brassy tripod. Then he waved the others back, flourishing a jammy piece:

'Awa, awa. I'm takin a verra careful shot of thae lads, an I want a clear background. Awa, all o ye, now! '

'Groogh,' agreed the Doctor through an ice-and-tongue sandwich under his immovable neck. 'We can't, oorgh, stay here, grrgh, like this all, urrgh, damned day.'

'Aye,' added Wull, catching on. 'These lads wants awa, they're no verra firm whaur they are. Hurry on doon tae yir bus, there's mair snaw comin in.' And he drove them off, breathing heavy experience.

Well, eventually they extricated us. It was a long job, for they were careful, gey careful, and every step they cut along the horizontal frozen bog (of course they had brought their axes) had to be brushed out and tested several times and their rope (of course they had brought their rope) had to be tied and untied several times and tugged and pondered over and discussed repeatedly; but by evening – and another couple of inches of snow – they had released the Doctor's axe, watched wonderingly our subsequent excruciating and arthritic manoeuvres, had rubbed us down and had helped us carry back the various blocks of mud and ice impounding our gear (we had dared not chip too close). We thanked them with the bottle of Glen Reechie the Doctor had brought for our celebration, and watched them pack it away unopened in their van. As they left, Geordie promised to send us a print of the picture he had taken: 'It would be a better reproduction, like, than the one we would see in the *Journal*.'

'A fine climb, The Thweepie, in itthway,' concluded the Doctor over his mutilated tongue as we drove stiffly off. 'Hardly the Bwenva, or even Minuth One or Pawallel B, but gwand for exerthithe; and for teaching you thomethin about Thcottith Ithe.'

Behind the back seat, the glaciers – and their accompanying moraines – retreated silently from our 39 points into his – fortunately open – rucksack.

# A YACHT MEET

It was not long after the unfortunate episode of the Cave Meet, and we should have learned to leave the nineteenth century alone. The Doctor was reading out of a recent Club *Journal*, carefully keeping its pages above the spirituous rings on the table in Daddy McKay's.

'...that supreme Victorian event, the Yacht Meet of 1897, and the desperate race back off Sgùrr na Ciche before the Presidential Yacht sirened finality and sailed away down the loch.... Whisky in the panelled smoking room and piping on the after-deck, with the sun setting over Skye beyond the loch and the President dancing a reel ....'

'There,' said the Doctor. 'That's what we should have. A Yacht Meet.'

'Lies,' pronounced the Apprentice, who had suspicions of that particular *Journal* editor. 'Lies. He made it all up. Always did. Even invented his contributors. The biggest liar out.'

The Doctor defended the now retired office bearer, though he looked thoughtful. Several of his own articles ('the best ones, too') had suffered editorial Improvement.

'No,' concluded the Doctor, 'it's perfectly true. It's described away back in volume four, in 1898. We should do something like it now. Trouble is, who has a boat big enough these days?'

We thought. 'Macassar?' suggested the Apprentice.

'Lord, yes! Of course, Macassar! He has several, by all accounts. And his place is just by the very loch....'

On the next Thursday we were informed that arrangements were complete. The Doctor had phoned, and had been answered favourably. A large ocean-going motor yacht, complete with crew and stateroom, lay at our disposal for the following weekend. All we had to do was drive over. It sounded most attractive. I put off a visit south and the Apprentice, to the amazement of his fellow-Weasels, forewent a promising line on the Ben – *Wedgewood*, a little to the left of *Sassunach*. Early on the Saturday morning we were cantering along a West Highland road in the Doctor's old Mercedes. We discussed our benefactor.

Sir Hector Macassar was, by universal agreement, a remarkable man. Unanimity stopped there. The Doctor had known him as a

student, and had climbed with him in the J.M.C.S. Even at that age
the youth had organised things – bus meets, expeditions abroad,
convenient loans. With the greatest breeze and aplomb he had risen
in the world, by means that no one – not even the Doctor –
understood. There were hints, of course; but doubtless prompted by
envy. The Macassar expeditions became world-famous, his films and
books universally applauded. That description of how he sank a
pursuing polar bear with his canoe paddle had been translated into
a dozen languages. Both Poles he knew, the Himalayas and every
big range in the world. Amazonian jungles, remote Polynesian islands,
world-renowned political figures. For some of these activities – which
ones were not divulged, but rumour included two international
business men, a hundred thousand dollars and an ex-Prime Minister
– he had been knighted. Yet he remained essentially the same
Macassar as in youth, jovial and unpretentious. The motto above his
arms read *Faill ill o agus ho ro eile*, and only cynics regarded this as
his considered comment. He kept close connections with the Club
and established the Macassar Trust; this presented emulators, if their
expeditions had been successful, with a medal showing himself on
both sides and offered them a complete set of his books, fully
illustrated and at reasonably reduced prices.

Such was the man whose estates we were now approaching.
Invercannilie Castle, an enormous Victorian pile, had belonged to an
admiring reader of his, a rich old lady. Sir Hector had naturally
returned the admiration, and had been duly bequeathed the castle
and a few thousand acres. As the rich old lady's next-of-kin employed
counsel unversed in the balance holds of Scottish law, he had
remained there, and now held court in Renaissance splendour. Or
so we had been told. We waited dry-mouthed for our first glimpse
of Invercannilie.

Our first glimpse was a huge signboard and a menagerie of
shanties – *Invercannilie Caravan Park*. Sir Hector was a well known
environmentalist. To prevent the coastline (previously inaccessible)
from being overrun by Sporadic Development, he had constructed a
road and this park. Sportingly, he had built it on his own land. The
inmates appeared suitably subdued and the charges not unduly
excessive.

Beyond the caravans, a high wall and gates. We were admitted,
somewhat doubtfully, by the wifie at the lodge. Within, the grounds

were peaceful. We dipped down to the loch. Through spires of *Sequoiadendron* we saw whitewashed turrets, gleaming in the early sun. Above the highest flew Sir Hector's own flag. It much resembled that of the Bank of Scotland, but the *roundels, or,* were replaced by small golden cuboids. 'Liar Dice,' averred the Doctor. 'Sir Hector's favourite game.' Below it, on a smaller turret, flew the national flag, of the authentic azure. Sir Hector was a devoted patriot.

We crunched to a halt outside the main entrance, the Mercedes cringing on the half-acre of gravel. Impressed, we mounted several flights of steps. An attractive young lady of eastern appearance received us at the swing doors and ushered us into a huge vestibule. She took our names, and vanished.

'Do sit down' – another, equally attractive, young lady. We declined. We were, unashamedly, amazed. Invercannilie entrance hall had been vast enough to begin with, designed for some megalomaniac Victorian stockbroker. Its eighty-foot-high vaulted ceiling would accommodate smoke from several board-rooms of cigars. But Sir Hector had wonderfully increased its guest-humbling magnificence. Walls flaunted spears and harpoons, targes, totems and gongs. From the invisible ceiling hung sails, kayaks and outriggers. About the floor lay skins of half the larger *Mammalia.* Stuffed heads eyed us severely from every corner. It was easy to see, as the Apprentice remarked, that Sir Hector frequently took his holidays abroad. And all around, immense bustle, a tripping to and fro of attractive young ladies, mostly of exotic origin, carrying piles of papers.

'Secretaries,' explained the Doctor. 'They help in the house. Sir Hector has so little time. And now this Oil....'

A tremendous crash. The Apprentice, stepping back to admire a secretary, had tripped over the open muzzle of a rug and dislodged a complete set of *samoura-oura,* rare Amazonian blowpipes. They were fortunately not properly poisoned, and he was being reassured by a circle of secretaries when our names were called and we were led out of the hall along a trilling conservatory bright with humming-birds and into a swift and silent lift. It deposited us on to a plush air-conditioned corridor. A door opened. A great hand extended.

'Wonderful to see you!'

Sir Hector was huge, bearded and beaming, in nondescript tweeds and a pink shirt. Waved to chairs, we listened as he leant back, boots on the desk among the telephones, and explained why he was sorry.

Our yacht, it seemed, had already been booked. Only for this weekend. But by a *great* friend of his, the Emir of somewhere or other (Sir Hector's Arabic was too colloquial to follow). Visiting on business. And the Emir had only this week in Scotland, whereas we lived here. We would understand. We would be fair. Next weekend? The other big yachts – only five since that affair at Ekofisk – were hired out – were lent – all the summer, but this, the best, would be free next weekend.

None of us could face the build-up of another such day. Had he nothing else?

Sir Hector considered. He jumped up. A telephone fell.

'I'm sure we must have. But small, very small. Some of the girls go sailing. And we hire a few to caravanners. Let's go and look. You're sure you don't want a power boat? We've plenty of those. The boys love them. And old Donald Archie. They're great fun.'

The journey to the boats was memorable. Our host's breezy commentary on everything we passed, from Patagonian firesticks to a newly-installed computer console ('a prototype I got from the Mitsubishi people to try out here') dazed us. We were briefly introduced to Donald Archie, the head keeper. He was sitting on a stool at the swimming pool Coke bar, next to the jukebox. His eyes said nothing – with considerable emphasis.

Down at the quay floated a duckweed of small boats.

'Now, which would you like?'

They were all very small. The Doctor, who had brought his pipes to play on the after-deck at evening, gazed glumly at a snuggle of two-seater Mirrors. Sir Hector could not have been more helpful. He skipped, with ease long born of killer whales and icefloes, from bow to bow. We followed, skidding on fibreglass, clutching diminutive masts.

'Why, here's a trimaran. Didn't know we had one left. That's big enough. You could have a hull each.'

But we declined. They were chancy things, the Doctor said. We decided on a G.P.14. Fourteen feet. *An Sgarbh*. The Cormorant. It would just about be able to cram us all in.

'Excellent!' said Sir Hector.

We gazed wistfully offshore at the great glittering vessel that lay under the black sardonic mountains of Knoydart. Men ran about its decks, polished its white hull from cradles.

'You know,' said Sir Hector, 'I'm really sorry you can't have the *Mobaidh Dhic* this weekend. But any other time, remember, she's yours. Unless, of course, we have sudden guests. They all like a trip.' I avoided the Doctor's morose eye.

'Raeburn was a good sailor,' remarked the Doctor reassuringly from the helm as we battered up the loch. 'Damn,' he added. A large wave had stared in and jumped aboard. The wind was increasing, gusting from the dark hanging glens above us. Sgùrr na Ciche vanished ahead into mist. Waves broke white on the shore we were making for. Our rucksacks were sodden. We recalled that cormorants frequently travelled long distances underwater. It was not very enjoyable.

The crew did their best. The Apprentice, despite twinges of *samoura-oura*, leapt from gunwale to gunwale at our skipper's command, leaning well out, at times half-immersed. I held various ropes, sometimes dodging the boom, which uncannily anticipated the Doctor's intentions. His subsequent 'Gybe ho!' was delivered apologetically, while the victim groaned in the bilge.

Some thirty feet off shore, the inevitable happened. The *Sgarbh* took the bit in its beak, and went for a dive. Despite Sir Hector's lifejackets we swam fairly well and beached most of our kit, including the distraught Doctor's pipes. Then we beached the boat, well up on the silverweed. We wrung ourselves damp, and helped the Doctor wash and lay out his reeds ('*just* blown in!'). Then lastly we plodded towards our peak, trying to forget last night's anticipation of today, the Apprentice gloomy with imagined Amazonian toxins.

It was a good peak, though, high and sharp above low cloud. The cloud considerately hid the loch, the *Mòbaidh Dhic* and the unrepentant *Sgarbh*. A large piece of seaweed, found in the Apprentice's rucksack, was placed on the cairn, to disturb the next Munroist. The Doctor added a crab's leg from his pocket. In the sun we dried, convinced ourselves we could see Ben Wyvis, and tried to forget the sail back. To walk to the car would take too long, and would be discourteous. There was, moreover, the *samoura-oura* to be humoured.

Halfway down we heard a curious noise. A wail. The Doctor was furious. 'Some ass trying my pipes!' But the wail continued, with a full-throated urgency no marinaded reed could aspire to. It was so like a ship's siren. Unmistakably like.

We looked at each other, and misery returned. The irony. Ah well. We dropped down through the cloud, despondent.

The cloud cleared. The siren roared. We saw the loch, slicing sunlit between Morar and Knoydart. And on it a white ship, just off-shore beneath us. Sirens again. And a powerboat running about ecstatically like a small dog. The Doctor pulled out his Trinovids, wiped off the salt, and gazed.

'Lord, it's the *Mòbaidh Dhic*. And there's Macassar in the speed-boat. Pink shirt. What on earth.... He's seen us. He's waving. Do you think...?'

We did think. We ran, leaping hags and boulders, falling, floundering, to the motherly bellowings of the *Mòbaidh Dhic*.

That evening the Doctor piped indeed. On the after-deck. Not with his own set. The prawns were still in it. But with Sir Hector's gold-mounted Robertson's. As Sir Hector's piper was away at a wedding for that month, the Doctor played uninhibitedly. Fortified by a fine meal and much Glen Rauchle, we heard him in peace. Then Sir Hector had a blow. He played surprisingly well. 'Better than he used to,' remarked the Doctor, 'but it's the pipes, of course. A great thing, gold.'

We danced a reel, unsteadily. Our host, the Emir, beamed among his attendants.

For the ship *had* been lent to the Emir. But Sir Hector's conscience, resilient as ever despite forty-odd years with its master, had whispered in His Eminence's ear. About our upset plans. And the Emir insisted on helping us out. He insisted, too, on a Blow. The three of us, Sir Hector, the Doctor and I, held his wavering instrument upright while the attendants raised their hands and marvelled and the drones roared farewell to the great sunset hills at the head of the loch, to Sgùrr na Ciche with its piece of seaweed and its crab's leg, and to the two MacDonalds and a MacRae who were trying, between drams, to hammer the centreboard back into *An Sgarbh*. The chanter, for its part, frequently managed to achieve low G.

The fourth of us, the Apprentice, was not on deck to appreciate this glorious consummation. Not because of the *samoura-oura*. Because of a secretary.

# A WET DAY

'One should always,' said the Doctor, 'climb something on a wet day. Anything; so long as you get to the top. It gives the day a point.'

We lay in our bags, disagreeing at length. The Apprentice clinched his view by turning over and re-burying his head. It was the fifth day of rain, and we appreciated the Doctor's tent, massive in architecture and material. Warned by the forecast, we had helped to carry this edifice, improbably folded and in puffing sections, up from the old Mercedes. So that if our own more portable shelter should decide to admit the overwhelmingly liquid phase of a late Scottish October, we could with a dry conscience beg accommodation.

We had climbed, the first three days, hard rock, easy rock, and finally a stretch of bog elevated by Munro to undeserved eminence. The Apprentice and I had spent the night before last mopping about us with towels: toasting tent walls and edges of bags with an urgent primus; and squeezing ourselves further up the ever-diminishing non-tidal area of the groundsheet. The Doctor's crowded *salon* was luxury to that. Why should we leave it?

The previous day, climbing had not even been suggested. Rain was heavy, our shirts were wet and the Doctor had decided to beat us at chess. He promised a new opening, to confound us. But it confounded him also, and I managed a draw; nor could all his beady-eyed craft and pipe-smoke preserve him from rout by the Apprentice's resolutely marching pawns. So we had veered towards music, the Doctor with his chanter, the Apprentice with his moothie; I had tried to read. A literally potted banquet – four courses in an alloy cauldron – occupied the remaining hours.

Yes, we were bored; but not that bored. The rain was still heavy. Even the ridge of the Doctor's tent, stitched from dinosaur hide, had softened to dampness at one corner; the flysheet, a melancholy kind of canvas mainsail, beat and wept on it continually. To go out on the hill would risk abandoning the only dry square inches in Argyll to penetration by a slowly-moving depression southwest of Iceland. Ridiculous.

Then the opening darkened. Voices.

'Ay, they're inside. On a day like this. Terrible.'

'They'll be wantin to keep out of the rain.'

'Verra likely.'

The Doctor extended an arm, and raised the flap higher. Drips shuddered from canvas on to flattened grass. Beyond, we saw two pairs of woolly-socked pillars, booted and gaitered, fit to support a Clydesdale. Two heads, moistily balaclava'd, bent down to join them; and peered in.

'Ha,' said the Doctor. They were a couple of wellknown heatherbashers, impervious to mist, rain, sleet, insult or lightning; and liable to be encountered on any undemanding mountain. They were referred to by all as Geordie and Wull. Both were heavily prudent, disliking rock, or snow above 10° in steepness. Wull was particularly cautious. He carried two of everything, just in case; maps, compasses, pairs of gloves, bootlaces, braces, primuses, even a spare rucksack – packed, somewhat illogically, within the other one; he should have hung them fore and aft.

'Come awa out,' said Geordie.

Wull squatted in front of the door. He gleamed all over, moisture and wool, grey moustache, spectacles and both wrist watches.

'Dinna stay in there,' he said.

The tedium of our surroundings was such that we greeted these worthies with interest, if scarcely with rapture. A temporary brightening of the sky, coupled with now three-fold urgings, lured the Apprentice and myself out of bags and into cold damp breeks and boots. We had already breakfasted, and the Doctor now spread pieces.

Meanwhile Geordie was inspecting the tent, tweaking the flysheet powerfully.

'A braw tent,' he concluded. 'Strong,' he added, leaning with all his weight on the front pole; 'gey strong', leaning equally unsuccessfully on the rear pole.

The Doctor grew more anxious to go. Geordie was a good thirteen stone, and liable to continue his inspection.

We were in fact ready to go, but Wull was still squatting at the doorway, staring benignly within.

We crowded the exit, pointedly.

'I'll be in your way, like,' admitted Wull, and hoisted himself up by the front guy. Geordie genially replaced the peg. 'A gey strong tent. No many like it the day.' He gave a final appreciative slap to the flysheet. The Doctor turned him about firmly, reinserted the rear peg and checked the rest of the rigging. We gathered, chilled and unhappy, in the resuming rain.

Where were we going?

'Come with us, lads,' suggested Geordie. 'We're daein Meall nan Adharc.' Meall nan Adharc? We hadn't heard of it. Hardly a peak, not even a Munro, not even a Top. Geordie explained: it was one of the Five Hundreds – a ghastly list of every Separate Mountain over 500 metres ('that's 1,650 feet', translated Wull), compiled by some besieged and lunatic extremist. Our visitors had of course done all the Munros and Tops within, and Furth of, Scotland (Wull had done them twice, to make sure) and were well on the way to completing this lower debris; how many hundreds I cannot bear to recall.

'It's just another hump of bog.' We were sceptical.

'Na, na' – Geordie and Wull rolled weighty glances at each other – 'it's *rocky* at the top. You lads'll like it fine. Mebbe you could look after us – eh? See we come to nae harm?' 'Keep an eye on us, like?' added Wull. It is difficult to define the extent of – or the existence of – Geordie and Wull's sense of humour. Their smiling amplitude betrays no irony. Perhaps it was rocky. Perhaps they had, seeing the Doctor's car at the road, looked us up for this reason. They were always careful.

'Right-ho, we'll look after you, then,' cried the Doctor. We moved off. The Apprentice and I felt we were being imposed upon. Wull sidled up to us. 'You see, it's *rocky* at the top,' he confided. 'Nan Adharc means: of the horns.' Geordie overheard. 'That's right. Horns, you see. Rocky at the top. Nan Adharc. Of the horns.'

Not a rock for hours did we see. Peat hag after hag, imperceptibly higher, perceptibly wetter. Even the Doctor became subdued; his pipe, reserved for such occasions, went out. But Geordie and Wull stumped on through the mist, unperturbed. Wull took off his balaclava occasionally, mopped his brow and turned and gleamed at us (it was hot inside two cagoules – one cotton, one terylene), but never stopped. This was nothing to them. A good solid plod. Restful. They took bearings, double-checked by Wull.

'Well soon be there,' said Geordie.

'No long now,' added Wull.

Then we heard it. A deep roaring. Silence. And a roaring again, nearer.

'Stags,' said the Doctor, 'rutting. We're probably walking into somebody's territory.'

We continued. But Geordie and Wull exchanged glances again. They halted. Wull fumbled in his rucksack. He brought out mysterious packages and shared them with his companion. We looked, questioningly.

'It's stags,' said Geordie.

'Stags,' confirmed Wull.

Seeing our continued incomprehension, Geordie explained more fully. 'Paraffin on a rag; matches; pepper.' Our eyes widened further.

'For the stags,' he added.

'In case they attack,' said Wull.

They always carried these antidotes in October and November. If a stag came too close, you would light a match to frighten it. If it was not frightened or, more likely, if the match was wet, you still had three chances. As it knocked you down, you thrust the paraffinny rag at its nose; it would dislike the smell, and desist. If it continued to molest, perhaps by then another match would light and you could set fire to the paraffinny rag, with consequent terror and fleeing on the part of the stag. If all that failed, you could cast the pepper at his eyes or his sensitive muzzle as he bent over to gore you.

This thoughtful procedure had happily never yet been put into practice.

'But they're dangerous beasts,' averred Geordie.

'No safe at aa,' agreed Wull.

Both perspired freely, perhaps not only with exertion. Maybe this explained their desire for company.

We – though never hitherto driven to such precautions – were less inclined to demur in that thick mist, heavy with hoofbeats and reverberations. Meall nan Adharc was obviously a favourite spot for rounding up one's hinds and protecting them from enterprising neighbours. We remembered tales of unpleasant accidents to trespassing primates, and drew closer to each other as we plowtered on.

Then it all happened at once.

The bog levelled off into scree and the summit appeared through cloud a few yards ahead: boulders and two central quite rocky pinnaclets some ten feet high – a fascinatingly unsuspected tour de force from the landscape, which retreated on all sides pleased with what it had done. Geordie and Wull beamed at us. 'You see, horns – *rocks!*' said Geordie. 'Rocks – *horns!*', said Wull.

An appalling roar drowned everything else, and a great black-throated red-eyed bellowing stag leapt into view, with dozens of other dark shapes cavorting around in the mist. Antlers flashed and tossed; roar after earsplitting roar....

And, exactly as when we met the cave bear under Beinn a' Ghrunnda, we panicked; or, more respectably, our ancient reflexes belted us out of danger.

When I recovered my current self I was on top of a sizeable boulder; the Apprentice and the Doctor on tops of neighbouring boulders – and Geordie and Wull out of sight. We anxiously searched the ground beneath the beating hooves. No sign. Then a quavering hail from above, repeated more faintly still. Geordie was straddling one summit pinnacle, Wull the other. Their rucksacks and safety measures lay scattered below.

But we were not finished with the stag. A monstrous brute, a Royal if ever, it stamped and blew and trotted, bucked and swore and re-offered challenge. It was piqued by our refusal either to accept or to retire decently backwards, with our antlers lowered submissively. It raced round and round our boulders, twenty peat-bedabbled stone of fury, nearer every circuit. It could – brow, brez and trez – sweep any of us off, especially the Doctor, whose boulder was a mere aspiring stone. Foam flew through the air. The Apprentice and I replied with pebbles, ineffectually. It concentrated on our companion.

'Shoo, blast you!', he shouted, and waved his arms.

Irritation increased. A maddened roaring, right up to him. He kicked at its snout. It withdrew, growling. Then it began to work up for a final attack, twisting and writhing, rolling eyes to heaven as witness, mobilising all its androgens. Hinds gathered about, adoring. It could not afford to make a fool of itself, this time. Dozens of sardonic young staggies were lurking nearby, to enrol disillusioned females.

The Doctor remained calm, hat jammed down. His eyes took in the distance between his tiny perch and the safe summit rocks. Too far, surely. To steady himself he groped in his pockets and began to re-light his pipe.

The stag was fully inflated for its final, pre-charging, roar, drones erect, when the match was struck. In the late afternoon mist and gloom the flare did all that Geordie and Wull had prophesied. The stag, too astounded to deflate, shuffled backwards, swollen. The ladies tittered.

The Doctor, seizing the psychological moment, struck again, bounded from his rock, swept up large pieces of scree and flung them at his foe. He roared most effectively and brandished arms long and antlerlike, sputtering occasional fire. The Apprentice and I leapt from our posts and joined the charge, pelting furiously. The stag disappeared, still backwards, still pop-eyed, drones in disarray, and full of unemitted roar. The girls shrieked with laughter and danced away beside him; one or two lingered to gaze admiringly at

the Doctor. Other roars broke in below, from anticipatory rivals. We heard him far away, drones rattling, regurgitating a feeble and largely-digested bellow. He was finished.

We left his successors to it, and hurried to the central rocks. Geordie and Wull leant an arm from their respective pinnacles. The crux was a definite Easy.

'They're dangerous beasts,' said Geordie. Wull agreed. 'No safe at aa. You canna *trust* them.'

'It's the time of year,' said Geordie. 'It's October, ken,' Wull pointed out.

'Now's when they're bad,' said Geordie. 'It's the rut, like,' explained his companion.

We got them down, complimenting their stiff-legged agility. Wull had to go up both, in case the lower turned out really to be the higher. 'You canna tell by just *looking* at them.' The Doctor helped him, though less effectively than the stag.

When we regained the Doctor's tent the rain had abated. But a small burn behind, grown out of its banks, had fully explored our site. Cursing, we waded to the entrance. A quantity of burn was within, and fell out through the opened zip. The tent itself was unharmed.

'Gey strong tent,' observed Geordie. 'Canna find them like that these days,' said Wull.

But they were kind souls and we slept that night in Wull's two tents while they slept in Geordie's van. Wull's spare clothes were plenty for the three of us. While our bags were drying over primuses, Geordie and Wull entertained us with comic songs: duets. Geordie, unlikely enough, produced a guitar from behind the driver's seat, and Wull had his (two) tin whistles.

As we crawled, well past midnight, pressure-cooked, out of the van, Geordie leaned over in confidence from the back doors.

'It's a right good name for the hill – eh?'

We tried to reassemble thoughts.

'Meall nan Adharc – hill o the *horns*?' He grinned and put two fingers on each side of his forehead. He bent his head and said 'Urrrgh'.

'Like a stag – see? Eh?' suggested Wull.

They clanged the doors shut. We heard them laughing long into the small hours. By morning the rain had stopped.

# AN OCCASION

'Of course we should go,' said the Doctor, sternly. 'The least we can do. He's a Good Man, and has been kind to us.' The Apprentice and I groaned. The back bar of Daddy McKay's gleamed in sympathy. There seemed no way out. Our consciences shared the same rope: the Doctor couldn't go alone. But he frowned. He drank thoughtfully; a good fifty pence of Glen Bogle. 'It might even be an enjoyable occasion.' He was unconvincing. We stared into our glasses; Glen Bogle stared back.

The occasion was to be the Last Munro of old Zero. Old Zero, *alias* The Reverend Zoar McKinley McSigh, M.A., B.D., had been a friend of the Doctor's at college. 'He always was an elderly-looking youth,' the Doctor recalled. Twenty-five years later he resembled a grave and active septuagenarian. He was the respected minister of a Wee Free flock in Glasgow, a staunch teetotaller and tireless campaigner for the Light, a diligent visitor of the sick and uncared-for. Distressingly admirable. He made us fidget. 'Excellent fellow,' the Doctor would say; and reach for Glen Bogle or its equivalent. The Rev. McSigh had nevertheless one fleshly weakness. He climbed hills. As a student he had climbed Salisbury Crags; but he gave up such doubtful adherences on ordination. A long hill walk inspired a wider view, and he persuaded his congregation that no trespass was involved. Certainly his Saturday excesses brought them fine draughts of fire and resonance the following day, in both Gaelic and English.

The path is slippery, however, and the Devil had whispered 'Munros.... There was no excuse. True, the first Compleater, No. 1, had been a minister, but the Rev. A. E. Robertson was not of the Evangelical Free Church; and therefore no fit person to emulate. As with lesser men, totals inflated the head of McSigh. Pride lifted him continually above 3000 feet; outlandish hills were followed. Little by little. Until Auld Hornie had sold him the lot, and the last one was coming up this Saturday. It was Càrn an t-Sagairt Mór. Would so auspicious a name avert retribution?

No. To ensure infernal success the Tempter took on the irrepressible and rotund form of A. J. Evergreen Smith, who had completed them all – Separate Mountains, Subsidiary Tops, Eminences

Furth of Scotland and the whole litter of Corbetts, Donalds, Dochertys and Maxwells – a dozen times.... Evergreen, a compulsive organiser, happened to organise the Boys' Brigade in McSigh's district and soon swept the straying minister into intemperate and browknitting enthusiasm: the ascent of his Last Munro should be a Real Occasion.

Not only would the youth organisations of all the kirks in McSigh's district take part, but even the more able-bodied of his own congregation. And also as many as possible of the previous Compleaters would be called out, each identified by the number of his or her position in the Official List of Munroists as published (shamefacedly) by the editor of the *Journal*. All would assemble at the summit, where the Rev. Zoar would exhort them before psalm-singing and descent. Exceptionally blameless, if somewhat Apocalyptic. And the Doctor and ourselves were especially asked to share his pleasure. How could we refuse? Glen Bogle gave no answer. It glumly retreated beneath our eyes.

Well, we were there. At the foot of Càrn an t-Sagairt Mór. As expected, mist and drizzle. Last Munros are usually, despite the weather, scenes of alcoholic mirth, often of excess. This occasion would be decorous. At first, no stimulating beverage was considered; but the diabolical inspirer of Evergreen Smith persuaded minister and elders, in view of the cold and exertion, to allow a little weak medicinal wine for those frailer members of the congregation who might need it – no beer, and certainly nothing spirituous. After all, a sip of Bouvier or suchlike celebrated physical thankfulness on these occasions in the old days. He even persuaded, with the extensive nether forces at his disposal, McSigh to agree to savour a touch of weak, very weak, medicinal wine himself at the top. McSigh had never – not even as a divinity student – tasted alcohol; his Communion wine was non-alcoholic; this was indeed a victory for darkness. He had wrestled; but – the Last Munro: just once, just once; to do it *properly*.

The Doctor had no objection to wine on the hill; he toasted Alpine summits with aluminium and *vin-du-pays*. But that week a rich and thankful patient had given him a bottle of Lochaber No More, the finest and rarest of malt whiskies, 16 years old and 100° proof.... The temptation to alleviate the strain of duty was too great; he brought it with him.

From the busy group round the cars and buses that morning,

McSigh came over. As a special mark of friendship he presented us with a bottle of wine, wrapped in brown paper. 'Just like my own – of course I shall take only a sip – but I expect you fellows will nearly empty the bottle!' And almost a wink from that clear blue eye: then he swiftly returned to the black-coated huddle of elders.

We unwrapped the brown paper, and stared. 'Sister McVittie's Medicinal Wine. Extra Weak: Formulated Specially for Invalids and Similar Persons.' Sister McVittie, unexpectedly rubicund, eyed us firmly and therapeutically from the label. She pointed unflinchingly at the small print: *Guaranteed to contain less than 0.5% ethanol.* We unscrewed the bottle and sniffed. Ghastly. The Doctor hurried behind the car. He emptied the bottle, washed it thoroughly, and almost filled it with Lochaber No More. He put it in his rucksack for the hill. He did not wish to hurt his old friend.

We relaxed, and set off. As we left, crates of Sister McVittie were being unloaded and dispensed, each bottle wrapped in brown paper, to the many Invalids and Similar Persons of McSigh's congregation; they stuffed them hurriedly away in pockets and bags.

It was no climb. Wet heather and grass, uphill. Visibility, a dozen yards. Interesting yards. Across them passed a succession of improbable figures. Not only the elders and congregation, puffing and mist-dripping, in gumboots, goloshes and steel-rimmed spectacles, clutching black plastic bags and wilting umbrellas; not only the pink and uniformed Youth carrying banners; but also more familiar figures in rock-torn attire, some already well-stimulated and each bearing his number as a Compleat Munroist; the Mark of the Beast, as arranged by Evergreen's Infernal Master. (Prudence compels the narrator to change the numbers here and To State Clearly That They *Are* Changed....) Several, as a token of respect requested by Evergreen, were repeating for McSigh's Last Ascent, the self-imposed conditions of their own Last Ascent. They paraded like sufferers out of Dante. Number 112 was carrying a set of pipes, No. 105 a folding stool, 87 and 101 drove golf balls before them; 125 was having trouble with his skis. Number 172 was in evening dress, No. 230 in nothing but a kilt and a false beard. Number 83, who had carried his fiancée up, a wee smasher, in his arms, now followed obediently her matronly shadow; No. 76 experienced similar difficulty with his baby, grown too large for the rucksack, who stalked gloomily beside him, six foot three and desirous of Hampden.

Halfway up we came across Sir Hector Macassar – No. 56, an old vintage – sprawling on a plastic Inverness cape. Unashamedly, he was enjoying his whisky. He offered us some. The Doctor slung off his sack and in turn proffered our disguised Lochaber No More (Sister McVittie continued to point, unmoved). Despite Sir Hector's indignant refusal, we poured it out, pressed it within olfactory range. Whiskers twitched. Eyes widened. Mouth opened. Savour. Gulp. Savour.

'Terrific stuff, man, terrific stuff.... Where on earth...?' The Doctor signalled silence.

McSigh had appeared. Well ahead of his flock, only the fittest of elders beside him. He came up to us. Sir Hector, also once a fellow-student, welcomed old Zero and offered him a drink.

'No, no. No. But – ' and here McSigh glanced almost gaily at his elders, who smiled grimly and inspected the turf – 'at the top I mean to take a wee mouthful: of weak, very weak, medicinal wine.' And he produced his bottle. Macassar sat up, unwrapped it and held it at arm's length.

'It's real!' insisted the unbecomingly enthusiastic Zero.

'Disgraceful,' observed Macassar. His further remarks were lost in the arrival of others. Among them were those two inevitable old summit-scavengers, Geordie and Wull.

'Awfy wet day,' volunteered Geordie.

'Could dae wi the sun,' suggested Wull.

And of course Evergreen himself, leading battalions of the young, his bald head gleaming with drizzle and pleasure, his twelve cards twinkling. About him dangled also multicoloured buttons, symbols of the various groups of sub-Munros he had conquered and reconquered throughout the four and a half countries of the British Isles.

We extricated ourselves, put Lochaber No More back in the rucksack and steamed on. 'Keep it for the top,' advised the Doctor.

At the top, there was some delay. The battalions had to be mustered, the flock folded and stragglers accounted for. Number 76 had lost his baby, No. 112 his low G. But it was a gallant throng. Banners dripped determinedly.

An elbow nudged me, hard. It was Geordie, offering a can of Export. 'Aye, doon wi it,' urged Wull, holding two. We quaffed. The Doctor was about to open our supercharged Sister McVittie: but the ceremony had begun.

Cries for silence. Banners dipped. The Rev. Zoar McKinley McSigh was balanced on the cairn and about to address us.

'My friends, this is a Happy Occasion. We have taken a rest from our Everyday Toil, and are gathered here together in the Clear Upper Air....'

Geordie, beside me, nodded and wiped froth into his moustache; drizzle beaded his sweating brow. Zero then elaborated the parallels with the Spiritual Ascent – the steepness, the backslidings, the mists, the rewards of perseverance. We wondered how soon he would come to the wine. Quite soon.

'And now we have reached the top. This Earthly Top; that is yet, friends, also a Higher Top. And we shall celebrate that Higher Top shortly, with all our hearts. But before celebrating that Higher Top, let us pause, and celebrate this Earthly Top. In an earthly way: for have we not reached here, friends, by an Earthly Way?' Geordie nodded. Wull drank noisily behind him; too precipitate – steel spectacles turned and frowned.

'Let us celebrate this Earthly Top in an Earthly Way, in the customary manner, before we go on, before we celebrate our greater ascent. Let us drink a toast to the friendly earth and stones that have helped us up, so far, so very far – though not, friends, far enough.' Geordie clouted my ribs again – 'Man, he gies ye an awfy thirst, ken,' he whispered hoarsely, 'dither-datherin awa like yon.' But the Rev. Zoar signalled down to his elders. Furtive rustling of brown paper behind the cairn.

'Let us therefore drink a toast. Some may wish water, fine burn water, others the juice of fruits, others, others' – he hesitated – 'others may be forgiven, perhaps, a mouthful of weak, weak, medicinal wine, for such an occasion, for such an occasion. O, it is a weakness, a failing of the flesh, for the flesh is weak in climbing a mountain; it is like embrocation for the stiffness or plaster for the blisters, on a mountain.... A weakness, a failing, but' – (he was clearly anxious to get on with the experiment) – 'in-human-sympathy-with-those-before-us-who-sought, amidst all difficulties-of-stress and-storm, these-heights-of-our-earthly-kingdom, we-will-celebrate, each-in-his-own-way, our-vouchsafed-and-happy-arrival-here.'

He bent down and was handed a large cup(!) by a frozen-faced elder. It appeared remarkably full. It winked over the brim as he stood erect. He raised it to his lips. A hundred other cups, glasses, flasks and bottles of coke were raised also.

'To our Bonnie Caledonian Hills and our climb beyond them to greater and more blessed Heights....'

He downed it. All downed it. Very felicitous. We were moved. The Apprentice ventured not a joke. We were all brought up in good kirk-fearing households. And old Zero was so excellent a man.

He was also a thirsty one. His mouthful drained his cup. He looked surprised. The wine – even under the resolute supervision of Sister McVittie – affected him severely. He was quite unused to alcohol. He coughed, sneezed, grew red and watery-eyed. He swayed, and was helped down. Great applause, rapturous from the like of Geordie and Wull and Macassar, dubiously tight-lipped from the umbrella'd and goloshed throng.

Buzz of conversation. Then a psalm began.

Having no book, the Doctor hauled out our bottle. He unscrewed it and offered it to Geordie and Wull. They read the label, glanced at each other, and shook their heads. The Doctor winked and grinned broadly, poured some into a plastic glass and handed it to Geordie. Geordie tasted it, blinked, and handed it to Wull. Wull sipped it, twice, and handed it back.

'Good, eh?' asked the Doctor, pouring some out for us. 'Sixteen years old, 100° proof, *and* the best!'

'No bad,' said Geordie; 'but no like whisky, mind.'

'Ay, whisky'd be the thing,' agreed Wull. 'Gey cauld here the now.'

We stared uncomprehendingly at their lack of taste. The Doctor shrugged, and swigged his glass.

'Grooogh!' He spat it out.

'Wine; damned medicinal wine! Evergreen's damned medicinal wine!' We all spat in sympathy, upsetting the damp-leaved psalmists about us.

'Some swine's switched bottles!' choked the Doctor. But his rage, and the countering belligerence of our shocked and hitherto tuneful neighbours, were lost in a growing tumult.

The psalm had ended. The crowd pushed forward. The Rev. McSigh, clutching his cup, refilled and respilling, was endeavouring to climb his cairn. Two elders were trying to assist him, three to restrain him. On hands and knees he reached the top. He was excited and flushed. He perilously straightened and stood, swaying. Then he began to bellow.

It was a rousing sermon, graphically if unconventionally illustrated. More of Paisley than Chalmers. Much was in Gaelic.

McSigh was above and due west of us; it was a westerly wind. We sniffed....

'Lochaber No More, by the Devil' hissed the Doctor. 'He's been drinking our bottle!'

I glimpsed Macassar a little way along, gold teeth filling his whiskers, cigar in hand, gazing happily. It had been him; while we were distracted by Geordie and Wull and Evergreen....

A rousing sermon; but the preacher was profoundly drunk. One hundred proof, 16 years old.... We listened and watched admiringly. He maintained precarious balance, on both cairn and theology. The congregation stood enthralled. Never had flames roared brighter. Calvin stoked furiously. Knox brought more faggots. Heavens! Another gulp from the cup....

The Doctor was about to scramble up and snatch it, risking unseemly altercation; when further fruits of error, rewards of Satan, tumbled to earth. A body of police, waterproofed, radio'd and ominously bulging, pushed amongst us.

The Inspector – our old friend McHaig – seized the Doctor. 'Ah, thank heaven, it's yourself, Doctor: what *is* going on here, now?'

A very puzzled man. We explained. He stopped breathing. Then he stepped back, slapped his thigh and began to curse, most frightfully and unsuitably. Our black-coated neighbours, breathless in their turn, white with horror, turned and engulfed him. One furious lady shook him, another slapped off his cap, another hit him with her umbrella.

Violence breeds violence. His men breathed deeply, felt under their raincoats, bayed, and likewise surged forward, grabbing most ungently. A regular brawl developed. We saw the helpless Evergreen, betrayed by the False One, delivered to judgement; his glittering badges proclaimed him ringleader. The Inspector ran about trying to call off his keepers of the peace. Scuffles, cries. We began to imagine a CS edge to the westerly drifts of Lochaber No More. Above us, the sermon continued, a uniformed interrupter being disposed of by an accurate kick.

Eventually the Inspector, with the Apprentice's rather too eager help, drove his men out of the fray. Order was more or less restored. Silence fell.

We all looked up. The cairn was bare. No preacher.

He was lying flat beside it. Two elders lay beside him. Uproar again. Hysterics. The Doctor hurried forward. He knelt by the victims, undid collars, felt pulses, listened to chests.

We saw, with relief, the bodies stir, and sit up. They rubbed eyes and groaned. Two fell back and began to snore. The Rev. McSigh, a man of steel, accepted a hand and was helped up. The Doctor, ever sagacious, leapt on the cairn. He called for silence. He explained that Excitement, due to the unfortunate error of our gallant police – who were looking for... for burglars (unlikely, we thought) – that Excitement had caused Mr McSigh to lose his balance. The fall had stunned him. But no injury whatever; perfectly fit. Though naturally he might be somewhat giddy for a while, with a headache and perhaps difficulty in communication for an hour or two. And the elders? Ah, the elders had also suffered from Excitement, but they were older men, and might take a little longer to regain their feet; but nothing serious, nothing at all. Plenty of willing hands. Let us continue with the service. Not spoil so happy an occasion. Another psalm. Eighty-four? To *Martyrdom*? Let our good friends the police join in....

Cheers, clapping. Singing. The Doctor rejoined us through an accolade of black gloves.

'Tight as owls,' he said, 'all three of 'em. The elders sooked the bottle behind his back. Old devils. Hardly any left. Let's go and finish it.'

A hand tapped the Doctor's shoulder. Inspector McHaig. Sad and embarrassed. He drank the proffered glass without a word. Then, nervously, he explained why he had been summoned.

'A damned old fool' – a Major Pigstrap (the name sounded like that, but surely could not be) – had rung him up excitedly. Pigstrap lived just outside Balqueenie and had been taking exercise from his car, near the track up the glen. He had seen strange motor cars, vans and buses arrive. From Glasgow. *Glasgow!* Nosey-like, he had investigated further, with dog and walking stick, and had seen troops of people, some with curious bags, some with badges and numbers pinned on them; some in paramilitary uniform and carrying banners. All disappearing up into the mist. Some secret rendezvous. Many young, many older – old enough to know better, obviously there to lead them on, furtive, desperate looking dark-clad buttoned-up people, grim-faced, determined – Real Reds they must be, Fanatics. And they were carrying, and trying to hide from him, brown paper parcels that looked like bottles – inflammable liquid? Petrol bombs! That's what they would be! *Petrol bombs!* And he had heard bagpipes – *Nationalists* there as well. He had asked a youth what was going on: the answer was sinister – 'A special occasion. Arranged for No. 293. *The Big Event.*' Secret, you see. Code. Cells. Pigstrap had crescendo'd by describing it, through foam, as an armed meeting of activist extremists who would afterwards descend on the, on the... McHaig looked grave. 'You ken WHO's staying there the now....'

The Inspector wiped his brow in anguish. It had *seemed* so genuine. Why, as they had puffed up – too misty for helicopters – they even heard singing. Impassioned singing. The SAS man attached to them (McHaig peered anxiously around) had unhesitatingly identified Old Hundredth as the Internationale.... 'Ye cannae blame the lads, like....'

Nothing would happen, we reassured him. Errors were too evenly distributed. He came down the hill with us, his men limping behind. He ignored the ribald staggerers to right and left. He ignored the obviously unsuitable would-be drivers singing on the road beneath. He ignored the piper on the bonnet, hugging his recovered low G. It was enough to have avoided arresting the Rev. Zoar McKinley McSigh, M.A., B.D., for being drunk and disorderly and/or inciting to riot and/or civil disobedience and/or armed insurrection on the summit of Cárn an t-Sagairt Mór at 13.15 hrs on the 11th October, nineteen hundred and whatever.... A narrow escape. He pressed both the Doctor's hands silently as he left. From high above came wafts of (devoutly-led) thanksgiving.

The Doctor let the clutch in, rather cautiously. In the back seat, the Apprentice and I passed between us the much diminished but authentic bottle of Lochaber No More. We had left Sister McVittie behind in the ditch. We lay back, content.

The Doctor swerved skilfully round an errant sheep.

'Quite an occasion,' he said.

# A STIFF UPPER LIP

'It certainly could be an aid,' agreed the Doctor. We were discussing the Apprentice's most recent acquisition, a moustache, in the not displeased presence of the new owner. It had germinated in response to his latest girl friend's desire for more public evidence of virility. It was indeed robust, disguising his normally sardonic upper lip with coils of easy splendour. He had grown it remarkably quickly.

'Could be very adherent on steep ice: should steady you, cutting out of balance,' continued the Doctor. 'You could lick it, to freeze in front of you; then breathe it off again and move up.'

The Apprentice swore it was not in the least an artificial aid. 'Grows naturally. Shaving's artificial; that's an aid. A right hairy bearded guy could get stuck in Raven's: never get up, whiskers jamming one side then the other, freezing on as fast as he's breathing 'em off. Shaving's the real Aid.'

Parallel B was coming that weekend. But when we arrived there, a violent freezing wind and snow squalls sent us up Raeburn's instead. The girl friend was Munroing nearby and we would all meet that night in the Inverfyvie Arms.

Raeburn's Gully is reasonable on a foul day and the Apprentice stormed it bravely, moustache as spinnaker. I gathered metal at the blunt end. The Doctor makes an excellent second on such middling routes, being tall, thin, and multijointed, and his long, prodding axe and nimble tricounis ran many messages.

Halfway up, just on the steep ice, came a prolonged halt. I peered through drift. My companions were crouched together on a minute stance, examining something inside the Doctor's anorak. Hell of a time. I shouted. No reply. I tugged. A tug back. Then the Doctor's eager beckoning. They had found something interesting.

Too interesting to take in the rope. I clambered up, cursing and coiling, points exploring powder snow. When I reached them, they were still in earnest conclave, the Apprentice fixedly eyeing his companion's bosom. The Doctor, looking down in a curiously strained position, explained.

A krab had jammed with ice. To thaw it the Apprentice had

unzipped the Doctor's anorak and thrust the metal against his warm Shetland jersey. He had breathed on it to speed the process. Just then, both were drenched in a flurry of snow from above. Both had crouched farther, and the Doctor had instinctively zipped up his anorak.... Muffled roars indicated that he had zipped it up into the Apprentice's moustache....

Painful trial had proved it jammed, not just frozen. Though, since then, tears and other secretions had welded the jam. The Apprentice was too sore to speak, and any attempt to move, let alone continue the climb as a joint lead, when so intimately and inconveniently mated, was clearly impossible. Yet they couldn't stay there. We had to think quickly, or permanently disfigure our leader.

As we had all forgotten to bring shaving things, I produced an ice-dagger. The Apprentice gurgled and clutched his companion appealingly. But I couldn't insert between whiskers and lip, and the zip was tough metal. So, to the Apprentice's howls and the Doctor's cries of horror ('...it's *quite* unobtainable now!'), I sawed through expensive Grenfell and cut, tore out, the offending zip. It dangled free, and the Apprentice now bore a mandarin-like extension of moustachios. But he clutched his pegs with relief and straightened up, sobbing with drool.

The Doctor wrapped the ravaged garment about him and grinned at his leader. 'Looks just like that damn great catfish I caught on the Arkansas. Marvellous beast.'

It was impossible to stow the two ends away without painfully restricting movement, so the zip dangled freely as the Apprentice raged up the rest of Raeburn's, fleeing from our merriment and roaring when, as often, an end jammed suddenly in a crack. ('Try a tension...' the Doctor would call up, unfeelingly.)

An hour later, he burst on to the plateau, through a goosefeather cornice. His moustachios now carried a fair weight of ice and snow and his appearance unnerved the two elderly climbers sheltering behind the cairn (we *had* to get to the cairn; the Doctor always insisted). We explained it was a special kind of moustache. (The Apprentice had signed us not to betray his shame; he was very sensitive by now.) They seemed to understand. 'It'll be a prob... prob... *feelers*, like? For finding the way? Like insects, like?' We nodded. They were relieved and offered us hot broth from a flask.

We sipped gratefully. The Apprentice, however, went aside and proceeded to pour his share sideways onto his face. But the zip did not thaw; it was jammed. Instead, the broth froze; carrots and peas and things were added to his burden. He gesticulated at us as if imploring the kiss of life. But he was most repulsive, and only to be embraced by the desperately hungry.

It seemed he particularly 'desirrghed a drinnghk – cogghle?' We smiled, as at some defective, and patted him. 'Never mind; when we get down.' The Doctor, unusually, was whiskyless that day.

We roped down an easy chute. Descent was uneventful, though one tended to tread on the moustache at narrow places. Afterwards, an unhappy sojourn in a dense sitka wood. The Doctor, as always, encouraged the sufferer. 'Damned useful, in a place like this; how cats hunt at night. You know your own width exactly.'

At the edge of the wood we met a large party. The Apprentice being nearly all in, I approached them for tools – a hacksaw or nail scissors – for zip or whiskers respectively. Neither; they stared, wondering. Feeble groans of 'cogghle' again. Alcohol? Was that it?

The victim nodded vigorously, holding his ends, by now long, icicled, white and stiff. No wonder the others were startled. Their leader reluctantly opened his rucksack and, amid mild protests, handed over a well-furnished half-bottle of whisky. The Apprentice, to louder protests, scuttled off and, to violent protests, was seen pouring it over – not into – his face. Even the Doctor was irritated. 'That won't unjam the thing; it's a shocking waste – even of a blend.'

But the Apprentice continued to pour and began to tug at his adornment. He tugged and poured, tugged and poured until, by the end of the bottle – and to the stupefaction of everyone – he had tugged off all impediment: zip and whiskers....

'Good Lord,' exclaimed the Doctor.

It was a fake. A false moustache. Beautifully made, expensive, cemented by an alcohol-soluble gum. That explained the speed of growth – and possibly the short-term romantic intentions of the owner.

Who had been punished enough. He returned, nursing his lip, promising whisky at Inverfyvie. The Doctor meanwhile wrenched out his zip; it seemed more injured than the moustache. He pressed the latter to his own lip. Wonderful sight – a moose among seaweed.

It fell off. We cheered. He rubbed it in some resin on a sitka trunk and pressed it hard once more. It stuck. It preened itself, if a bit squint and somewhat defeathered. As the late bearer refused even to look at it again, the Doctor wore it proudly all the way back to the car.

We entered the Inverfyvie Arms. Noise, lights. Then silence. All eyes on us. Eyes especially from some posh persons in tweeds and from a jazzy-looking wee smasher. The Doctor met the gaze of the next-of-kin of a wealthy patient he had just recommended for psychiatric treatment: and remembered he was wearing a squint moustache. The Apprentice met the gaze of his girl friend: and remembered he was not. Panic seized both. Both leapt at the misplaced appendage....

Next Thursday at Daddy McKay's, they drank much and spoke little. Each fingered thoughtfully a small pink and white memento of surgical plaster.

# MAN'S FAITHFUL FRIEND

'Barking,' said the Doctor. 'Must be a dog.' We agreed.

We were engaged in a delicate traverse on Cir Mhòr; unfamiliar ground, but we had long looked forward to this week in Arran. We hoped for a good haul of routes, both classical and spontaneous.

'Still barking,' said the Doctor. The pitch of canine communication reached a fresh urgency. 'Howling: blasted thing must be stuck somewhere.'

We scrutinised the crag above and below us. No sign. Yowl; yowl.

Five minutes later we passed a fierce rib (a triumph for the Apprentice, who took us round on a tight rope) and entered an echoing cacophony of distress.

'Down there – on the ledge below that slab. Poor brute. Could have been howling for days.'

We other two felt that the vigour of its summons indicated a healthy, recent and presumably uninjured beast, but followed down the Doctor's compassion, the Apprentice muttering rebelliously. A fine traverse ruined.

The Hippocratean oath did not specify dogs but, as the Doctor pointed out, there might well be a human casualty it was guarding. Greyfriars Bobby and all that.

But the dog was alone. It looked up at us appealingly as we descended the plump granite on small holds, the Apprentice keeping a good belay. 'It has the sense to lie still. Sagacious hound,' observed the Doctor. Its appearance was nondescript, a sort of Labrador collie, coffee and black and what could have passed, after a prolonged bath, for white. It lay quivering, tongue out, eyes rolling up at us.

'There, there, now, old chap, don't worry, we're coming for you,' cooed the Doctor soothingly as he slithered the last few metres.

His kennelside assurances turned to alarm as soon as he landed. For then the beast leapt up, barking and shrieking, slapping him all over like an ice cream cone with its tongue. It was a good five feet of fervid hairiness, and a difficult partner for so exiguous a slab.

'Get down, blast you, get down – Groogh!'

The Apprentice held us taut. 'Seems grateful,' he said.

The Doctor fought off the gratitude as best he could and sought to encircle the convulsive belly with a sling. 'He seems – geroff, poogh – he seems uninjur – foogh – uninjured; we'll have a job, though – hoogh – keep still, damn you, groogh – he's heavy.'

Gratitude, however, did not seem to include being roped up. The beast disengaged itself and retreated to the very end of the ledge, lay down, muzzle between paws, and whimpered, rolling eyes again.

'Come along, laddie, come along, then,' wheedled the Doctor, inching closer and wiggling his fingers persuasively. A rude gaffaw from the Apprentice above. 'He's panicky,' explained the Doctor, 'could throw himself off any minute. Poor creature.' He advanced slowly, whistling and beckoning, along a ten-inch ledge on eight hundred feet of rock towards a bunched and apprehensive dab of fur.

Then just before he reached it, the dab exploded, leapt up past him (he grabbed the rope, I grabbed the rope, the Apprentice leaned on his belay – miraculously we all stayed put) and with a horrible scrabbling of claws the animal writhed up a groove at the edge of the slab, up a longish rake, bounded over a crack, scrabbled some more and then stood above us on another ledge, looking down, feet apart, barking loudly and tail wagging furiously.

'Nothing the matter with the bloody brute,' bellowed the Apprentice, getting his breath back.

The Doctor was not so sure – some mental derangement – perhaps it had fallen on its head. 'No such luck,' grumbled the by now hostile Apprentice, dodging a shower of fragments loosened by the tail above.

Indeed, as we painfully clambered up towards its new ledge, the beast, joyfully exclaiming, leapt about upwards and downwards with astonishing freedom. To prove its point, it even revisited, briefly, its original ledge and marked it in conventional canine fashion. True, it slithered about a lot, and rolled over once, but was quite obviously at home. It needed nothing from us.

Bitterly, we resumed our traverse, having lost a good hour and a half. The remaining couple of hours were devoted to completing the route and cursing the dog. For it did need, apparently, company, and appreciated ours greatly. Barking above us, slavering (and worse), was the least of its demonstrations. After a tricky crossing of some wall you were met by a jumped-up fusillade of paws. If you grabbed it, it would clutch delightedly back and both of you would swing perilously over the abyss, held by your other two companions. Curses were instantly filled with (extremely dirty) hair. You would select the next foothold, step confidently towards it when, horrifyingly, a coffee and cream object would flash between you and the rock, brushing you off, and eagerly occupy the very place, slobbering down at you with pleasure as you sucked your knuckles and tried to clamber back. Kicking and beating were of little avail. They could not be too vigorous, for reasons of personal equilibrium, and the prods and punches we could give were accepted enthusiastically as part of the fun.

When we at length stepped on to the ridge, scree yielded more pointed argument; we beat the brute off, determinedly.

'I-say-I-say-I-SAY: what d'you think you're doing, eh?'

A string of disapproving tourists, wrapped in new cagoules and waterproof accents (it was of course raining by now), on their way back from the summit, stood and eyed us severely. The men were tight-lipped; the ladies murmured together. All fresh from Cruft's.

Too full for words, the Apprentice and I left the Doctor to explain, and trudged towards our next climb. He did not convince, and returned dejectedly, swearing beneath his breath. We heard bursts of barking along the ridge and cries of 'Heel, sir!'; and hoped.

But no. We were only halfway up our route when the damned creature appeared again. We were the preferred companions. It was a climbing dog.

This route was obviously too severe even for it, and it leapt about above, below, on all sides, yelping excitedly. It dislodged showers of stones, some quite large.

'Keep that bloody tyke under control,' roared a helmeted Glaswegian voice from below. 'You should all be on a —— lead,' confirmed another. Further comment was extinguished by a basinful of gravel sent obligingly in their direction by our companion. We made haste. I saw a disapproving member of the Club on a nearby line.

And then there was an even louder noise from above. The all-too-familiar barkings were interspersed with shriller yappings, and then with feminine (human) screams. We groaned. A dog fight.

The racket increased as we neared the top. The Apprentice was greeted there by the boisterous hound and three shrieking women, clutching each other's windproofs. The altercation deepened with the Apprentice's own angry baying, so we hastened up, the Doctor, our diplomat, leading through.

'O – your – dog – your – horrid – horrid – dog has chased poor Manfred over the edge. O he is killed – listen to him, listen to him....'

The dead animal was yapping nonstop below us. It was a miniature pug, or some such affair, on a miniature ledge. It had obviously been led there by our – NO, not *our* – *the* great gangling brute, and couldn't get up. Its leader danced about, roaring advice.

The Doctor gave up trying to make himself heard, patted the least unattractive lady on the arm for comfort, nearly got assaulted by all three, and fled down to the puglet's ledge. He was still roped and a spare coil flicked the creature a few feet further below. Renewed and intolerable squealing from the trio.

'Shurrup!' bellowed the Apprentice, somewhat rudely. Open-mouthed silence. He felt he had to add something: 'Let the man concentrate....'

The man concentrated, on picking the furious Manfred up with least damage to himself. Carrying it was impossible – it wriggled, spat and snapped continually. So – to bubbling terror from above – he bottled it, probably upside down, in his rucksack. He knotted the loops with satisfaction. Then he climbed back up, undid the loops and offered Manfred to the bosoms of his family.

'O, O he's fainted, there, there, there – ow! – poor, poor Manfred – ow! – he's so shocked!'

We were pleased to see that Manfred's irritations included his owners. He bit unhesitatingly. A most unpleasant little beast. Fortunately they managed to fix a lead on him or he would have been off again with his companion, who sat regarding the scene benignly. He was dragged away protesting, chewing his lead with rage.

Animosity was general. 'Would you believe it, not a word of thanks....' 'They all deserve each other.' '*Fancy* letting a dog like that run about on a place like this!!' Etc.

We had had enough, and turned down to the glen. V   were too dispirited to kick, and throwing more stones was pointless. Whether they hit him or not – he was extremely agile – he brought them all back in triumph and ran off backwards, shouting for more. We had looked forward to food on the way down, but our pieces were in the Doctor's rucksack, and his oaths, unseemly for one of his clinical experience, gave us to understand that Manfred's excitement whilst confined had been intense. We washed the outraged equipment in a burn. Rather than let the hound enjoy our pieces we flung them into a deep pool. But he was looking and, leaping in, devoured them paper and all before they touched bottom, emerged grinning, and shook himself all about us at intervals for the next hundred feet or so of descent.

Our tent was fortunately fairly high up on the hill, away from any of the day's human contacts. The dog squatted, damp and odoriferous, outside. It had tried to enter several times, but was beaten back; its claws had been difficult to disentangle from the flysheet, and its smell still remained. We did not feed it (any more), but it did well enough off the Doctor's mince, put – for a fatal forgetful halfminute – outside to cool, and a slab of mint cake left in the Apprentice's rucksack. Everything, bar the dog, had to come in, and we spent the night cramped and apprehensive. Circumambulant sniffing and probing, punctuated by ominous and probably three-legged silences, plagued us and drove the Doctor, the unfortunate owner of the tent, to despair. Once he undid the door, shoved out his boot and struck a snuffling object. It was a sheep. But he woke the dog.

The next day we decided to traverse Arran, if necessary, to escape. We packed up everything and staggered under the weight towards the N.E. face. Our companion trotted behind, tail erect with well-fed affection.

At a signal, we stopped, abseiled down, traversed slab after slab, raced round the cliff, over the ridge, down, up and down again. We followed burns, splashing and tumbling with laden sacks, to shake off the scent. Up, and down again. Somewhere beyond Caisteal Abhail we paused. No sight or sound. We pitched camp, illegally, in some remote glen. We trembled and spoke in undertones. We encircled the tent with pepper, and slept with our food inside.

The next morning the sky was blue, the wind soft. Silence, glorious silence. The cliffs stood clear above, perfect. We climbed off, happy once more.

Then, the Doctor froze. We heard it, too. Barking. Just up on the left, halfway among the slabs.

A terrible outburst of oaths was preparing, and the Apprentice had looked out a specially-sharpened piton, when we saw a line of climbers on the path below us. We waited and scrutinised them. They were ideal. Not VS men. Decent, washed, guidebook-clutching, mild-eyed. They doubtless fed blackbirds and cheered Royalty. They had pleasant innocent English voices and clean ropes.

The Doctor went over and explained. There seemed to be a poor dog trapped on the cliff over to the left. We would have liked to have rescued it but the way looked steep (we sat on our ropes and krabs) and his companions had injured themselves (our arms were stiff from hurling rocks): did they think *they* could...?

Hook, line and sinker. They set off with a springy philanthropical step, thanking us for the opportunity, and marvelling amongst themselves at the probable agonies of the wretched, abandoned animal. 'Remember to feed it well,' called the Doctor. 'And see it safely off the hill....' They waved, happily. They had a first-aid kit.

We did a small dance, and moved rapidly to the right.

# ONE OF THE LEAST FREQUENTED
# PARTS OF SCOTLAND

It had been an interesting ridge, for that area of the West. We carried no rope apart from the Doctor's usual 5mm line, brought to assist any red-faced retrieval or, as the Apprentice suggested, in case we had to do up parcels on the way. We did not need it for either purpose, and enjoyed the day, wet as it was.

We came down on the seaward side. 'It's a pleasant route back; quite remote sea loch and glen. One of the least frequented parts of Scotland,' said the Doctor. Through the mist we glimpsed liquid confirmatory gleams. Also some sharply conical glints. These last resolved themselves into the turreted roofs of a Baronial edifice.

'Ha; Duntilty Castle,' remarked the Doctor, inspecting his map. 'And some shacks round it. Must have been done up recently.' Then clouds resumed.

Slopes levelled out. A track appeared, unsavourily trodden by man and beast. It led through a dyke. Leaping from slimy stone to stone, we became aware of a figure waiting on the grass beyond. Tall and thin in the mist, possibly potentially taller than the Doctor, but bent and wavering on the way. It was dressed in a kilt, a stick, a fawn raincoat and a Balmoral bonnet. It dripped. It eyed us askance, wavering more evidently; then, presumably reassured by the Doctor's tweeds – always our passport into the higher bourgeoisie of such regions – it straightened and approached. We stopped. 'Aah, hello.' A limp hand was extended. The Doctor, opportunist as ever, took hold of it for the requisite second. 'Aah. Howdyedo. Mkerrchkghnn.'

We stared. The accent was understandable; English Home Counties, of uncertain reach. But that last word? It included a much-practised guttural. Even our privileged companion was at a loss. A repeat. '*Mkerrchkghnn....*' Obviously we were expected to reply suitably. Then the Doctor justified his diagnostic reputation. The kilt, overlong like its owner and stitched together equally close to the Thames, could have been Henderson. The Doctor, well-versed in Telfer-Dunbar and suchlike sociologists, noted also the moist Clan Badge on the bonnet – MacEacheran? MacEacheran. A name. He offered his own in return; these intimate canine preliminaries concluded, conversation could begin. MacEacheran and the Doctor stalked gravely on, avoiding the puddles. We, as befitted our mucilaginous garments and the Apprentice's increasingly far-Left expression, followed incognito.

Nevertheless, we gathered that Duntilty was now an Outdoor Centre. 'Toughening 'em up,' drifted, not unexpectedly, from the mist ahead. At that moment, of course, They appeared, from the mist on our right, a breathless and stumbling downhill string of cagoules in all those fluorescent hues most suitable for evening rush-hour traffic. They were shepherded or, better, dogged – for he was tirelessly at their heels rounding them up from declivities or growling them back from watercourses they took for paths – by a short square-faced man in an anorak as clarty as ours, and possessing a sharp black Yorkshire bark. The convoy vanished ahead, at a double-up. 'Rather reserved, you could say; but very capable. Very capable.' Clearly MacEacheran preferred someone else to administer the toughening process.

We reached Duntilty. The shacks were to feed and sleep the wearers of the cagoules. They were spartan enough, and moss already dripped from their asbestos. Our host, continuing his leisurely discourse, flung open the occasional door: we smelt authentic wet socks and peat smoke. It was cold and damp. Eyes peered furtively from within.

'Toughening, toughening. We make a *point* of Doing It The Hard Way. All the three days they are here, they Really Go Through It. That's where we *score*. When our clients go home and say they have been to Duntilty, then they are *respected*. Their friends *know* they have Done Something Worth While, in these Too Easy Times. And, of course, Duntilty is' – he paused to enable us to take in the gleaming turrets, misty protuberances, invisible loch, wet gravel, and plastic St. Michael brogues – 'truly *Highland*. Scottish. Not like' – and he named a few of his good-clean-English-public-schoolboy competitors up and down the coast. 'Those places would be just the same in Cornwall or Wales or anywhere else in England.'

Not only Mountain Courses could be undergone by his clients. There were yet more expensive ways of getting wet. We saw ponies cropping the rushes; they raised mild and blameless eyes at us, and continued chewing. We saw dinghies, canoes. And all these courses were run by Dan, the anonymous sheepdog. 'He really likes doing it. Curious fellow. Doesn't seem to *bother* about money. Must say he's rather *valuable* – aah, ha. Now, you kind of people would be interested in this' – his uneasily seigneurial gaze included the Apprentice, who recoiled as from serpents – 'this Rock Climbing Boulder. Dan has fixed it up with all the latest gadgets. Like to try it out?' We demurred. A monstrous collection of cast-iron pitons and multicoloured ropes trussed up a glacial erratic beside the shore; it snarled helplessly behind them, awaiting the next Milankovitch cycle.

We also refused, politely, a not very pressing invitation to enter the Castle, where our host was installed and where his clients, after their gruelling three days, could recuperate, sampling Highland hospitality at an even higher exchange rate with sterling; but where doubtless the food and facilities, however dispensed, were an improvement on those in the sheds.

'Well, keep on down the *drive*. Then follow the road out through the *Park* – Glen Awley Park.' Glen Awley Park? The Doctor rapidly checked his map. On it, beyond that dot of Glentilty stretched, obediently, an unspotted Gleann a' Thuiltidh. 'Oh, the *map's* quite wrong. *We* call it Glen *Awley* now. *Anyone* can pronounce that.' Park? 'Yes, the Company's Executive Holiday Estate. Luxury homes you can buy, in a *quite* unspoilt setting. Swimming pools, saunas, air conditioning. And Sports Palaces. Everything essential to get away from it all. You seem to like this sort of country – have a look round. Mention my name. Sam Goldfeiner's the manager. Though I *know* they're all bought up years ahead. But we *are* building more, further down. Aa-ah....' And he withdrew.

Our subsequent conversation may be guessed. The Doctor soothed the Apprentice's Knoxian denunciations. He had visited workers' mountain camps on his Caucasian trip and agreed that in fact they were much better – 'Great fun if you like that sort of thing.' But he was principally amused by our late host. 'Marvellous Front-Man. Wonder what his real name is?'

So we traversed Glen Awley. Some of the white settlers' houses – the partly invisible ones – appeared reasonable enough; most of them resembled MacEacheran and his kilt. The glen, moreover, like the clients, had suffered Landscaping. The consultants' choice of Executive Vegetation perturbed the Doctor. *'Prunus serrulata* "Pink Perfection": my God!' Still, a few natives had been reinstalled, at the back, respectful and peasant-like. Birch, for example; each one clean and firmly attached to an establishment pole. Behind them glared suckers from the *Betula* scrub uprooted to make room. The Lake – several boggy lochans commandeered into one – was redispersing to its constituent rushes, its willows beyond weeping. The tennis courts, however, introduced a pleasantly formal aquatic feature in this weather; beside it the copper-sulphate of the swimming pools appeared *arriviste*. We crossed a new but uncertain bridge and, except for the danger of drowning, could have knelt and kissed the honest hillwater thundering through; after three weeks of rain it sounded more like the cartographic Allt a' Thuiltidh than the Awley Burn its rustic notice indicated ("River Awley" must have been insufficiently Scotch). Yes, Glen Awley Park was plainly an Encampment, soon to join the other nettled patches on the hillside, a few of its Horticultural Society genes maybe ennobling the local flora.

Our sentimentalising was halted by the arrival of an expensive car, driven too fast for the road or its own motorway suspension. It slithered to a stop beside us. The driver was fat, pallid, bright blue-shirted. Obviously a Resident, presumably an Executive. The Apprentice examined his Class Enemy with interest. Residents had been hitherto invisible, no doubt at home scanning the oscilloscopic tartan of Highland television, or at the various Leisure Centres lightening their purses. The clouds of midges, attracted by such rich feeding, would have kept them in.

But this resident appeared worried, even anguished. 'Look, you're climbers. You can help. You must!'

The Doctor skilfully calmed him, and we got into the car out of midges and rain, now both heavy, while he explained.

Between mops of the brow and eyerolling through the drenching midge-beaten windows, he told us how his son, in the Fourth Form, a clever little chap, was up for the hols. A clever little chap, very unusual, fond of nature, archaeology and all that. He had left the previous night, with food and torch and all that, to climb that little hill – a shaking corpulent finger described an ellipse – to see how the rising sun shone through some old stones and all that. We glanced at each other: prehistoric astronomy again. 'You see, it has something to do with predicting times of the moon and tides and all that – to tell when it's safe to cross the' – he jabbed a more accurate finger towards the distantly-glittering Marina – 'to cross the kyle, in a coracle; and all that. So his book says. He took his book with him up the hill, O they shouldn't allow these hills, O he's such a clever little chap....' The gifted youth had promised to be back by breakfast; he *had* to be back by lunch. And now it was after *tea* time.... The hand-wringing gastronomic chronology indicated how gnawing the anxiety. Yes, he had contacted Mr Goldfeiner. Mr Goldfeiner had then contacted Duntilty, but Dan – who naturally ran the Mountain Rescue Course – was just now away again with clients taking the course and coaching them for the Pitfoulie Cup – for the best Vacation Volunteers. No! he had not left a note of their destination.... Police? No, Mr Goldfeiner did not like troubling them yet – besides, he had heard three *climbers* were walking down the road.

The parent broke off, hands apart in supplication.

We patted him physically and psychologically and set off. We followed the boy's likeliest track from the house. We quartered the ground, calling and listening. Just as the sun was setting and the yellow security floodlights of Glen Awley Park were switching on, compound to compound, we thought we heard an answering shout. It re-answered, and we found him, down a hole between peat and boulders. The Doctor scrambled in; we stood respectfully by. He climbed out, cracking a joke, feebly responded to from below.

'Not bad. Coming down. Reading. Fell in. Broken ankle. Pott's. Clean enough. Need the usual.'

The Apprentice and I departed rapidly to the Castle, while the Doctor rejoined his patient, discussing the likely over-enthusiasm of Professor Thom. We found Dan and his team there. Also Mr MacEacheran, who was glad, because Mr Goldfeiner had *hoped* there'd be No Trouble. 'Most unfortunate for us if the Press got hold of it.' He phoned the parent. We heard, 'Aah – my dear Mr Chancy, happily I have found your boy safe and well....'

A Front Man indeed.... When I steered the enraged Apprentice back to Dan, a crowd of refugees had emerged from the sheds; they seemed for the first time alive. They besought. Could they join us? I looked at Dan. He looked at me. He spat on the ground: Yorkshire for yes. We all set off, the Apprentice with Dan and his team, myself sheepdogging the others, picking up dropped torches, separating gigglers, counting called-in heads every few minutes.

We met the rescue party coming down. The Doctor was galloping alongside the stretcher, still deep in equinoxes, the bearers well in the running for the Pitfoulie Cup. They left my excited gaggle far behind.

When I reached Duntilty, I found the Doctor laughing heartily with a broad shiny individual beaming from disgraceful tweeds; surely Mr Goldfeiner? Even the Apprentice was grinning. All held large glasses. Mr Goldfeiner swept them aside, spilling precious millilitres, and thrust a paw at me.

'Great work, great work! Now everybody is fine and O.K. The ambulance is on its way, the statements have been taken, Mrs Chancy is happy and in tears, Mr Chancy is happy and in tears; and the boy is asleep.' (No wonder, after two hours of the Doctor on Alexander Thom.) He refused to listen to anything we said and bundled us off in his limousine, louder and plushier than even Mr Chancy's. As we left, we waved to the cheering clients. Dan raised lips from orange juice in acknowledgement. Mr MacEacheran, tired by the exertions of his rescue, had gone to bed.

I recall little of the rest. An enormous meal chez Goldfeiner, unlimited whisky (all, to the Doctor's well-concealed dismay, Dependable Blends of Staggering Expense), tales and stories (and information on Malts), songs in Cockney and Doctorial Gaelic, ballads on Brixton and Great John MacLean, a Yiddish aria by the ample Mrs Goldfeiner: and eventually blissful sleep in an executive suite of execrable taste, one for each of us. Then an early rise, an appallingly cheerful Mr Goldfeiner over a shuddery breakfast (we refused a further glass of Stockbroker's Pride), and a dawn whisk by himself, not his chauffeur, to our tents (and if ever we wanted a site and a *good* house, mind, a real *good* house, not their usual sort, and at a *sensible* price, mind, we were just to let him know...). Followed by a rush south to work.

We snored in the back of the Doctor's fusty old Mercedes, a wagon proper to our station. 'Astonishing thing,' the driver remarked as we boomed through a 6 a.m. Tyndrum, 'the number of people you can meet, in even one of the least frequented parts of Scotland.'

A fortnight later the Doctor received, with best wishes to us all, three cases of Glen Speerie, 80° proof, 18 years old, distillery bottled, smooth as milk; from Mr Chancy, a director of the firm. The accompanying letter added that he believed his grandmother had come from Scotland.

# BLÀS NA BEURLA

It had begun in Skye some years ago, when the Doctor, fresh from leading Collie's Route, had met an old man in the Sligachan bar who claimed to know the original name of Sgùrr Alasdair. 'No, no, it was nothing *like* Sgùrr Alasdair: that one is – an *invention*.' The Doctor, impatiently drumming his glass, had to listen through an hour and five drams of explanation concerning who invented the invention, and for whom it had been invented – all of which he knew already from a more accurate if less inspired account in the Club Guidebook. And so skilled had been the old man in the oral tradition that they parted without the Doctor having been told the Original Name. That might have been divulged the following night or, less improbably, *implied* several nights and bottles later; but the Doctor had been recalled to Edinburgh and an urgent case.

'You can only get these things if you have the language,' was his firm conclusion, based on that episode and on the proven extractive skill of his Gaelic-speaking friends at the University's School of Scottish Studies; their prowess was undeniable and often provided them with significant liquid contributions from us all in the back room of Daddy McKay's. The Apprentice and I, admirers of their bilingual persuasion, doubted if the Doctor, elutive enough in English, could coax even one drop, so to speak, of information in so athletically metaphorical a tongue as the Gaelic.

But he had worked away, building with grammars and tapes from our common foundation of the language laid in the JMCS; hardly a foundation, rather an odd half-brick or two serving to distinguish (for us) a necessary mountain or a greeting from a farewell – but, when dropped accidentally and sonorously among native speakers, liable to engender uncomfortable silence. He did not involve us in his studies; we learnt, however, to interpret *'Tha mi sgith'* or *'Seadh, tha mi sgith'* or, more daringly, if emphatically, *'Seadh, is e mi-fhein a tha sgith'*, delivered, after some thought, in an off-hand manner following a hard day on the hill. Similarly *'Tha an t-acras orm'* signalled a slinging-off of rucksacks for a bite. We would reply encouragingly 'Buachaille Etive Mór!' or, more determinedly 'Stob Coire nam Beith....' We learnt also to live with, as with midges, his at first frequent outpourings (by torchlight in the tent) of Donnchaidh Bàn or the great Somhairle, versions which might have astonished the authors; but these books, too heavy or too expensive, gradually dropped from his climbing kit, and we believed the fire extinguished.

But Sròn Ulladale revived it. The westerly winds of Harris brought conflagration. Unsparing of our embarrassment as crass visitors from the *Gallteachd* and claiming proudly to host the linguistic genes of a native-speaking grandfather ('I'm only carrying it on' – or, rather, *'Chan eil mi ach a leantuinn ri mo dhualchais'*) he insisted on demanding food, drink, petrol or a night's camp site in the ancient tongue. Almost invariably, communication required restatement in lean unlovely English, due to insufficiencies in the Doctor or in the local inhabitants; one of whom remarked in unmistakably Lancastrian tones to his wife as we were leaving, 'That's the third Germans we've had this week.' The rare success spurred him out of all sense of proportion.

For we were most threatened on the climbs themselves. Sròn Ulladale at its mildest is, literally, still off-putting. We had gone there, after preliminary races over the sun-dappled Forest of Harris, to strengthen our characters, and for the Apprentice to liberate a few Artificials. Dangling in stirrups and harness, pulleyed to right and left, requires, as our unhappy experience on the Ben with *Constipation* demonstrated, swift unambiguous communication.

It was therefore just the place for the Doctor to announce that, as our progress in the language needed encouragement, he would speak for the rest of the holiday only in Gaelic. 'Even on the Climbs?' asked, with incredulous oaths, the Apprentice. *'Eodhoinn mar a tha sinn a' streap, a'bhalaich.'* (I shall rarely translate these italicised Doctorial utterances; the reader might as well appreciate how we ourselves felt at the time.) We did arrange mutual understanding of the terms for (or in the Doctor's mind approximating to) 'tight', 'slack', 'take in', 'ready', 'coming on', 'right', 'left', 'up', 'down' and so on. Even 'I'm coming off' was put into the tongue of the Garden of Eden, as befitting the preface to an imminent Fall. Mercifully, the Doctor was not (yet) familiar with the dialect of St Kilda, or we should have had further subtleties concerning the state of reliability of the guano underfoot (it usually dropped clear, anyway, from the Sròn).

It says much for the well-proven determination of our companion that he stuck to his decision, even when the choice lay between adherence to it or to Sròn Ulladale. His ribs became very sore. (*'Tha* *m'asnaichinn gle ghoirt. Tha.'*) The Apprentice suffered strain on his rope, his memory, his glottis and his temper, and fury drove him to spectacular successes, often virtually solo. He also took to going off alone towards the crag in the long evenings, while we lazed by the tents or fished. 'He's probably – aah – *Is docha gu bheil e ag obair air* – aah – *rud ris nach eil duil againn,'** remarked the Doctor.

On our last day this surmise appeared correct. The Apprentice, strangely pleased with himself, led us to the most overhanging part of the great overhang. He announced he would lead it to the top, and then the Doctor would follow. Only the Doctor, for he couldn't risk two passengers. I felt somewhat nettled. '*Mi-fhein?*' asked the Doctor. 'You-*fhein*' confirmed our leader.

I sat on the heather and watched. A stupendous lead. '*Schön, schön,*' cried the Doctor, gazing up, switched to the wrong waveband by admiration. '*Sgoinneal, sgoinneal,*' agreed a soft voice behind me. I swung round and saw a highly attractive young woman, not a climber, and presumably a passing local. The Doctor overheard. He called out to her. '*Tha, gu dearbh, nach eil!*' She sniffed and moved away. It was clear what he had meant; I wondered what he had said....

He had no occasion to say more, for the noose tightened – 'Come on,' roared from above. '*Tha mi tighinn,*' answered the Doctor, and began. He did not perform too badly. But he was no Apprentice, and went for short voyages in space, scrabbling unbeautifully. The Doctor is far from vain, but he is human and male, and this exhibition, following the consummate artistry of his leader and so exposed to the gaze of an otherwise pleasing young lady, must have proved abrasive in every sense. It might almost have been planned by some illwisher.

Finally, he stuck. How, was not clear. Maybe the Apprentice, so far above, had misunderstood. The Doctor dangled, gyrating. Clearly he could continue if his leader freed the lefthand rope a little way up. He roared hoarse instructions – manfully as ever, in Gaelic. The Apprentice did nothing. I thought I heard the fair one sniggering. I turned round again. She was, but so were half a dozen other people. Some had plastic cases slung over their shoulders. Heavens! Photographers? Journalists? Film men? Actresses?

My heart bled for the poor Doctor. I bellowed instructions, in full Sassunach, to the Apprentice. He remained silent, flicking the ropes occasionally to ensure continued Doctorial rotation. He could be a hard man, provoked long enough.

* 'He's probably working hard at – aah – a surprise for us' *Translator*

But the Doctor was equally hard, and even more provoked. He gave up shouting to his leader and directed instructions to his audience, for relayed transmission. His period of rotation was fairly constant, so that the resultant intermittent foghorn, rebounding from Sròn Ulladale's impassive walls, was indeed ludicrous. I hoped the audience were laughing at that, and not at the Doctor's syntax – which under the circumstances, if not *foghlumaichte*, was certainly *bho gaisge*.

At last this Mórag creature (that turned out to be her name), flinging back locks yellow enough to enchain the most experienced poet, let fly at the crag a torrent of Gaelic. It echoed sharp and beautiful among the rocks. Then silence. What did she expect? The Doctor, as he spun, spun openmouthed, like a goldfish circumnavigating its globe.

She got what she, the madam, expected. An answer from the top of the climb. From the Apprentice, none other. A long, apparently authentic, peroration – *anns a' Ghaidhlig*.... Full and orotund.

And then, communication having been achieved, he wound on the Doctor; it had seemed to require, not just Gaelic, but correct Gaelic. (Being humane, he let his companion scramble fairly unaided to the top; but being human, he stepped carefully away before the Doctor got there.)

The Doctor, however, acknowledged a victory when he saw one. How it had been planned was celebrated that night at Angus John's, the nearby house of a *seannachaidh* whose remarkable songs and stories the other members of the party were recording (they carried tape machines, not cameras). Those long evenings had not been devoted to Sròn Ulladale, but to Mórag. And they had hatched together a pleasing revenge on the stubbornly monoglot Doctor. We did not enquire if the Apprentice could interpret all that his *ban-sith bhoidheach* shouted up at him, nor all that he so convincingly replied; but it was clear that night that some understanding had been achieved.

I cannot comprehend how we caught the Ferry next day. For weeks after, the Doctor hummed and chanted Angus John's nephew's cathartic playing of *Is fhada mar seo a tha sinn*: other pibrochs lapsed into mathematics. I could not forget Mórag's mother's singing of *Mo run geal dileas*, one of the greatest of the *orain móra*. And until the next weekend, when we tackled a tremendous new route on Garbh Bheinn, the Apprentice could not forget Mórag.

# A DAUGHTER OF THE REVOLUTION

That Harris episode brings to mind our experience with another young lady, rather different from Mórag. It is too long to tell here, indeed it is not yet concluded; but how we first met her and her companion may be of interest.

It was a damp August Sunday afternoon at Craig-y-Barns. Dismal; and the Doctor does not like popular outcrops of polished severity. They remind him of humiliation on the Junior Climbing Wall at Meadowbank. 'Like the end game in chess. Pure mathematics. Just no scope for the imagination. Mistakes are your own stupidity. Can be most embarrassing.'

The only thing he enjoyed about Craig-y-Barns was the firing, in the eighteenth century by some Planting Duke or other, of tree seeds from a cannon to the most inaccessible buttresses, as part of a re-afforestation scheme. 'Long term provision for decent belays. Curious how time disinfects ethics. Quite proper to use the trunks now; only the seed was artificial.' So he moodily scanned the botanical fringe. We had just arrived on our way back from the north, and stood beneath the Upper Tier of Cave Crag, wondering wetly what to do – if anything. But the rock was fairly dry.

Towards us came a Glaswegian hard man, with two people in tow. He muttered briefly to the Apprentice, handed them over, and was gone.

We gathered they were two of the very top American climbers. The Apprentice had seen them at Joshua and appeared duly awed. One was a dark intense bony girl about the height of the Doctor's anorak pocket, who moved as if on over-tightened springs. The other, a vast shambling ape, grinning from earlet to earlet, pink to the blond shadow of his crewcut. He raised a paw. 'Hi.' Both were in abbreviated shirts and jeans, the lady's being torn off some ten inches above the knee; which, for one of her height, was a fair way up.

The Doctor found himself beaming down at her. She eyed him from a set hickory face, attractive but for its likeness to some Aztec god of prey. He introduced himself. She appeared unmoved, regarding him fixedly with black unblinking lizard eyes. Her lank midnight hair disappeared behind into a grimy headband.

'I'm Virginia Prusik.'

'Ah.'

'No. NOT the knots. Before my time.'

She turned away. He endeavoured to regain her attention.

'Ah, Miss Prusik....'

'I'm NOT Miss Prusik.'

Unhappily: 'Mrs Prusik?'

'I'm NOT *Mrs* Prusik.'

The Doctor orchestrated all his bedside skills to suggest she tell him what she was.

She raised flawless precision-ground teeth, grimly.

'I'm *Ms* Prusik.'

'Ah, yes. *Ys*....'

The giant oozed across. 'Call her what you like, pal. Virge, Gin, Ginney, Pru. That right, gal?' He playfully nipped her arm. No impression on smooth hickory.

The Doctor, still fiddling with
with his wavebands, then tried to
describe a meeting with Layton
Kor on some North-West Orient
flight. Kor had remained
asleep until landing. Equal
lack of interest here. She
turned back to the cliff,
devouring it hungrily, nibbling
the turf of well-bitten nails.

The huge paw circled
above us again.

'I'm Sep.'

Much less complicated.

Sep and Virge had been
in Europe all summer.
They had just come from
Sweden (why Sweden?).
They were in Scotland to...
climb the Castle Rock at
Edinburgh. Of all places....

'Castle Rock?'

'Sure....' That broad

easy smile extinguished further interrogation, even doubt. They would climb Castle Rock. Sentries, rockets, radar, would melt before them.

'Got a guide?'

The lady was back. The Apprentice meekly proffered that not inexpensive publication.

'That Rat-Race?' Jerk of polished head.

That was Rat-Race. 140ft (42m), Extremely Severe, E4. She handed back the guide and minced towards the wall with a curious springing step, like a female spider sizing up its prey. Then she returned.

'I'll need a diagram for later.'

The Apprentice handed over the book, she opened it, tore out the diagram, and handed the rest back to the astounded Apprentice. Then, still piercing us with a fierce visionary gaze, she fumbled in the debatable region between short shirt and shorter shorts; hauled out a grubby purse on a string, stuffed the crumpled diagram into it, and pushed the whole thing down again.

'O.K. Fine.' She turned away.

But we had been fascinated by the momentary revelation of a long twisting red and black tattooed snake down her middle, one end up under the shirt and the other presumably finishing below at some metaphysically suitable site.

Sep loomed over us. A great grin.

'You seen Ginny's Nature Trail?'

We gulped facetious nothings and followed him to the cliff.

They climbed of course solo. No ropes or that jazz. We were prepared for this by now. Most people on the crag were not, and clutched Perthshire appreciatively. Virge or Ginny or whatever was halfway up more or less the line of that E4, moving like a lizard on a 5.12: stationary, plotting, then a flash to another position; waiting; then another flash up to the left, to the right; and so on. Her limbs, though, held her bunched body well clear of the rock; they curved in below like those of a spider. During these momentary waits she was slipping, often from all four press-ons, but slowly, and just before the movement blossomed into a peel she transformed its momentum into another upward leap, became again a trembling bud, even higher above our heads. Unreal enough on The Titan or any suchlike desert pillar. Here, in a nose-dripping Caledonian drizzle, a *montage*. But firmly pinned. She would not fall. Only flesh and blood fell. She vanished beyond an overhang.

We resumed respiration. From up on the left croaked a fitting opinion: 'Weel done, Cutty Sark....'

'Ye-e-e-eah.' Sep shuffled to the cliff, tapped it with a shapeless finger, beamed a great smile, and began *his* climb.

The technique was quite different. He flowed, rippled, up the rock; but not elegantly. Like a huge *Amoeba* or pink bathmat, extending amiable wrinkling pseudopodia right round his periphery, tirelessly examining, rejecting, accepting, moving on, using the whole of his oceanic frame, inside of limbs, belly, neck or where his neck occasionally revealed itself in the ebb and flow of that roseate tide. When he revolved his head to gaze happily down at us, the infinitesimal bristles of his cropped poll added their friction. He was dead safe. The very rock relaxed.

'That's not a route...' faintly pointed out the Apprentice.

Sep apologised, and hoped he hadn't damaged anything.

The Doctor congratulated him on making a new route so soon.

Sep included the whole Upper Tier in an ample gesture, without affecting his adhesion in the least:

'Guess they're *all* noo. Ain't never *bin* here before....'

And continued his vertical amble. We felt somehow refreshed, as if windows had been opened. He coincided at one point with part of the spring of *Mousetrap*.

Two Dundee mice had taken the bait, both very white. Sep paused to offer advice, then generously wandered up a little with the rope to thread an aid.

'Now: that's just dandy!' And undulated on. (The leader did not return to Craig-y-Barns; but developed into quite a good canoeist.)

So Sep also vanished from our ken.

We waited below, but they never came back. We could have given them a hitch to Edinburgh, too. Why didn't the Apprentice and I, at least, climb after them? Well... as the Doctor said: after listening to MacFadyen for one night, he put away his own pipes for a month.

We heard nothing for a long time. They never turned up at the Castle Rock, either. When we did hear, they were at the Calanque, more suitable than Craig-y-Barns. Yet we were fated once more to meet with them.... But that is a different tale and, as I said, not yet over.

# WINTER HOMES FOR ALL

The subject of snow-caves and igloos confines the Doctor, the Apprentice and myself to a frigid, glass-staring and cold-sipping silence. The whole bar contracts. These dubious habitations may well succour the sudden exposee or the ritualistic masochist; but to us were havens of disaster. They were frankly dangerous. The only two we managed to build each sent us back through the daily press as 'Climbing Casualties', an indignity which the more vexatious of our colleagues are too fond of recounting. I say *we* managed to build, but that is just decency; the author of their construction, and of our downfall, was – as usual – the Doctor.

Apart from himself, we doubted the value of what the Apprentice scornfully termed 'fall-in shelters'; though we had suffered much clubroom experience of snowholing and igloo-rearing from the extensive slide shows of Sir Hector Macassar and, less loquaciously but more factually, from the grubbyfingered syllabuses of earnest purveyors of Winter Certificates. We had also spent the odd blasphemous night 'up there' in a mush of polythene baggery reminiscent of a deep freeze two days out on a power cut. But we had never done the thing properly. We had never climbed a hill for the sole purpose of indulging architecturally in the Polar Vernacular. Until the Doctor met a long-lost nephew. He was an Antarctic geologist, and kindled our companion's creative fire with robust tales of roasting ice-baked nights, poker played in shirt sleeves, at minus seventy outside.

The Doctor thereupon bought a snow shovel, a large and glorified aluminium trowel, which accompanied us everywhere that winter until a certain day. Tied to his sack, it clattered irritatingly up rock, jammed behind ice in Parallel B, and at nights visited everyone's sleeping bag in turn. He would never leave it outside. We protested in vain. As demonstrated on our Cave Meet, he loves such incongruous apparatus. He reproved us sternly.

'You should always keep a shovel *inside* an igloo; in case of collapse.'

We pointed out that we were in a tent.

'Ah, well, in winter, heavy snow overnight: can't rely on

terylene.... Anyway, a damned useful thing to have around, a shovel. And this one fits in anywhere.'

We bore out his last sentence, groaning and prising the implement from between our shoulder-blades. But we had dissuaded him from purchasing a snow saw, presumably even better equipped as an aggressor, and considered ourselves relatively fortunate. The fad would surely pass. It was, so far, a bad snow year.

One February weekend we were bound for the Coe, but drifts blocked Glen Ogle. We left the car at a dripping farmhouse low down and planned a round of Stobinian, Ben More and Cruach Ardrain, staying a night on the hill. We carried the Apprentice's new mountain tent that would sleep two at a clinch, and the Doctor brandished his shovel. 'An excellent opportunity!'

It was not. The strong wind blew the hills clear. Nothing but icy scree of the irascible and malevolent Stobinian variety. The Doctor poked and scrabbled below the unforgiving clifflets of Ben More late that afternoon, like an old yowe scraping for pasture. But only flour and marble, a few inches deep. No nourishment for his hopes.

Darkness fell as we clambered down the last rugosities of the steep north side. We were not very sure of our whereabouts. Bivouacking makes one cavalier of general topography. Our interests ferreted local cubic yards. We found ourselves below most of the wind, and the snow under the rocks looked flat; and proved deep. A similar scarp reared up beyond. A good site for a tent, even for a snow cave.

Indeed, excellent. The Doctor, uncharacteristically and execrably, began to sing as he wielded, at last, the glittering instrument. Blinded by his effluvia, we were forced to help and, despite ourselves, enjoyed excavating a roomy chamber in that huge soft drift bridging the trench between the lines of cliff. Although rock was a long way down, and flat, the Doctor dislodged a piece of quartzite after a deep lunge – 'Remarkably symmetrical crystal. Rarity. Museum might like it.' We dug midway in the trench, away from possible stonefall at either end. Scale was deceptive in that poor visibility: a Sudwand could be rising before us. The Doctor busied himself with ventilation. We, under continual instruction, modelled cooking shelf and sleeping benches. An ideal home, compared with the entropy outside and – for this once anyway – better than struggling with half-rigged nylon and string; mountain tents in particular seem designed on the windsock principle.

Supper was soon roaring inside. The Apprentice twiddled primuses, and the Doctor, to demonstrate the indubitable heat and to dry his breeks, lay stretched in sark, pipe and long johns on a luxury of plastic foam and eiderdown. Poker appeared imminent. Before joining them, I retired to a call of nature, cursing the wind and snow.

Returning, I noticed a glow to our east. The moon.

The moon? Rising very quickly. Surely, too quickly....

Showers and gobbets of snow streamed up through the illumination, heavier each minute; billowing hypnotically.

I struggled along the trench towards this odd phenomenon.

Then the moon rose.

Two moons! Two huge eyes of light, centres of roaring snowy Catherine wheels. And a smaller yellow intermittent light above them. Twinkle, twankle, twinkle....

Somehow strangely familiar....

With horror, I guessed the unguessable. A snow plough!

Snow plough!

On Ben More....

Topographical niceties aside, it had to be stopped; or our house-warming right in its track would be rotovated, my companions likewise.

I staggered in front, and danced about.

It continued, bellowing and gnashing, sooking up the stew.

I leapt at the choking bank, nearly slithered into its threshing maw and rattling chains; I beat the heartless yellow flanks.

It kept on, masticating furiously, head down.

Only twenty yards, at most. I bashed the side window so hard it nearly split. The brute felt that. It reluctantly slowed; and stopped, panting and grinding with impatience. I nursed my numbed wrist. The window screwed down. A wool-encumbered orange-hooded scarlet head peered out.

'Ay, ay?'

I attempted to shout an explanation. The head, as ponderously deliberate as the rest of the vehicle, turned to another, unseen, head within. Then returned to me.

'Oo, aye; we'll get ye oot as soon as we can!'

Disappearance of head.

Fearsome revving and, Lord, the contraption began again. I clung to the lurching window and tried to convey an urgent necessity of stopping BEFORE they got my companions out.

Fifteen yards on, it did stop. My information had maybe penetrated the well protected epidermis of the Coonty roadmen, substantial enough in its own right; but probably more effective in instilling a sense of the unusual was the capering figure of the Doctor, aroused by the glare and thunder, his bare feet and shirt-tails flapping, horrific in the stormshaken – but now mercifully stationary – headlights. The Apprentice, eyes popping and primus still in hand, filled in a confirmatory corner.

'What's all this; like?' Heavy consternation at the windscreen. Three heads.

We had stopped them; but explanation was impossible. They were too well wrapped in years of rescuing foolish but grateful motorists. And were they not this very night grinding up from Killin to liberate more of them stranded by Loch Dochartside? And were not their rivals from Strathyre, Dalmally and Glen Falloch nosing at the same harvest, muzzles lowered, diesels wagging?

We gave up; and dragged, still shocked, our belongings out of the centre of the A85, stuffing everything – including a pan of hot fried bacon and two cupfuls of soup – into the nearest rucksack. The Doctor's museum specimen – most likely a reflector from the invisible white line – was not included. The roadmen had climbed down stiffly, and stood in a group, hood-scratching, bemused at finding no car, but a Hole... like. While the Doctor once more endeavoured to explain, pulling up his breeches, the scene changed dramatically. *Blue* lights flashed. A police Land Rover, two Land Rovers, appeared. Torches.

Explanation was clear to them. Our open rucksacks, dishevelled attire.... Lost climbers, distraught, about to collapse from exposure, gear scattered despairingly. Obvious. We were led away amid scribbling and earphones, protesting unavailingly against omnipotent sympathy. There were flashes, clicks: reporters occupied a third Land Rover....

The second occasion was still worse. Let me continue. It is good for the character.

Many weeks elapsed before the Doctor dared mention the subject again. He took us in fine vintage style (the leader must not slip!) up a spring-ice S.C.Gully, and we relented. On condition that whatever edifice, or declivity, he raised, or lowered, should be well away from danger of Public Intrusion. We wanted a quiet home of our own. Not too near a main road....

'Quite so, quite so. How about a summit plateau? Safe enough there, eh? Not the Gorms, of course: that's a helicopters' main road. Somewhere else.... Splendid at this time of year. You can get good windpacked igloo snow; and lie at your own door drinking-in the sunset.'

We agreed because it sounded impracticable. Wind would remove snow, not pack it, from so exposed a position. Alas, that very week in late April snow fell heavily high up without a wind, and was then compacted by tiresome zephyrs. So the following Saturday found us on the top of Meall Chuaich – remote enough – in cold sunlight, being supervised in fetching and carrying, and even in cutting and shaping, blocks for an igloo. A Thick-walled Igloo, best for Scotland.

The Great Pyramid had scarcely required more expertise. Mutterings and hummings. Angles and tapers. Punctuated by a long description of anchorites' cells on some Irish island. 'Not a trace of earth or mortar. Drystone beehives. Much more difficult than an igloo. And devotions five times a day as well. Devil of a job....' But we enjoyed silkily carving the sighing whiteness, so light and firm; pressing the blocks to mutual embrace; subtly aligning blue joints of shadow.

It was a beautiful object when completed. On the white dome beneath cloudless azure, it glistened irreproachably. The grimy summit cairn, its nearest rival, was half-buried a good three feet lower.

The Doctor patted it continually, unable to resist paring here and encouraging there. 'You know, it's almost a Thinwalled Type. A perfect hemisphere up top. Pity we didn't have that snow saw: would have been much quicker.' We shuddered; we had tripped over the shovel several times already and anticipated another night of its pressing attentions. Yet it had performed well. Ample room for three or four, even for itself; an ice age howff, with almost full headroom and built-in kitchen and bunks. A tunnel led up from the entrance, to drain cold air. A primus polished the interior finish of Glacier Blue to non-drip gloss.

We duly lay outside a little in the Doctor's sunset, cooling off, watching the round miles of snow about us redden and purple, above the dark glens of Laggan. Then, a flaring feast inside, the decor now Primus Orange. We relaxed on foam and feathers. A tiring day. But the Doctor insisted on poker; just to demonstrate.

A comfortable night. No damned snowploughs. Dispensing with adiabatic aids, we corked the tunnel with a rucksack to deter inquisitive summit winds. Snug, we trusted the ventilation holes. Jerseys, breeks were discarded. We were very warm. The Doctor purred. 'Even at seventy below....'

Carbon dioxide is soporific, poker (with the Doctor) exhausting. I remembered nothing. No dreams. Not even a shovel. We snored long, disgracefully long, into the Sunday morning.

The Sunday morning was clear and fresh, and under its genial spring sun the high eastern plateaus gleamed and sparkled. Ptarmigan chattered, skiers queued, and up to the welcoming heights wound a bright and early crowd of Young People, shepherded by the eternally ebullient A. J. Evergreen Smith; eager for their first real Munro. They stomped on to the plateau and streamed towards the distant cairn, hullooed by the perspiring Smith. Evergreen's dog, a large exceptionally brainless redhaired creature, Doggie by name, barked in encouraging circles. They reached their cairn, their dream, and danced round it in snow already trampled by previous triumphant Munroists. Doggie claimed it as his own several times. In great excitement, all twenty were successfully counted. Then there had to be the group photograph. As many as could, clambered up the cairn, Doggie as well. Evergreen teetered at the apex, dangling the two jumping smallest. The rest clustered about, buzzing and singing round their ample queen, swinging hands and kicking toeholds. They hurrooed and kicked and barked again and again as the camera was set up. They hurrooed and kicked and barked once too often.

They all fell through.

The whole clamjamfrey. Right through.

On top of us....

I was dreadfully wakened. Avalanches, earthquakes, stampeded through my brain. I glimpsed blocks of ice and daylight, boots, legs, hairy socks, a sort of tail: a haggis of snow, shouts, barks and screaming. An inexplicable, appalling chaos. I sank back, refusing to believe, buffetted and pounded....

They scrambled off, pulled each other out. They were counted again, all heads extricated and dusted free of snow. Twenty.... Twenty... two. Twenty-two!

Evergreen, agape, counted once more. Who, how?

The Doctor and I found ourselves hauled to the front, through a forest of legs and a tail, I still half awake, the Doctor hopelessly disoriented; and, unhappily, again in his underclothes. Young Folk shrank away. Silence reigned, even over Evergreen.

As I felt someone should say something, I opened my mouth; but found myself describing the second Pyramid. The Doctor, collecting his agitated neurones rather better, took over, though he did begin with a few words on the Great Skellig. He soothed them, had them (inevitably) cheering again. Someone hung a cagoule about his knees.

Then we remembered the Apprentice. Scattering brats, the Doctor and I plunged into the ruins. But Doggie had found him, probably had claimed him as his own, and was now affectionately slorping over his furious purple face. He was iced in, halfway down the cold air trench, and felt like it. He was fortunately gagged by a largely unbitten block and before removing it I drew his attention to the younger and more innocent of our visitors. He was, however, beyond swearing. I prised the shovel from the small of his back.

Swearing began when he found he could not kick at the dog nor even rise without pain; and when the Doctor, now more professionally back in breeches, diagnosed a couple of cracked ribs: probably the shovel, but possibly the still wondering thirteen globular stone of Evergreen. He refused to be strapped up, still less carried; and as he clearly could not walk down, a dilemma ensued. It was resolved by the presence of an attractive darkhaired student nurse, a slender but firm pillar of the Youth Group. He consented to be strapped by her, in decent privacy beyond the rubble; and accepted her unyielding arm on the long limp down.

Doggie galumphed about in front of the Casualty, cheering him on. Boots were restrained by painful ribs and Nurse's grip, but when the feckless animal bundled once too often against his legs, the Apprentice got in a good Penalty before collapsing. Howls (from the dog) brought Evergreen bounding across from a short tutorial on pollination in *Juncus squarrosus*. 'Ah, poor, poor Doggie, THEN....' They clung together, the hound casting large white reproachful eyes back at an unrepentant Apprentice, now suffering Florence

Nightingale's tongue. There is no malice in Evergreen. He twinkled at us brightly: 'Ah, yes, Doggie *can* be *very* troublesome.'

But Doggie won. Next day his picture was larger than ours. Heroic Doggie. Who smelt out an Injured Climber Buried Under The Snow. A complacent hound across the front page. Beneath that, a horizontal Apprentice; a third, much smaller, picture of the Doctor and I, merely rescued together. A long, graphic story. Doggie's master is a dab hand at the newspapers. But nothing about a collapsed cairn. No shred of malice in Evergreen.

The Doctor and I, gloomily predicting all this, hobbled down after the excited gaggle. Painfully the Doctor stopped, painfully felt behind, painfully slipped off his sack; and rummaged within. He looked up, stiffly.

'Blast. It's not here. Must still be under the snow.'

The shovel. The bloody shovel.

We called it a spade, and left it there.

KENNEL NOTE: We were of course too hard on poor Doggie; we felt savage that day. Doggie is a kindly beast, only a little less intelligent than the average M.P., and quite guileless; not like that vile Climbing Dog of Arran. We have frequently met him since, and fondled his long floppy ears. A thing we would not do to the Climbing Dog of Arran. Nor to the average M.P.

# OLD MAN AHOY

Even before this, I had not liked sea stacks. They were so crude and digital, mere exclamation marks against the solid statement of cliffs about them. And, looking down from their tops, one lurched slowly and flatulently to and fro on a smearing tide. But the Apprentice revelled in their verticality, and the Doctor elaborated on their character – 'you get to know them from every side,' he said.

They all had similar names – Maidens or Old Men – and this one was an Old Man, an Am Bodach, off the west coast; its precise location, for reasons obvious later, cannot be given. The Doctor had climbed some of its fellows with Patey, but they had never got round to this. It stood some way off a steep deserted shore, racked by savage tides. Approach needed planning, and several days.

That summer the Apprentice and I, after a week's climbing, were to be met by the Doctor at the coast not far from the Bodach. He was driving up with his new rubber boat and its powerful outboard. He was late, and when he did arrive he was a bitter man.

'Wrecked,' he said. How? we asked. 'That blasted beech!' he said. What beach? 'A huge brute, right over the road. Couldn't avoid it.' Our disturbing impression of some massive maritime incursion was soon corrected. The boat had travelled on the roofrack, the road was narrow, and a damned caravan ('those *damned* caravans!') had swung inexpertly at him; he swerved to the verge and ripped the port float end to end, on a bough of *Fagus sylvatica*. The deflated ruins draped the back seat. In the boot reposed the 10 h.p. Volvo outboard.

'We'll have to look for another boat to fix on the end of it,' was his conclusion. But no boat could we find. Nothing that dared to wear such internal combustion. The few houses along the coast were occupied by old women ('no, no: no boat') or holidaymakers (largely inflated ducks). The Doctor refused to enquire at the numerous caravans. Someone (a harmless Frenchman or southern Englishman – it was difficult to tell, his vowels were so confused by the Doctor's expression) suggested the Warden at the Nature Reserve. Still badtempered, the Doctor strode along to a No-Entry sign. We lifted the wire and walked on. A terrible smell (soon to be familiar): rotting seaweed, birds. Birds everywhere. Feathers in the air. Continual squawking. Not *still* breeding?

The warden was a mild man, Jim Twite, holding a revolting bald gosling-like individual in each hand. So guileless were his eyes that the Doctor did not like broaching the boat business right away. We therefore, as supposed bird lovers, underwent the story of how the Twites (his wife joined him, nursing two equally repellent, but smaller, neonatal *Anser anser*) had tired of living in Blackburn, and how rewarding they found it up here, re-establishing a colony – he indicated the clamouring throng that crammed the bright green fields of an evicted township – and combing innocent feathers free of oil. The Doctor thought of his engine, and hesitated again; allowing a further half-hour's conducted tour, family to odorous family, before he could lay the problem before our hosts. We needed to hire a boat for rough seas and for a 10 h.p. outboard. Mr Twite – Jim – placed his pair of offspring – orphaned from the egg – carefully on the heads of the other two held by his wife, wiped his hands clean on his jeans and said:

'I'm not sure that I can help you, we've not that sort of boat, it's only for calm weather, pottering-about-like, it wouldn't stand the strain and the noise would upset our birds, wouldn't-it-Edie, but – why don't you try the old man?'

We explained we indeed hoped to go to the Old Man: that was precisely why we needed a boat.

'O but you can easily walk to the old man, it's only a couple of miles up the path isn't-it-Edie?'

We said that the Old Man was out at sea – didn't he know?

'O he *has* been out at sea some time ago, and he still goes out a bit, but he's really more or less fixed on dry land now, isn't-he-Edie?' Jim flashed a smile, returned thinly by Edie. They peered at us intently.

This further suggestion of coastal mutability worried us. The Apprentice, scenting confusion, volunteered that our Old Man was known as the Bodach.

'So is Donnie, by the old people here,' said Mr Twite, 'they call him the Bodack.' He looked at the Doctor. '*Bodack*, they say, used to mean "old man". That's because he's an old man, you see.' Dawn broke.

Mr Twite, resuming his fostering of the pimply and objectionable pair, who were now calling loudly, stretching skinny winglets and performing other physiological functions, pointed the way to Donnie McIsaac's; he held a bemused infant at arm's length to the north-east. 'Up there,' he said.

'Eh, it was funny,' he went on, 'getting mixed up like that, wasn't-it-Edie. Now Donnie is a very old man, over 80 isn't-he-Edie, but he's very active and I know he has a lobster boat with an engine, too, he's a nice old man but can act strange, can't-he-Edie? But you do know, don't you, you're not allowed to *land* on that rock,' he added, 'it's bad for the birds.' 'There's an *order* on it,' hissed Edie, thrusting up her spectacles, 'but you *can* have a sail *round* it – it's very *interesting....*'

The track passed more caravans, glassy packets of suburbia parked on the Precambrian. The inmates protected themselves, pot plants and small pet carnivorae from the blast of wind and landscape by plastic embattlements. We did not disturb their privacy. From one, to the Doctor's consternation, came the News in Gaelic.

As the track got worse, his temper improved, and when it had disappeared and a hut, presumably Donnie's, had come in sight, he was the familiar Doctor again. He discussed plans for hauling the outboard all this way. 'Perfectly possible. With determination. Or a pony.'

But before we reached Donnie, a wire fence blocked our progress. Twelve foot high, bristling with barbs and – unpleasantly – with insulator-like things. A large red and white notice announced, aggressively, 'Keep Out'; another, still more aggressively, 'Ministry of Defence'.

We were probably near a N.A.T.O. frontier. We had noticed English and American Army trucks back by the Nature Reserve, and an emptiness of beer cans about the place. We trod carefully, the Apprentice, a dedicated dissident, this time indulging a rave.

Donnie's house was outside the fence. He had refused to move, not desiring the generous financial reward offered on behalf of Democracy. As the ultra-left-wing *Oban Free Press* printed his picture several weeks running, he had to be allowed to stay. The fence bent in, and then out again. It gave good shelter for the tatties in an east wind.

Donnie himself understood at once; we could see Am Bodach from his doorway, like a fractured Statue of Liberty standing out from an iron band of cliff. We might, yes we might, be able to drag the outboard here. But that would be no help at all. Because he would not let us use it on *his* boat. His boat had an engine of its own. What use would another one be? Moreover, the stern was not *built* for an outboard. Just look. Not *built* for an outboard. He gazed placidly over his pipe at us. He was as tall as, as erect as, and had been considerably broader than, the Doctor. It was pleasant to lean on the stone wall of his gaze, after the uncertain journey hitherto. Only his right hand – not unnaturally at eighty-three – shook a little as he shifted the bowl of his pipe.

Would *he*, then, take us to the Bodach?

What would we be going there for? Would we be geologists, hydrologists, ornithologists, ichthyologists, algologists, ecologists, divers after the sea urchins? He rolled the catalogue past his pipe stem. He had suffered them all.

Because if we were – No. He would not hire himself or his boat. Puff. A ghost of a hard smile.

The Doctor warmed to this excellent rock.

'We only want to try and climb it. Nothing else.'

'Climb it? And what is the use of that to anybody?'

'None whatever.'

It was the right tack. The Doctor can afford 10 h.p. Swedish outboards, even under the National Health, because of skills like that. Puff.

If we only wished to visit Am Bodach for our own enjoyment, he would take us there. But he could not guarantee an easy landing, or a take-off on the same day. The swell.

No matter; we had bivvy bags, spare food. Am Bodach had been climbed?

'Who would want to climb it?'

The Army, we suggested.

His eyes fixed bayonets. No; not even the Navy.

It was expensive, but promised to be worth it. We lugged our gear to Donnie's, and camped on the foreshore. Behind some rocks, because The Army was always watching for people.... We understood.

The next day was fine, but with the usual swell. We pushed out Donnie's boat and loaded her up. He swung aboard, poled out a little, then lifted wooden hatches. Still bending, he gazed skyward and turned and turned a handle. Eventually a splutter and clangorous rumbling. He replaced the hatches, took the shuddering tiller, adjusted his pipe, and steered us out of the bay.

It was a frightful coast. The base of the cliffs – two hundred feet high or more – heaved and seethed; foam broke and was swallowed, was vomited out again. All in silence. Nothing could be heard above the engine's din. We tried to plant a conversation on Donnie. It blew off. He puffed, unmoved.

There were terrifying incidents. Just out of the bay, where we met the swell (delivered straight – but for some irritation about Lewis – from Labrador) and where the bow began to rise and smack, smack, each shouldering monster and the spray flew, just out of the bay and beside the great guarding incisors of basalt, the engine stopped. A rushing, drenching silence. We were slung sideways at once. We had only one oar. 'Hold her out,' said Donnie, resigning the tiller to the Apprentice. He bent under the hatches. Minutes, minutes. We kept her bows out, but were driven ever nearer to that boom and suck and explosion at the root of the cliff. He rose and held something in his hand. He lifted it up, looked along it and blew. He inspected various other objects, staggering as the boat staggered. Heavens – parts of the engine! If he dropped one.... He picked up an old bait can from the scuppers. He leant over the side, swilled out its molluscan residues in a passing wave, shook it, and poured in petrol from a rusty container. He was washing the pieces of engine. He took them out, examined them, blew, replaced his pipe and stepped back to the hatches. We had only a dozen yards to go; the backwash from the cliffs drenched the crouching Apprentice in the stern. We wondered if any gear could be saved. The plunging and thunder and rock promised little enough for ourselves. Donnie inspected the sky from the hatches; he was turning the handle. A sputter. A stop. A sputter, a stop, a jangling roar, hatches back, he took the rudder, away we went.

'Dirt in the carburettor.' The message was passed hoarsely each to each, as we clutched the gunwales.

It happened twice again, but seemed safer farther out. Then the stack was above us, rising and falling.

'Because it is calm the day, we can get near enough,' shouted Donnie. We were only six or so feet from a curling slab that lifted and dropped almost that height as the swell travelled along it. 'This is the landing place. Where we used to come for the eggs. Take your rope and jump for it.'

The Doctor, anxious to board first, flung off his jacket, gripped

the coil, balanced on the prow and awaited the next upward lunge of
the slab. As it appeared, he jumped; but just before he jumped, the
engine sputtered again. We lost way, and he plunged straight into
deep water.

When he came up he ignored the boat and struck for the slab,
was lifted over it by the swell and, jamming his fingers into crevices,
clung to Am Bodach. He curled up legs, survived the next swell, and
then clattered (he was in nails) up a barnacly abutment into a crack.
There he turned and hauled in the rope.

'It's a good place for landing,' said Donnie, 'but not for getting off.'

Thus encouraged, the Apprentice and I, having passed the kit over
on the rope, followed the Doctor; gripping tight, we avoided complete
immersion.

Donnie swivelled away, raised an arm, and vanished into a rush-
hour of grey shoulders. He was to return next morning. The weather
was forecast fair.

Technically, the climb was Mild Severe, but the exposure, the guano,
the smell and the feathers – horrible. Am Bodach rocked like the boat
and squawked like a poultry farm. The Doctor employed an extended
length of car aerial to prod baby fulmars in the belly from a safe
distance; they voided their horrid oil before he reached them. Some of
it fell on us. I held my own stomach down. Guillemots, razorbills,
gulls of all dimensions packed this riotous high-rise, balconies screaming
and flapping, corridors trundling debris. How could *we* disturb them?

The Doctor led the last pitch. He stood on the summit in the sun
– we had come up the north, the only possible, side – and exulted. To
help his drying, he climbed down south a little, into a sentry box; and
took off his clothes. They fluttered in the wind on a length of line, to
the indignation of our fellow-tenants, who dived about them and
marked their displeasure. The Apprentice and I relaxed on the summit,
a sloping desk lid, batting the occasional too-inquisitive fowl. The
Doctor had raised a small cairn – half a dozen stones or so – at the
base of the lid. We piled more rocks and stones on to the Doctor's
embryo and by the end of the afternoon had built a massive structure,
proof obvious to all the coast of our success.

The sun cooled; the Doctor was putting on his clothes. We slid
down to his niche. Warm. He was brisk and contented. Dry now.
'Wish my wallet was, but I didn't risk bringing it down here. Left it

at the top for safety, under some stones. Hope you haven't knocked 'em off....'

It was dark before we had rebuilt our cairn, a shadow of its former self. Hard words had been said. But the sunset restored us.

We roped down to the platform selected for the bivouac; set up our bags and brewed a reasonable meal. We beat off skin-headed urchins and irresponsible parents. Eggshells, and worse, were dropped on our heads. We were pecked, intimately, during the night.

We woke to the roar of wind and wave. Settled weather....

Rain lashed us all that day. The coast was hidden in cloud and spume. The boat? We laughed hollowly. Birds wrung themselves dry above us.

The next night was calmer, but for birds; the next day quite calm. But no sign of boat. We had eaten most of our food, and eyed the birds with more personal interest. We climbed the summit, and shouted. We drank chicken soup from the rain puddles. Small clouds sailed above us, white wings beneath us. Donnie can act strange.... Or perhaps dirt had finally stuck in the carburettor....

Almost evening. And then a boat. Two boats, fast launches. We roped down to the landing slab. The launches came closer. They were huge. One was grey, with numbers and letters on it – U.S. NAVY; the other was darker, and labelled POLICE. Lord....

Both were too clumsy to get very close. Both addressed us with loudhailers, simultaneously. Breaking waves drowned the confusion. They hailed at each other. They almost collided. We were pleased to see a fist shaken, not at us.

A helicopter appeared. U.S. NAVY.

This was becoming serious. Perhaps Am Bodach was somebody's Secret Weapon; a lot of money at stake somewhere.

The police launch – and was it Edie and Jim in there with them?– was smaller, and nosed nearer; its opponent retired and loud-hailed vigorously, with aerial support. Then it disappeared behind the stack. The police drew still closer in – and then faltered, swung round, and vanished behind the stack also. The helicopter cried in distress and it too fluttered behind the stack. Nobody came back.

The Apprentice rattled up and traversed south. He called to us. He was leaping about dangerously. We struggled after him. In the evening sun, a police launch tended a slowly disappearing one-end-up unsinkable U.S. Navy launch, the water marmaladed with orange jackets. Above, a bereaved helicopter wrung its blades, beating wingless and helpless, dangling ineffectual wires.

The Bodach long ago had a crony to the south, centuries gone to his rest; but his boots, so to speak, remained, and at low tide (as now) poked up to the surface.

We did not wish our rescuers ill, but their concentrated approach would now be diluted. Yet, another night on the Bodach? We turned and longed at the coast. Nothing. At the sea. Nothing. Below, at the landing place. Lord!

A small boat. Donnie.

We clattered down, slithered over slabs, tossed rucksacks and ropes and jumped ecstatically but accurately into the sputtering craft. Donnie swung her round, revved up, and off we went.

'I was delayed,' he said, puffing.

No other conversation was possible in the noise. We beached and hauled up the boat. Two police officers came down to meet us; one senior, red and sauntering, the other pale and earnest. Inspector Macleod introduced himself. 'Better weather the day.' Och, he just had a few statements to take. Perhaps we could go up to the house together. The tents? Och, the tents would be safe. Donnie stayed, poking under his hatches.

Round Donnie's austere table, we learnt a little of the confusion. The Inspector pushed back his cap; his neck and grizzly hair sweated across his collar. The constable leant intensely at a notebook on his knee. Mr Twite had been worried about his birds, and had telephoned the police. The police tried to contact Donnie, but Donnie was away.

'The Yanks had got him.'

Yanks had got him? Yes, he was being questioned by the United States Authorities across the fence. The Inspector jerked his thumb. Donnie was always being questioned by the United States Authorities across the fence. 'They think he's a spy,' chuckled the Inspector. 'What, Russian?' we asked, agape. 'Aye – or English...' was the answer, 'but he's probably paid by the C.I.A. to see what they're up to.' Certainly, Donnie's other room, through the half-open door, bristled with wires and dials. 'He was a radio operator in the Merchant Navy,' explained the Inspector, 'and still likes tinkering with the wavebands.' He chortled wheezily. 'They thought he was mebbe landing agents on Am Bodach...

they saw signals flying' (the Doctor's washing?). More chortling. 'Mind ye, my opinion is that Jim Twite's the Fifth Man – no doubt whatever.' Wheeze. The lack of whisky in the house made itself almost audible. Donnie came in and sat amongst us. The Inspector set to business.

'Well, then, *did* ye land at all?' The assistant's pencil was poised, recorders were no doubt buzzing in ample blue pockets.

Yes, we did.

'Did ye *intend* to land, Mr McIsaac?' – question to Donnie. He answered calmly that no, he did not.

'Then how was it these gentlemen found themselves on the top of Am Bodach, frightening the birdies and the U.S. Navy?'

Donnie impassively recounted how the Doctor had fallen into the water while we were admiring Am Bodach. How he struggled to the rock and climbed it for safety. How we two had joined him for further security. 'Is one man by himself in a dangerous position on rocks like those?' the Inspector asked us. We assented, vigorously.

'Then, Mr McIsaac, why did you not stay and take them off again immediately?'

'I had dirt in the carburettor; and I went back to the shore. And then the weather was bad; and I had – Americans.' All true. The Inspector nodded. Statements were concluded and signed. We had had no wish to disturb the various species, subspecies or genera of Aves covered by the Order, or harm the fledglings. 'Wouldn't hurt a hair of their heads,' protested the Doctor, somewhat unzoologically. Notebooks were folded, recorders (probably) switched off. The Inspector stood up. 'You'll likely hear nothing more from us.' We went to pack up the tents. The Apprentice came rushing back.

'There's a sentry outside the tents!'

So there was. An at-ease very uneasy very tall U.S. Marine in full combat dress with rifle and bayonet, gazing awkwardly westward towards an invisible Old Glory.

'Aye, he's on guard. But take down yer tents. He canna stop ye. We're no in the Area here.' The Inspector forcefully reassured the still Caledonian earth with the square toe of his boot.

We packed the tents and left the sentry protecting the hard-pressed silverweed. No word was exchanged, but he appeared to be having difficulties with his candy. We went back into Donnie's house. The Inspector twiddled his walkie-talkie, glanced at his assistant. 'Mrs

Vortoff's found a man watching her caravan again. Away and check up, Constable. I'll join you at the station.' Having cleared the room, the Inspector relaxed and recounted amusing tales of life in the neighbourhood – catfights among the officers' wives, revolt and bribery in the native quarters. A flask had appeared. We all quaffed except Donnie, who sat a little aside, puffing his pipe. At length he rose and washed up the glasses. We followed the Inspector to his car. A lift along the road – behind the fence – to our car?' 'Safe?' 'Och, they'll no touch you.'

We were not so sure. We were less sure when we met a wellsprung and epauletted staff car, freshly serviced from the Pentagon. We stopped and were introduced to Major Altenheimer, of the U.S. Marines. Just then, the Inspector's radio crackled loudly. He listened and swore. 'There does seem to be a man watching Mrs Vortoff,' he said 'poor felly! I'll have to go there right away. The Major...' – some hurried conversation – 'the Major's going your direction, he'll take you.'

We meekly entered the staff car. The Major hailed from Denver, Colorado, and the Doctor soon had him happily back in radiant heat and electrical sun. But the Major had only driven up to Routt National Forest, never climbed Mount Dirkel or Dome Peak, and the Doctor's merciless description of these mountains, and of buttes, canyons and sagebush horizons brought tears to his eyes. He jerked inexpressibly at the dour evening bog outside. 'I guess you like this sort of thing but... Jeeze....'

Shortly after, we passed lights on our left.

'Look, why don't we go down eat in the mess? You guys must be starving.' We were. 'Sure, I'll get you in.' We had no choice, anyway.

In the mess we were plied with food, drink and eager young officers. All were desperately homesick – for Maine, for Vermont, Tennessee, Washington State.... The Doctor had been to most of these places, and laid it on thick. The Apprentice had spent ten days at Yosemite, and found an assault lieutenant who knew every route on El Capitan.... It was a bewildering night, littered with lone stars from Texas and inextricable trails from New England, yarns from Mount McKinley to Old Smoky, Katahdin to Crater Lake. But never a word on Am Bodach or a navy launch.

We explored most of that marvellous country, and then the Doctor moved them further east to the rival Elysium and enthralled them with tales of convivial alpinism in the Caucasus and ski-touring in the Urals.

They listened with shocked delight, as schoolgirls to rude stories. They peered behind furtively. He almost convinced them that the Laws of Gravity were applied more or less impartially throughout Russia.

Gorged with hospitality, we staggered to the offered beds. 'Why, you can't go back to an empty car....' But we demurred at pyjamas, and collapsed in our clothes.

The next day after breakfast (no Major) we were respectfully chauffeured to the Doctor's old Mercedes. But the Doctor had been booked, for two bald back tyres. The pale young constable attended, pencil and radio. The victim protested vigorously, produced calipers and micrometer and might possibly have proved his point in the High Court. But the walkie-talkie crackled, Am Bodach winked, and it was easier to compromise and buy two new tyres and have them fitted, at fearful cost, by the garage opposite. Then – the crackle assured him – the charge need not go forward: och, yes, the tread might be enough just now, but not by the time he'd reach Edinburgh, and he might be – stopped – on the way. Of course. He paid the bill. No sign of the Inspector. But the garage proprietor turned out to be his brother; and would convey our greetings.

We had suffered memorable experiences, but thought it best not to publish an account of the route; still, my companions had taken photographs enough to loosen the floor of any lecture room.

A fortnight later the Apprentice burst into the back bar of Daddy McKay's, brandishing a box of slides. He spilled them on to the liquid table – blank, blank, all of them. All those wonderful shots of Am Bodach, the Doctor's washing, the sinking launch.... He had been sent, by Kodak as consolation, a little booklet on 'Do's and Don'ts for Beginners' or suchlike. He cursed and swore.

'X-rays,' said the Doctor, pleasantly.

We remembered our rucksacks in the corner of the bedroom at the mess....

'Don't worry, mine are all right,' said the Doctor, 'we'll duplicate 'em. Some excellent ones. I took out the film in the tent before we left; kept the spool in my pocket. Best thing. And always sleep in your clothes.'

We were aghast.

He tipped back his glass.

'Learned that in Russia,' he said.

# NOTHING SO SIMPLE AS CLIMBING

# NOTHING SO SIMPLE AS CLIMBING

G. J. F. DUTTON

Illustrations by Albert Rusling

Published in 1993 (in cased and tradepaper edition)
by Diadem Books, London

# CONTENTS

\* First published in the *Scottish Mountaineering Club Journal* (between 1984-1993)

\# First published in *One Step in the Clouds* (Diadem 1991)

§ First published in *Mountain* (130)

# BECAUSE WE WERE THERE

Our sport is frequently misunderstood. We are not socially irresponsible. We go out of our way to help others; if there is no alternative. Take one evening when the Doctor, the Apprentice and I were relaxing by the bar in the unlovely hamlet of Kilmoggie – that last hitch of the Industrial Belt – after a pretty hard day. The Apprentice had led three new E1s; and I had followed with drawn breath, adhering by the resultant suction. The Doctor, fresh from some meeting or other, was running us back. Not to be outdone, he tried a new route home, and got lost. We found ourselves in Kilmoggie and stopped at its single repellent hostelry for a belated celebration.

The Doctor was examining bottles for the next order when a boy's head poked round the door; stared at us; rotated, and howled ear-splittingly backwards: 'They're *here*!'

He approached, stepping over the sacks, rope and assorted gleamery which we uncharitably thought safer with us than in our car, whose boot would not lock that day.

'You climbers?'

We assented, with equal lack of grace; he appeared highly predatory.

He revolved once more; and shrieked: 'They're so: *climbers*.'

Then, to us, 'Come awa out.'

Mesmerised, we went out, the Doctor testily shaking his head and putting away spectacles.

Out there, a small group. Locals. A sort of delegation. A determined-looking wifie, well-endowed with shoulders and chest, disengaged herself and, accompanied by heads and eyes, marched up to us.

'You climb, eh?' We nodded. 'Then folly me.'

Ah, well; Fate had taken over. We followed. The rest fell in behind, muttering.

We turned down a small carboniferous lane. At the bottom, another crowd, larger. They parted, and we trailed through, the wifie striding in front. Then she halted and bellowed ahead:

'Here, Annie, I've brocht them Annie. Here's climbers for ya.'

Annie, an auld happit-aboot craitur five feet high and three feet away, raised keen – very keen – eyes to us. 'They'll help ye, Annie, they'll help ye.' All at ten decibels, for Annie was deaf; and then, fiercely, at ten and a half, to us: 'That right, eh?'

The Doctor summoned together all his professional bravura and replied briskly and with a dreadful gaiety, 'Of course, of course. Now,' bending towards Annie, 'What's the trouble?'

'I canna get it doon', she croaked, 'canna get it doon....'

The Doctor, with conclusions automatically oesophageal, laid a kindly hand on her shoulder. 'We'll have a look at it, then: let's go into your house.'

'Whit for ma hoose?' screeched Annie, eyes rounded, 'It's no 'n ma hoose!' The Amazon was more explicit. She grinned savagely. She smote the Doctor's shoulder. 'Up there, Chairlie, up there....' and raised her arm skyward. Reality was awaiting us.

Our gaze followed, and encountered a huge, a vast, tree. An ash of so straight and unhindered a trunk we had taken it for a pit-head lum. Above, far above, it blossomed into a billowing head of foliage. Once, it had paged the long-demobilised Kilmoggie Castle.

'What's up there?' asked the Doctor, like us prickling with horrid suspicion.

'Ma caat,' wailed Annie, 'ma caat....' and the appalling certainty dropped on us with eighteen claws. And dug in.

'Get it doon fer her,' demanded the first wifie, 'ye're climbers.' Voices from behind – 'Aye, ye're climbers, get it doon fer her.' An objectionable voice: 'Aye, and be some bluidy use fer once.'

But it was a terrifying tree. The Apprentice mumbled about the Fire Brigade. 'Fire Brigade? We canna get the Fire Brigade. It's twal mile th'ither side o Balweemie pittan oot fires.' 'Aye, fires stertit by campers,' spat out another wifie, evidently in the B & B business. They were not really hostile, just rightfully resentful of our intense desire to be elsewhere. Fortunately, we did not suggest the Polis. But we continued to dither. To strengthen a sense of commitment, the boy and some companions dumped our gear, looted from the bar, below the trunk. 'There y'are.'

Murmurs of approval. Multiple despatch of spittle.

Annie grabbed the Doctor's unsteady arm. 'Mebbe ye're no used tae climban trees, eh?' He looked gratefully at her. 'There's ladders....' –

she turned round – 'Pit thae ladders thegither,' she yelled. A formidable crone, and crafty.

The bole soared bald for forty feet. What ladders could reach that far? And an ash, the Doctor explained, was a very *unsympathetic* tree; the devil to climb. Horrible. Meanwhile, we searched the canopy. Helpful fingers pointed out various invisibilities. The Apprentice maintained that a beast bold enough and brainless enough to climb up there was equally well equipped to climb down again. 'Ah, but cats, cats,' sighed the Doctor, '...particularly young ones. Is this a young cat? 'he asked Annie, playing for time.

'Na, na, an auld yin: Tammas.' Tammas had done this before, when the Fire Brigade was not otherwise occupied, and his retrieval had become a local classic. Two firemen, it seemed, finished up in hospital. The outcome of his second expedition was therefore awaited with interest.

While the several ladders were being lashed, hammered and cursed together, the Rescue Team was disputing Honours. The Doctor emphasised that advanced modern techniques were required, and therefore the Apprentice was the logical choice; he himself would be worse than useless. The Apprentice, while conceding the latter point for most situations, compared a tree with the vegetated routes so beloved of the Doctor; our affair on The Craggie still rankled. He explained it was ideal for the Doctor – '... Vegetation all round, like a sea-stack of leaves, an Old Man of Chlorophyll – perfect.' 'No, it's purely...'

'Wheesht!' roared a large elderly man beside us. Sibilances rippled away. Hush.

We heard the wind beating the upper branches. Then a yowl; a small windblown yowl, but undeniably from a cat. Up there. Damnation.

'Here y'are, Jimmy!' cried our companion, slapping the Doctor's long-suffering shoulder. A gang of youths, who would have been better employed climbing the thing, were pushing a wavering company of ladders up the trunk of the tree. Four ancient wooden eight-footers, tied in line with minimal overlap. They collapsed drunkenly, and began to slide sideways. They were hauled back by knotted washing-line. A large splinter fell heavily, not from the tree.

'Jump on them, lads, it'll haud them doon!'

Some of the gathering mistook our hesitation. 'Ah, ye'd like fine tae climb it straucht aff, eh? Mair the thing, like? Na, na, tak the ladder's far as ye can. There's plenty climban fer yese efter that!' True.

The Apprentice trod the scaffold first. With a succession of slings, he bound the lower ladders to the trunk. They protested wheezily. When he ran short of slings an old body took a knife to our two 50-metre coils. This drove us all up the rungs, clutching equipment. We spiralled the ladders with precious kernmantel.

It was terrifying. Quite vertical. Rounded exiguous rungs, some missing, others rotten, slobbered against wet bark (rain had arrived to watch, as well). The trunk was much too broad to clasp, the ladder sides were loose and slippery. Looking down, the eye bounced off the bole and plunged into a flutter of white faces.... Surely the whole thing was toppling....

Above, the Apprentice, unconquerable, had left the topmost rung and was jerking one sling up the greasy pole inch by inch while leaning out from another. Then he clipped into the upper sling and repeated the process, coaxing the lower one above the upper. He pressed against pitons, deep into secondary thickening. Some fifteen feet were ascended this way, and darkness was closing in. Then, after two shots, he lassoed the lowest bough, fixed a line, and jumared aloft. Murmurs. Approbation at last. The Doctor called up to reserve the first coconut.

I reached the top of the ladder, sea-sick. Then a cry from the Apprentice – 'There's the brute!' And the rope whisked away. I hung out to watch. He was advancing, on hands and knees, along a large horizontal bough, preceded by the cat walking backwards. Each time he stopped to fix a runner on the branch above, the cat stopped. When he resumed, the cat resumed. The bough got thinner, and bent downwards. Both contestants began to wobble, but continued grimly towards the end. Clearly the Rescue would not come off; the Apprentice or the cat, or both, almost certainly would. If the cat – and, judging from the hate on the Apprentice's visage, that seemed likely – then lynching would ensue; enough rope, plenty of branches. So I, at centre of communication, managed to convey the logical (and convenient) solution that now the ropework was fixed, the Doctor, with his kind cat-loving heart, should replace the venomous Apprentice.

The cat, perched on a bouncing spray of twiggery, surveyed the resulting gymnastics without comment. Darkness had fallen, and we

were smokily floodlit from below by an old roaring break-down van. Drama was intense, as the Doctor, slithering desperately despite clinkers, edged towards Tammas. Employing all his vegetatious skills, he wriggled from fingertips to bootlaces.

We could not hear his blandishments, but they probably resembled those squandered on the climbing dog of Arran (a day of pleasure compared to this).

The branch dipped further. The Doctor began to slip. He shuffled backwards. His face was pale and petrified in the lamp beam; shining black branches scampered about him, sluicing water. Rain pelted.

It could not continue. It did not. The bough suddenly cracked and bent double, the Doctor, head down, heels up, swung under and wrapped himself about it like a newly-licensed sloth. The wee beastie, now below him, summoned its remaining lives and skedaddled upwards. It prepared to crampon daintily across his white streaming face. It paused, sprang at the bergschrund – and the Doctor grabbed.

He caught the cat, but lost the bough. He hung upside down by his knees for a long millisecond: and then gracefully slid off into the air.

Perlon plinged, we heard a snap above wind and engine, and a couple of runners broke free; twigs and leaves fluttered through the beam. But he stopped, spinning well below the bough and thirty feet above the ground. He was still clutching a small black object which even at that distance radiated fury.

We expected applause; or, at the least, pity and terror. But no. A degree of censure.

'Auld fule fell aff!' (the Doctor, not Tammas). 'Sayan they wis climbers....' 'Micht hae killt the beast....' 'Should hae left it tae the young lad....' 'I telt ye, they're no...' Annie, however, was peering up with a diabolical grin. 'Hey, Tammas, Tammas!' she cried. Tammas was no doubt longing for the relative security of a broomstick.

We faced logistics. The Apprentice explored, wreathed in ropes. He appeared and vanished among ebony branchwork, trailing ghostly loops through snatches of floodlight. Beneath him, the Doctor twirled, with his outraged burden. Tammas had lost dignity; and hell hath no fury like a cat so bereft. He held the creature now close, now at arm's length. Either way, he was being rapidly abraded. He could not be pulled up; and he could not abseil while acting as male nurse.

The Apprentice therefore threw down a length of light line for the little one. The Doctor was to tie him on it and lower him to Annie's bony grasp. This proved difficult, Tammas being a bonnie fechter and wet and slippery. 'Round its bloody neck!' roared the Apprentice, thoroughly fed up. But humanity prevailed, and a sort of Tammas splint was conjured by the Doctor and his foe secured, tail wrapped tight like a muffler.

Then the bulb blew in the floodlight. Pandemonium. When light returned it revealed a smaller rotating object below the larger one. Tammas, no hand – or paw – at abseils, had stuck. His line was jammed under the sodden capstan of coils above the Doctor. The Apprentice could not help, for his own branch was splitting. He retreated and tied the Doctor to a higher limb. But that didn't get Tammas down, and until that object had achieved its owner's skinny bosom we dared not descend ourselves.

The Doctor, from his gyrations, shouted for the crane of the breakdown truck; Tammas, counter-gyrating below, joined in through tail. At top elevation, the crane might just... Smoke and fumes, roars; a bold figure swarmed up its hiccupping vertebrae and held out hands. About five feet short.... The Doctor *could* cut the line; but if Tammas missed, he would be sure, that night, to break his neck.

The figure smote its brow, scrambled down and vanished into the crowd, which was boiling up to an Ibrox. He reappeared carrying a great salmon net, doubtless veteran of many another night. On tiptoe at full stretch of crane he could just tickle the enraged Tammas' toes.

'Right!' And the Doctor leaned over and sawed at the line. A fearful hush. The motor paused and the beam flickered.

Then, plop! He was landed. Right in the net. Deafening cheers, hoots, screams, whistles.... Goal. Everybody stormed the pitch.

Well, we got the Doctor down, too, eventually. But no one stayed to watch. They bore Annie and the tightly-knitted Tammas off into darkness. Fortunately, they left our light on.

We shouldered gear and trudged up the lane. We were sore, soaked, and the bar would be shut. A door opened and a blaze leapt out, the truck driver after it. The Doctor thanked him for his light. To our surprise, he enveloped us all in an ample grasp.

'Come awa in, boys, come awa in, we're aa waitan on yese....'

And they were. A memorable night, till late early morning. Unlimited food, drink, music and song. The salmon-netter buttoned an accordion wonderfully, the Amazonian wifie – a Higgins in more itinerant days – gave splendidly belligerent renderings of *The Blantyre Explosion* and *The Donibristle Disaster*; the Apprentice of course indulged to wild applause in *Great John MacLean*, Annie herself piercingly to even wilder in *Andra Lammie*; the Doctor tried out his new reel 'Black Diamonds' on a borrowed chanter bent like a pit-prop – there were marvellous stories and some scarifying wit – but I remember little. I do remember how they plastered the Doctor's slashes, scratches, bites and bruises with an emotional rhetoric of iodine. 'Terrible, terrible.' 'It's thae *claws*; an thae *teeth*.' 'An he *needna* hae done it.' 'He did it fer Annie.' 'No fer the bluidy cat, onywye'...

Tammas, rebuilding dignity, had sought his dubious blanket. We asked how he had so badly mauled the firemen that they had to go to hospital. 'It wisna Tammas.' Had they fallen off their ladders, then? 'Na, na.' 'What?' 'They wis jist fou.' They had fallen out of their fire engine's door, waving unbelted as it roared away after the previous Kilmoggie Gathering. 'Three weeks in hospital, man. Aa fer auld Annie's Tammas.... But they get *paid* for it, ken; they're no like Climbers....'

See what I mean?

We slept on the salmon-netter's bed till six o'clock.

# MIDGES

Midges have been much maligned. They not only protect us, provide an unsleeping Air Umbrella for our precious West Highland scenery: they can also help us to a First Ascent – or to understand what a First Ascent is really about. They are great teachers of ethics. As we discovered to our cost. Although we made that First Ascent – the Best-Seller of its day – with the help of midges, we were ashamed of ourselves, the Apprentice and I; we still are.

Yet, as a Munro is a Munro, so a First Ascent is a First Ascent, and nowadays nobody is perfect; moreover, the germ, so to speak, of this biological weapon emanated from the Doctor, hitherto so upright a man. He was not in the climbing team – the grade was too high – he was Base for the expedition; Base indeed. But he ensured our success; if it can be called a success when the vanquished, however disreputable, trudge off with the moral victory.

Enough of snivelling. To the story. It is a lesson for all climbers. It should be told. For, as the Doctor observed by the primus that evening, peering into his glass through a penumbra of equally thirsty uncountables: 'Too much competition – *poogh* – tends to obscure the – *poogh* – essential Spirit.'

The Apprentice had to cross to Harris for that first ascent. His fellow-Weasels were Alpineering and rivals were athirst. So I joined him; the crux coming last, I could at worst be hauled over it. The Doctor was there to cook, and watch the fun.

The weather steamed close and cloudy, after weeks of cold rain. We waded over a sopping hill, and the great cliff Sròn a' Mheanbh-Chuileag rose imperturbably before us. Our eyes scurried nervously about it. No one was there. We would be first! Straight up the centre unrolled the only possible line, Leac Mhòr, the Great Slab, that unclimbed new discovery everyone was raving about. It had been attempted only the week before by a couple of teams but, as the Apprentice pointed out, they came from Glasgow. They had, nevertheless, pioneered as far as the crux. *That* appeared impossible – it jerked outwards above us like a vast flight of stone steps seen upside down from underneath.

'Great,' declared the Apprentice, a little hoarsely.

We splashed down to the river gravel for a meal. Our domestic help began to make jammy pieces and set up the tent. The Apprentice and I, adhesive from sweat and apprehension, stripped and plunged into a fine bellowing pool, frothy with spate.

'Don't!' called the Doctor. 'It's dangerous!'

We looked at each other. We had all of us forded and swum (often by accident) much fiercer water than this. The Doctor had now turned not only cook but nursemaid. Nonsense. Perfectly safe.

'The midges!' he shouted. 'They'll get you when you come out.'

So what? We two were going up the Slab, not festering round the tent like him.

As we munched our pieces, vastly refreshed, and insulated by the Doctor's unseen rucksack from infinite bog, we ridiculed his prognosis. Ah, but immersion, he averred, removed the body's protective layer of oils. 'You mean dirt?' suggested the Apprentice, through his crumbs. 'Exactly!' It appeared that the accumulated greases of the skin impeded midgy mandibles. They found it difficult to sook. Washed, we would be a naked lunch to innumerable multitudes of *Ceratopogonidae*. This place in this weather would generate the most ravenous midges within the whole lengthy jurisdiction of An Comhairle nan Eilean. The Doctor had already identified them as the two worst of the whole bloodsucking bunch, *Culicoides heliophilus* and *Culicoides impunctatus*. So there.

A few of the brutes had already appeared that morning. They bit us even in our then well-enough-larded state. As the old man at the last croft had remarked, 'The midges is no very good the day.' So we rubbed in more midge-repellent and hurried across to the climb, the Doctor remaining entrenched behind turned-up collar, pipe smoke and Natural Oils.

I do not want to remember the rest of that day. Instead of climbing out of midges, we climbed into them. The Sròn was the west end of a high boggy tableland, its top and sides dribbled with bog; it stood in a bog. So, from bottom, sides and top midges screamed out at us, radars blaring, rockets firing. Faces, hair, necks, ears, eyes, backs of hands, wrists, crawled with a million engines, tracers incessantly stung and flashed. Torture of infinite needles. Jab, jab, jab. Hell, hell, hell; more hell....

I gave up half-way, blind and one-handed. The Apprentice lasted a little longer, banging in a runner at the crux. But he ran out of oaths, and midges swarmed into the vacated territory. We spun down, coiled ropes and vanished. Flies were nothing to this.

At the tent, we dived into bags, head and all. The Doctor, puffing valiantly, made supper. Midge-netting kept most outside, and those within – chastened by St. Bruno – congregated along the ridge-seams and were periodically incinerated by a brandished Primus. Numbers gradually decreased. We uncovered heads, warily.

'Midges no very good the day,' observed our companion genially, poking the pot. He remained unchastised, for cooks are the Sacred Fools of climbing, licensed jesters, dear to the belly. And he had warned us.

That night, sleep was fitful; we were iridescent with bites, and refugees wandered wakefully about our hair. The Apprentice tossed, in a rage of frustration. First ascent ... first ascent ... and last chance.

We rose late, to a midgeless morning. But the steamy weather promised another yesterday. However, the Doctor had not been idle. He produced two midge-helmets for us: his spare stockings, with slits for eyes. 'And you can wear your own spare socks as gloves, the ends pierced for fingers.' That, and the remaining midge cream, would see us up to – maybe over – the crux, now the way there was familiar. We blessed him as he stirred the porridge, twinkling grand-maternally.

The Apprentice crawled out, stood up, and gazed happily at the Sròn. Then his eyes popped. He groaned, swore, stamped, slapped thighs and cursed again. We all peered out.

Below the crag stood People. We were forestalled. Who?

'No, no; Oh NO!' wailed the Apprentice. 'It's *them*!'

'Who's Them?' asked the Doctor, beginning to regret his slit stockings.

'Wee Dander', sobbed the Apprentice, '*and* Greetin Jimmie; *and* The Porpus.' He named three legendary figures. 'And there's Else and Big Ian to look after them....'

We were suitably silent. Wee Dander was one of those youthful prodigies who – for a few years – climb apparently everything with unstopping ease and no little scorn. More than that, he would never write up his routes, never bother to record them. He had no use for journals or guidebooks, or other people. He was pure Oral Tradition, pure Hero, sheer Me; free as the wind. Hateful, no doubt; but enviable in many ways. His companions tied themselves always second and third on a rope that was invariably the best you could buy, like the rest of his kit – which he never did buy: the three of them, aided by Else and Big Ian, took whatever they needed from any unoccupied tent or car they came across. Hateful. Dangerously enviable.

They saw us and ambled over as we swallowed our now tasteless porridge. Wee Dander was indeed wee, a laddie, in tatty shirt and shorts, with an open expressionless very pale face and uncannily penetrating blue eyes; any age between twelve and seventeen. He bent over and picked a piece of bacon from the pan the Doctor was frying and nibbled it carefully. Then he picked a couple more pieces and threw them to his companions behind. All three masticated in silence.

We looked them over, refusing to speak first. Greetin Jimmie was a long skeletal youth in grubby denims and greasy shirt; his equally oleaginous hair sprawled to a thin pimply face, dreepy red nose and sparse fringe of unappetizing gingery beard – or he may not have shaved that week (it was indeed difficult to imagine him shaving). A dismal enough streak, from knocky knees to watery eyes. The Porpus – round and polished as the playful Cetacean – bulged from relatively clean sark and shorts; he grinned even while chewing, small pink nose and ears oscillating independently. He rolled an enormous boulder across and sat on it; it was one the Doctor and I had failed to shift when pitching the tent.

Before Wee Dander could appropriate more breakfast the Doctor smartly tossed the rest to us. Our guest was then moved to communicate.

'Saw yer runner. Been up, eh?' A hard, clear, raw-fish accent.

The Apprentice, wrestling with honesty, said he'd had a look and come down early, but would be up the day right enough.

'Like hell.' (Pause) 'But thanks fer the runner; nae use here – 'll dae fine fer the Ben next week, though.' (Pause) 'Well, we'll jist awa up. See ya.'

And he sauntered off back to the cliff. Greetin Jimmie nodded morosely at us and followed his leader. The Porpus, still managing the odd chew, beamed and waved a flipper. He clanked away uphill; they were particularly well-equipped that morning, having passed a Mountain Adventure camp the day before.

They paused at our pool. The Porpus gesticulated. He wished to gambol therein. Wee Dander scowled: and was moving away when the Doctor, to our astonishment, leapt up and shouted.

'Hi! Don't go in! It's dangerous....'

What the devil? We looked at him bewildered; then at the three. But the Doctor knew his man. Wee Dander stopped dead. His eyes unslung their Kalashnikovs. He was not going to be head-mastered by any what-ho! tweed-brandishing establishmentarian.

He stripped off and dived, right into the considerable whirlie under the waterfall; and stayed down a long while to prove his point. The Porpus rolled and splashed, gleaming epidermally, while Jimmie, even dirtier with his clothes off, waded in slowly, rubbing long thin shanks bitterly and fading gradually to a pale shrimp-pink.

The Apprentice smiled for the first time in twenty-four hours. That, of course, is why we climb with the Doctor. A practical man, so *good* with People.

We took it easy. We watched them rope up; we saw Big Ian and Else unfold some sort of encampment on the bog beneath the cliff. We kitted ourselves out, packing midge-helmets and socks carefully, and used up all the midge cream so we needn't tell a lie later. The Doctor stayed to guard the tent. We strolled across in the gathering fug, regarding emergent midges almost benignly. Of course we were a little dirtier now, more naturally repellent....

Wee Dander proved a marvellous climber. He was already entering the crux. He would easily get over, he contemptuously pocketed the Apprentice's sling, he flowed with a lovely movement, elastic as rubber. Greetin Jimmie stalked after him like a vertical pond-skater; multilimbed, impeccably adept. The Porpus, whose job was never to peel but to hold the others when they did, scuttled like a crab. It was a great team to watch. We felt ourselves almost wishing them success.

Then they began to jerk, increasingly. Early Warnings had sounded, the defenders were busy. Progress slowed, became intermittent. The rope twitched agonizingly; coiled, uncoiled, gave forth sobs and cries. It was not so nice to watch. A beautiful animal was being done to death. The leader crouched between moves, slapped bare thighs and neck, his second agitated beneath a cloud, the third man beat bongo-drums about his waist-band, jangling in disarray.

We came up to Else, a plump vaguely belligerent Amazon, and Big Ian, even larger and grinning hugely. 'Bloody midges,' he remarked, rubbing with vigour. What went on above was not of great concern to him. Else swore low and continuously, rummaging in an ample knee-length jersey, well adapted to supermarkets.

A great crash above us, and we all fled. Wee Dander, blinded by midgery, had peeled on the final step. Greetin Jimmie, enmeshed in his web, shot up – still scratching – to a sentry box. The Porpus, smacking his backside, sat down in space and held them all; a large sling of Mountain Adventure cutlery had meanwhile slipped off his tray and nearly brained us.

It was a curious sight; three in tension at various angles, writhing and scratching like St. Vitus. Somehow, Wee Dander fought back up, Jimmie slithered down to his stance, The Porpus swam to the surface. But all magic was gone. The lower pair, fisting eyes, faces and limbs in a frenzy, implored their leader to come down. Wee Dander tried again. And again; wiping his forehead – milling with millions – blindly against the cold Precambrian. Terrifying. At the very profile of the last step we watched him slip, slip, recover; slip, recover.

Then he abseiled down. And, yes; we were sorry.

They stood beside us, two of them rubbing and cursing. Wee Dander, his pale face bloodstained, crawling with tormentors, looked straight at us. His teeth had bitten his lips white.

'Any ... midge ... cream ... ?' It must have cost him.

We had used all ours up, the Apprentice explained. He displayed the flattened tube. He did not look at me; nor I at him. Silence.

'Aye,' said Wee Dander.

Else and Big Ian had packed up the tents. They all moved off, hunched and muffled, pummelling zipped anoraks, Wee Dander leading. He slowed, the others overtook him. He stopped, looked back and spun something towards us.

'Yer runner,' he said. And went on.

We deserved it.

# MIDSUMMER MADNESS

'Scotland is nowadays quite impossible! No peace any more: Always somebody messing about somewhere....'

This Doctorial outburst summed up our feelings. It was midsummer night – or eve, an all-night eve – on a Monadhliath top, a bump in the plateau. Miles, we had hoped, from anywhere; or anybody. We had camped there, after climbing on Creag Mhòr at Kingussie, just for the pleasure of doing nothing but laze, seeing nothing but the low rim of the northern sun beyond Wyvis – and perhaps a passing herd of deer; and hearing nothing but the occasional sough of wind to round off the silence – and maybe the cry of a distant bird. Aaaah.... Wonderful....

Instead, we had been disturbed by distressingly human shouts and shrieks, mingled with bugle calls and horn-blowings, that emanated apparently from every innocently humped summit about us. Swearing, we had peered beyond the tent flaps and witnessed lights flashing signals; and made out an occasional bowed and plodding figure against the rolling black horizon. Military exercises? Boys' Brigade? Nocturnal Munroists?

We had just pulled up our bags again after one such infuriating alarm, when the tent guys sang suddenly, and a guttural cry made us sit up. Immediately afterwards, the walls billowed inward and the Doctor was flung hard against the pole. We scrambled out, torches blazing in wrath.

Yes, some idiot had walked into the tent. With the whole deserted tableland to wander about in, he had to – walk into our tent. We fixed him severely with indignant beams.

He was a small man in a thin grey suit; around him lay long poles, balls of string, parcels and rolls of paper. And – a bugle. He looked unhappy. Shocked, in fact. To be fair, he in his turn no doubt did not expect, stumbling by dark across the summit plateau of the Monadhliaths, to have walked into a tent. But what the devil was he doing there himself, transporting such an odd assemblage of property in the middle of the night? Surely not... flitting?

We dragged him into the tent, revived him with Doctorial whisky and, since sleep was now impossible, brewed some tea.

When he seemed more in the world, we interrogated him. What on earth was he doing here?

'I'm looking for my wife.'

'Your wife?'

'Yes. Mrs Urania Grey-Mullett; you know....'

We did not know. Was she lost?

'Oh no, not at all.' We fancied a note of regret. 'She's been on Càrn Sgùlain, she's to meet me here at Càrn Ballach, and my daughter as well – she's coming from Càrn Dearg. And Edward, from A' Chailleach.'

Heavens, this was a Waterloo Place, a Charing Cross. 'I suppose you're all collecting Munros', observed the Doctor testily, striving for politeness.

But George – that was his name – George Grey-Mullett did not appear familiar with Munros.

'We've just been taking sightings,' he explained. 'Mrs Grey-Mullett, as I expect you are aware, is extending her studies to this part of the Highlands.' We were not aware; incomprehension remained mutual. We swallowed our tea and surveyed his pile of maps and poles. He began to tell us about his wife, about his daughter, about Edward, and about the studies that threatened to extend across our once solitary encampment.

His explanations were interrupted every five minutes – by his watch – with rushing outside to the summit cairn and flashing a large torch, followed by a melancholy toot on his bugle; then waiting for answering flashes and wails from his companions as they toiled up their respective slopes towards us. In between, we gathered that Mrs Grey-Mullett was an authority – or had made a name for herself – on prehistoric astro-nomical-observatory sites among the hills. Something after the fashion of Professor Thom, of whom the Doctor had once been so tiresome a fan. By sighting the sun, or moon, or stars, along cairns or pointed boulders or summit nicks, our forefathers could deduce the date: how near they were to important agriculturo-religious (George pronounced this twice for our benefit, with a sip between) agriculturo-religious festivals that punctuated the year and stabilised their society. Mrs Grey-Mullett had a knack, not only of lining up her sightings, but of identifying – in just the right places – the stones and slabs indubitably employed for kneeling on to take your observation, or for sacrificing your Sacred Victim. It required great skill – he might say intuition, also – to distinguish these man-made artifacts, smoothed by thousands of years of weathering, from casual effects of wind, water or Ice Age. And considerable knowledge. Mrs Grey-Mullett, if not perhaps a practising devotee of, was nevertheless very well instructed about, the Triple Goddess.

'All that bloody rot....' commented the Apprentice rudely, wiping his mouth of tea. We had suffered enough Professor Thom, Golden Boy Frazer, and of course Robert Graves. 'Loonie stuff.' But, as the Doctor more kindly observed, stirring up the porridge (for it was now clearly dawn), Midsummer Eve seemed an appropriate date to encounter the White Goddess: her real house-parties took place at this time.

George nodded, his face serious. '*And* at mid-winter.... Ah, I hear my wife now,' he added, and rose stiffly. We crawled outside.

We all heard Mrs Grey-Mullett. The earth shook.

The sun, already high in the east, was temporarily eclipsed as the lady climbed on to the summit above us. Mr Grey-Mullett raised his bugle and blew. A brazen blast replied, and his wife descended upon us, flumping in a thick tweed skirt, anorak and purple woolly bonnet. She stopped, slung her trumpet behind her, and peered closely.

'Why, Doctor!' she boomed, 'Doctor!' 'Urania Major!' gasped our companion, 'Lord, I haven't seen you, it must be, these twenty years, never dreamed...' Much mutual hand-clasping and arm-slapping. She turned out to be a sister of Ursula, the Mrs Cairnwhapple, M.B.O.U., whom we had met, booming as imperially, on Lochnagar during the Pitfoulie episode. Equally bulky, Urania too began as a birdwatcher – had indeed cornered her husband in a cramped nocturnal hide at Loch Skinaskink; but now followed more substantial quarry – stones and slabs, cairns and megaliths; and George had become her chief assistant – or porter, it seemed. He carried things. 'George used to be in Rateable Values', she explained, 'but I made him retire early; he is so Useful.'

One of his uses had been to sire her daughter, who now appeared from her own particular cairn; a fine bouncy blonde, a Spring version of her Midsummer mother. 'Hi-yi!' she carolled: 'God: who are all these people?' Her mother explained, and introduced us: to... Blod... Blodeuwedd. An old Welsh name for the Goddess as Maiden, Mrs

Grey-Mullett assured us. 'Most attractive, isn't it? George wished to call her Mary, after some aunt of his, but we just keep that as a second name.' We boggled at the spelling, but the Doctor, who as a boy had scrambled extensively with his uncle among the hills, valleys, double consonants and two-faced vowels of North Wales, performed the task expertly. ('Wonderful language – spelling perfectly phonetic'). We could not even pronounce it. 'You can call me Bloody, if you like – or Bloody Mary,' conceded her daughter, 'most people do.' '*Bloddy*, dear,' protested George, feeling among his parcels for sandwiches.

So we ate our strange breakfast together. There was no sign of Edward. 'Edward', announced Mrs Grey-Mullett disapprovingly, 'has had to go home. I expect he's Found Something.' She munched bacon rolls. 'He's always doing that.' Edward was an Archaeologist. 'Mother discovered him in an Earth-house in Fife', explained Blodeuwedd, 'and raised him to higher things.' His hobby, indeed, was Hawking.

'A dreadful nuisance, when he brings his – what d'you call it, Bloddy? – anyway, his wretched bird on the hill with us. He also', she added as an afterthought, 'speaks Pictish.' We gaped, as much at a loss for words as any dictionary of that much postulated tongue.

Over our meal we were treated to an exposition concerning the religious festivities associated with the midsummer solstice, once its date had been fixed along the lines drawn out by Mrs Grey-Mullett. The victims – Sacred Kings of the Waxing Year – were of course always male. They had been for six months consorts of the Goddess, in the glamorous person of her young Chief Priestess, before being flayed, impaled, thrown over a cliff, burnt, drowned, buried alive, eaten or otherwise ritually and entertainingly disposed of by their successors.

'But always', explained Mrs Grey-Mullett, 'castrated first. A bronze sickle. For fertility, for the crops. Afterwards, naturally, they became immortal.' She chewed bacon roll dreamily. 'Wonderful times to have lived in,' she sighed. Blodeuwedd nodded, munching, and unwrapped a Mars Bar with care. The Doctor scraped his pan. 'Human nature,' he noted, 'remains much the same.' The Apprentice and I thought of discussing Rateable Values with George; but he was asleep among his parcels.

The lady continued to address us and the nearer Monadhliaths. Winter, it seemed, the Grey-Mulletts devoted to theory; drawing lines and conclusions. 'But in summer, it's Practicalities, isn't it, Blodeuwedd? Stern practicalities.'

They finished their meal. Mrs Grey-Mullett briskly rubbed her hands on a napkin; George obediently tidied away.

'Now, we should not disturb you, Doctor, but we must look at our maps and rule in a few more sightings: there is a wind getting up – do you mind if we spread things out in your tent for a little while?' We escaped, before engulfment in George's unfolding preparations.

Within, the lady boomed; her husband tapped his calculator. We looked at each other. Then at Bloddy, who was seated, decoratively, on a rucksack and still eating chocolate. She stretched shapely shorts; and a shapely smile. The Apprentice, reassured, proffered his spare bar. She took it, and patted the rucksack beside her invitingly. Our companion, mesmerised, moved across. He would last, doubtless, until the 22nd of December, if George got his sums right.

They seemed right. Mrs Grey-Mullett emerged, beaming. She had again been proved correct. Càrn Ballach was a *most* important observational site. 'The name itself suggests that.' But surely Ballach is named after bealach, a pass? 'No, no, all these are *modern* corruptions – the last fifteen hundred years or so. Ballach is really from Beli (Baal, you know) which is from Belili, the Goddess' name in her very powerful Pig Form. We nearly called Blodeuwedd after Belili, the Sow Goddess; but it could have been unfortunate at school. Now, this area has possibly the greatest number of *Càrn* names in Scotland, look at them here.' She rattled out the map and reeled them off. '*Sixteen* contained within these *three* alignments (*three* for the Triple Goddess), sixteen being the number of Increase, besides being made up of *nine* (three threes) and the sacred number *seven* (days, planets, candlesticks)...' George interrupted with a correction: 'Ah, *fifteen*, my dear, that extra cairn is fly-dirt, the true summit is just outside the alignment.' The lady changed into third gear and continued unabashed, 'Well, *fifteen*. *Fifteen* is of course the number of letters in the Ogham alphabet they would have used, made up of *three* times *five*, the five fingers, Dactyls, the Five-Fold Knot for tying the Victim....'

Mrs Grey-Mullett would have been great, running a Bingo Hall or presenting Treasury Estimates. We thought of the fruitful opportunities she had (so far) ignored: the numbers of the Ordnance map sheets, their editions, the Grid References, positions in the Munros list, altitudes in feet and metres. But she plunged on.

'*Càrn* is of course from a Mediterranean form of the Goddess, Carnea – another name for Artemis, the child-eater. You see, the Sacred Kings later on postponed their Immortality a little while by employing child surrogates.' The Doctor ventured, but was brushed aside. 'No, *Càrn* is not from heaps of stones: the heaps of stones are named from Carnea. Now then, look at these *three* cairns on the map here (three again, you see), all in a straight line, pointing – when you have corrected for star movements and changes in the earth's rotational axis over the past few thousand years – due north, to Corona Borealis, where the Sacred King goes after death: Càrn Ballach, Càrn Mor, Càrn Leachtar Dhubh – and lining up *exactly* with that charming sacrificial stone we found in Gaick, remember, Bloddy?'

Eventually we retrieved our tent and packed up, Mr Grey-Mullett popping in and out to collect rubbers and tracing paper. The Apprentice trod on a ruler and snapped it. 'No matter', said Mr Grey-Mullett, philosophically.

No matter, indeed. You could draw straight lines through any three of the multitudes of local *Càrns* in a heavily-stalked area like this; every pony-boy had built one. But we held our peace.

The Grey-Mulletts huddled in discussion. They summoned us. The lady explained that Edward's desertion now threatened to spoil an exciting follow-up: another sighter was needed. Just for the day. 'Someone to run about and do little things with Blodeuwedd: George and I are getting too old and stiff these days.'

The Apprentice needed no encouragement. He would love to do little things with Blodeuwedd. The Doctor and I watched them troop off to the next top. We heard Bloddy's fruity laughter. We wondered if our reckless companion would ever return. Fortunately, he had never given us the impression of being particularly Sacred.

The day continued fine, and late that afternoon we admired the view, coming down into Gleann Ballach. A mile further on, a bounding figure hailed us: Blodeuwedd, hair streaming behind her like molten gold in the long lazy light.

'Mother says will you come and see something Very Interesting? Just up on the right.'

We went. A few hundred yards, and Mrs Grey-Mullett reared herself, stag-like, majestically from the heather.

'Ah, Doctor, now I can show you something! Just where I calculated it would be! Here on one side we have Càrn Dearg – the red cairn, red for death and blood, you see; and there on the other, A' Chailleach – the Old Woman, the Goddess as Hag, reinforced by Geal Chàrn – the Goddess as White Carnea! And right between them on the subsidiary line – a splendid example of my Class IIA displacement – where the rising sun shines down from the north-east: what do we find but this – a perfectly lovely little Sacrificial Slab! Now look at it carefully – this is where the priestesses knelt, a depression each side – see – for their knees, so they could hold the victim – drugged of course. There is the incised Spiral of Immortality. And here the little scoop to collect the blood. And this flat stone I've just cleared, is where the chief priestess would stand holding the dagger – or the sickle – in her hand. Quite, quite delightful!'

The Apprentice lay stretched on the slab, wearing a ghastly grin. Mr Grey-Mullett, as priestess, calmed him. Blodeuwedd took up her position, holding the most crooked of the Apprentice's pitons, anticipatory as Steffi Graf before the net. Mrs Grey-Mullett circled them hypnotically with a camera, no doubt subconsciously repeating the movements of the Crane Dance – *nine* steps and a leap. She reassured the Victim. 'No, lie quite relaxed. Don't try to smile, there's a good boy, I want it to look *realistic*.' She clicked from various angles. The Doctor and I cackled, safe on the periphery.

Then the ceremony was over. The red-faced Apprentice resurrected himself, dusting his breeks. He had not, it seemed, acted as surrogate for the Sacred King; this was only a minor slab, for an everyday kind of victim. No great calendar event, just a checking of the tribal clock. Mr Grey-Mullett scribbled notes, possibly on the low Rateable Value of this particular site of immolation.

The ladies had a few more little things to do; the Apprentice meekly departed with them. George was returning to prepare the evening meal in their campavan. We went down with him, being parked at the same road-end.

Two hours later, the midsummer twilight had still not illuminated any of the three. Mr Grey-Mullett shook his head; she must really have got stuck into something. 'Her studies, you know, go very deep.' He would wait there, anyway; we should walk back up – just to see. He lent us his bugle affair. He offered tuition: 'Screw up your lips like this – then grunt: *Booo!*'

We had almost reached the site of the photogenic sacrifice, with no sign or sound. We climbed fallen boulders below the face of Càrn Dearg and gazed about; self-consciously, we wound our lonely horn. Only echoes.

Yet one echo seemed persistent. We trailed it, blowing – or grunting – determinedly. Yes, it grew to independent tootling, and appeared to issue from below ground.

We pushed aside bracken and bony heather, among the piled rocky debris, injecting our two and a half notes into dark cavernous cracks and fissures.

At last we stood over a peculiarly jumbled crevasse system, an eviscerated stone whale. Mournful hoots percolated from beneath. Then voices, gusts of laughter. The Apprentice and Bloddy were within. They had discovered – at the end of another of Mrs Grey-Mullett's alignments – what seemed to be a tunnel to a burial chamber, and followed it. They found the chamber. They were in it. But now they could not get out. Why?

'Because Mother's in the way!' The Doctor and I stared at each other. 'Yes, she came in after us, and' – shrieks of undaughterly mirth; the Apprentice took over. 'The old b-, the old lady – ', slappings, more giggling – 'got stuck. Her backside jammed with the trumpet under the lintel....'

We busied about and found the entrance. We had to make it an exit. The delicate task of sounding out the hindquarters and trumpet of Mrs Grey-Mullett, and of suitably easing them both backwards as undamaged as possible, was best left to my clinical colleague. I shone the operating torch. Various particles of clothing, and a trumpet, surgically removed from the hindquarters, were handed out; and I discreetly retired as the Doctor emerged backwards, followed by ample billows of pink and a chokeful of exclamations.

When I returned, they were all recovering from their collective inhumation, like something by Stanley Spencer. A trumpet and a horn were deployed apocalyptically about. Mrs Grey-Mullett sat, still fanning herself and puffing with emotion, draped informally below with strips of skirt and anorak. The Apprentice was blinking and mopping his brow, and La Belle Dame, completely without *merci*, loudly chaffed the Doctor as she beat earth out of her shorts and smoothed her dangerous hair. Clearly, he was to be the next victim.

Fortunately it was almost dark on the way down, and we gallantly walked in front of Mrs Grey-Mullet, who limped and jangled with safety-pins.

'We must come back and investigate that burial. I am convinced it is a burial.' It nearly had been, anyway.

'Doctor, do you think I'll be fit to crawl in there tomorrow, or should we leave it a little while? Do you advise that I should, in the meantime, try and reduce my, my *weight*? Bloddy, do stop fooling with that poor young man; I'm sure he's had enough of you, three hours in the same burial chamber.... Why, I myself could hardly breathe!'

All the way to Edinburgh, the Doctor and I chortled and the Apprentice sighed dreamily. Despite our cheap jokes, he kept silent. He was not going to enlighten the non-Elect about his Day-Return to the Underworld. He only remarked that if he had been sacrificed, he would at least have been Immortal, living with Blodeuwedd in the nine-gated Castle of the North Wind, eating an infinity of chocolate.

(Significantly, the journey from the burial chamber home took us *three* hours, *dead*. We had, however, stopped for chips at Dunkeld).

# ACCESS

Ah, yes: access. That is a real problem.'

The Doctor shook his head and fingered his diminishing allowance of Highland Park. We were in Daddy McKay's, studying the map for next Saturday. The Doctor had been confined to his patients' beds for many a recent weekend, and we felt that this, his first free one, should be of his own choice.

To our politely-disguised chagrin, he had chosen Meall nam Fiaclan which, thanks to the regular orogenic free enterprise encouraged by the Ordnance Survey, had the previous year raised itself to Munro status.

As a result, it was being assailed every weekend by voracious hordes of metre-devourers, eager for more elevated fodder than weekday jogging could afford. As a further result, those unfortunate enough to farm, forest or shoot the lower slopes of Meall nam Fiaclan, a singularly isolated protuberance, had encompassed it with a Galvanised Iron Curtain. Approaches to the frontier bristled with barbs, swung with padlocks, blistered with exceedingly rude notices. Bulls, dogs and savagely uncomfortable retainers patrolled the fences.

Of course, one Route of Access had been discussed: that (the discussion) was only fair. The route was to be six feet wide, with no stepping off it. Ample; the Romans had run an Empire from only a few inches more. The trouble was that, naturally, none of the Owners would admit it might cross his particular land, and so its whereabouts – timidly signposted by various fund- and cap-raising Amenity Bodies – were bumped into, eased over or scornfully rubbed out by beast, bogey, bulldozer or busily underemployed whatnot. Wherever it went, it certainly would not take the only interesting way up Meall nam Fiaclan, a sort of craggy ridge that gave the heap its name; for that ridge rose above a very posh house indeed.

The Apprentice, numbly accepting the idea of walking up a Munro, warmed to the more attractive possibility of an Assault. The Doctor, to egg him on, read stirring accounts of climbing the Affric hills in the days of that dreadful American Mr Winans, when even the respectable had to skip delightedly from shelter to shelter beneath the telescopes swivelling daily from the ridge of Mam Soul.

We scanned the entry for Meall nam Fiaclan in the nervous little booklet on Access. Its message appeared clear enough. The Restricted Period ran, fairly comprehensively, from the 2nd April to the 31st March. The Owners' Names occupied half a page and read like an international Trotskyite hit-list – gone were those of our former doughty competitors, the double-barrelled English of both nationalities. The Preferred Route announced itself succinctly as 'None'; the Contact was a telephone number which no longer existed; the Remarks diplomatically concluded that 'an authorised footpath is under consideration.' It looked, as the Apprentice remarked, rather a good thing to tackle. We congratulated the Doctor. He beamed, called for the next round, and briefed us on the Order of Battle.

Following the dicta of Clausewitz, Liddell Hart, Guderian, Zhukhov and other internationally popular team managers, we were to attack where the defence least expected us. In this case, directly beneath that interesting ridge – straight up the fields beside the big posh house. Our General's temerity astonished us. The Apprentice, in his excitement, even paid for the Doctor's round.

'The point is', explained that military genius, 'Mowglie Castle has recently changed hands. The new chap's rather eccentric. Neighbours don't get on with him. Has queer ideas. Weak spot, eh? Name's pronounceable, too – Ulfsen; a Swede from Germany – a good honest European. Can't find much else about him except that he's a self-made man and doesn't like dogs: evicted all the old Sheikh's Rottweilers into the Canine Defence League. Should be no trouble of that sort, anyway.' As the Assault was to begin by night ('Much more fun; and they'll never expect us then'), we had worried about padding feet, hot breath and the odd fang. (We discussed further; but the rest of our debate is not yet Cleared for Publication).

We left the car a long way off, by the River Spray, with a wrapped-up tentpole like a fishing rod inside it to divert attention streamwards. When we climbed off the road to go over the top, we felt a tingling in the feet highly flattering to so humble a Munro of such recent creation. A mere V. Diff. took us through and over the barbs and mesh strung up by the old Sheikh to keep his doggywogs in. We were careful not to damage anything; sportsmanship is half the fun of battle; victory is sweeter to the chivalrous. These high-minded consolations of the criminal suffered severe abrasion during our next half hour among late-Arabian-now-Swedish Sitka spruce of southern Alaskan provenance; we decimated their infinite spears with xenophobic fury.

And emerged on to a wide, horribly open moonlit field. Above us rose Meall nam Fiaclan. On our left, pale gleaming turrets among tall timber. On our right, and beyond the field, a dark wood of similar trees.

The air smelt naked and ominous. Our necks prickled. And – surely that was a distant bark, or – even – howl, in the silence? We imagined paddings, breathings. We looked round; and round again. Nothing. 'Ulfsen hates dogs,' insisted the Doctor hoarsely; he obviously felt the same as we did. Our genes manned Action Stations.

We tiptoed across the field, beside the wood on our right, as far as possible from the house.

We had almost reached the end of the field, and the house was below, when I swore I glimpsed a Shape fitting between the tree trunks beside us. I froze and pointed. The others looked, said nothing. We shrugged, and continued; but we moved faster and faster, led by our gallant Chief of Staff. Then: a Howl. A long, low howl. Lord.... And worse – other long low howls; from all sides, it seemed. Very soft, hairily menacing, howls.

'I think', said the Doctor, moving forward faster, 'we had better get out of this.' 'A good job', gasped the Apprentice moving even faster, 'that Ulfsen doesn't like dogs....'

We panted uphill into the dark, followed, we swore, by Ulfsen's pet aversions.

Tree after tree silently slipped below us; we were gaining height. But so were They. Howls, sobs, moans, kept pace with us, swift, swifter as we puffed and stumbled; we dared not use a torch. At the last tree before the bare open hill, with a hint of dawn beyond that black vanishing ridge far – too far – away, we spontaneously stopped, backs to its trunk. We stood breathless, strained eyes into the night.

At first we saw nothing, heard nothing but the paddings about us. And, Lord, the breathings. Then, paddings stopped; and whatever They were, they were watching. We became aware, horribly, of green eyes surrounding us. In pairs, each pair capping a deeper patch of darkness. Dogs.... Dogs.

'Ho, there, boy....' suggested the Doctor, uncertain how otherwise to introduce himself.

A sort of snarl; like slowly torn-off sandpaper.

'There, there; boy....' he continued, rather desperately.

Another snarl, on the right. On the left, a long howl. The Apprentice examined the trunk for boughs. It was, mercifully, an old Scots pine not a Sitka, and we could – if threatened – leap and scramble up.

It was growing lighter; and our mouths dried with what we gradually saw. A whole pack of dogs encircled us, some staring at us, forefeet splayed, heads down; some sitting on their haunches, gazing at us with Red Indian gravity; others stretched out, regarding us chin on paw. Huge dogs, long grey dogs, curious sleekit hunting kind of dogs.

It was the Apprentice who voiced our mounting horror.

'Dogs! They're not bloody dogs: they're bloody WOLVES...!'

Wolves!

We leapt and scrambled furiously, chimps up a tree. I regret that I trod on the Doctor's face on the way up, but Nature is red in tooth and claw, and I needed a foothold just there.

On the third branch, we sat and considered the next move. Our General was clearly nonplussed. Still, Scipio Africanus eventually overcame Hannibal's elephants. We surely could out-manoeuvre Ulfsen's wolves.

But we did not. They came right up to the trunk, jumping and slavering, moaning and howling dreadfully. Hell of a row. The only consolation was that they never bared their teeth. 'Perhaps it's just play, perhaps they're quite friendly,' hoped the Doctor. But he was unwilling to test the assumption.

By eight o'clock we were sore and stiff but fairly familiar with the social habits of hungry wolves. Their sudden cessation of howling therefore aroused our interest. The Leader, then his Deputy, loped off; the remainder followed, leaving only a handful (*sic*) on guard beneath our tree. We were plotting, monkey-like, how to demoralise these obviously reluctant picketers when they began to howl again, noses skyward; and were answered by the others, evidently coming back. Our curses died in our mouths: accompanying the returning wolves appeared two men. Men – walking contentedly amongst them. One – a huge blond bear of a fellow in sandals – was actually roaring with laughter. He came and stood beneath our tree, slapping its trunk with one great pink hand and twiddling the Leader's ears with the other.

'Zo! You meet my vrens! Eh?'

We could not but agree.

'Kom on town, sey are harmless, harmless! Aren't you harmless, eh?' – this to the 'vrens'; the Deputy-Leader wriggled, all grisly two metres (it seemed) of him, with delirious acquiescence. We descended. Embarrassment is too mild a term for our scarlet confusion. But at least we had remained undevoured.

'They are... ah... fine animals,' volunteered the Doctor, unhappily.

'Vine – of course sey are vine. Sey are Vine Animals – but for von sing, von sing...' and he prised open the Deputy-Leader's jaws (the Leader being above such demonstration) – 'Look – sey haf NO TEES! NO TEES!

Indeed they had not. No teeth. None of them. And they set up a low wailing, as if lamenting that unfortunate (for themselves) absence. Ourselves, we felt immeasurably better. The Doctor cautiously tweaked a passing ear; its owner bared up at him a yearning demilitarised gum.

The other man had reappeared with a Land Rover and trailer. Out of the trailer he poured gallons of mash into troughs. 'Zee, ve veed sem here – for you! Sey vill not kom to seir eading place – zo! ve bring seir vood to sem. Sey vould not leaf you: sey are vond of you! Ho, ho, ho!' And he roared again, beating the tree till needles rained about us.

This was obviously Ulfsen. After introductions, he explained a little further.

'I am vond of Vulfs. My name it is Ulfsen, vich I zay means Zon of se Vulf.' He beat, this time, his own chest. A few wolves looked up from their troughs and growled agreement. 'Zo, I like keep vulfs all round me. But – ,' he leaned down at us, brows knitted (he was even taller than the Doctor, and three times as huge) 'I cannot keep vulfs in Zkottland – sey zay sey vill ead se TOURISTS!' – a great shout of laughter, in which we feebly joined – 'and zo, zo – I get sis Shenetic Breed of TOOSELESS VULFS! TOOSELESS VULFS! Sey vill not ead anybody!'

Toothless Wolves. All his fenced land was running with Toothless Wolves, that rare inbred strain from some Scandinavian genetics institute. We marvelled. We felt small. A Night Assault was nothing to this.

'Now – ' he darkened – 'tell me sis; vot vere you toing on my lant? In se night.... EH?'

We left it to the Doctor to explain. Which he did, admirably, with much Svensk lore, ancient and modern, thrown in; and a great friend of his at the Karolinska happened (naturally) to have treated Ulfsen's cousin for some condition as rare as that of his own wolves.... So all was well, very well. We drove down to a splendid breakfast ('NOW I ead se Zkottisk bregvazt, zee?') and were then accompanied by Ulfsen up the ridge to the very summit of Meall nam Fiaclan. He was enormously interested in Munros, Munroists and the story of Sir Hugh ('But I do not like your real glimbing – too dansherous – I like my vulfs!'). He would set aside a Route, a wide, wide Clearway 'up se rogs right to se Topp' himself: 'Sen, many many people can go!' But it was not all on his land? 'Pooh, pooh, it is von mountain. Only my vulfs I haf to keep in se vire.' And he brought us down to supper and fierce Skansk refreshments.

We asked him if it was really true he did not like dogs. 'Togs? Togs vorry my vulfs. Sey haf tees. My vulfs sey haf NO tees. Sat is not VAIR? Eh? Zo I zay – NO TOGS!' And he handed us another Finnish aperitif, some three to four degrees above Absolute Zero.

Yes, a very satisfactory ending.

And all this fuss about Access? Well, clearly, there is no difficulty of Access which is not readily resolvable through an appropriately adult approach.

# A RESCUE

'This is worse than Princes Street the day before the Festival. Or Zero Gully at Easter.'

It was. We were pushed, jostled, poked, stood on. People overtook us, some very rudely. We overtook others, more rudely still. Children and the aged dithered in front, were helped aside, were cursed at. Luggage dented us. Infants hooted and howled. We kept losing each other in the turmoil. A few fanatics even fought against us the other way, pale with exhausted hate.

We seized a rare opportunity when we were all together, and ducked to the left, under an overhang. Traffic thundered above us, turf and small stones trebled past us, the odd whispering sweetiepaper see-sawed beyond us 2000 feet to the A82. Aah.... Relax.... Stretch....

It was the Aonach Eagach on a fine day in late summer, and we had gone there for Doctorial 'old times' sake'; for a simple scenic stroll after the Apprentice had shown us, the previous day, some of the latest things across the glen. It was certainly a ridge of high pressure; we hoped it would remain unbroken.

'We'll wait here till sunset', declared the Apprentice, 'when the pubs are open and they've all gone home.' Otherwise, he'd be up for manslaughter; simply walking on, he'd knock dozens off, either side: satisfying, but morally wrong. The Doctor's suggestion of a descent by The Chancellor ('It's a good route, for 1920.') met with an expected response: equally morally wrong, much less satisfying. One ecological expedition sufficed for one day. Anyway, every gully would be pattern-bombed by these remorseless squadrons. We would wait. It was a fine afternoon.

At least you did see people. Fascinating. We clambered up our overhang and surveyed the procession. Occasionally friends appeared but were borne away by the current, their greetings submerged. Many parties were roped up, often only a few feet apart, lurid in astronauts' anoraks, tintinnabulating with promenade ironware; so the tanglement at times became epic. One of the helicopters droning above would have been useful in traffic control. Our detached and lofty superiority provoked, though, occasional misinterpretation. 'Are you stuck? Can we give you a hand?' called out one eager Youth Leader from the van of his bright-faced progeny. It was left to the more genial Doctor to smile him on, dismissively. Little did we know.

As the sun went down, so did most of them, and we were about to resume our nostalgic traverse when an agitated figure approached from the west, swinging and jumping through the slap-happy pinnacles.

'It's Sandy Oliphant!' cried the Doctor, 'Without babies, for once, or kids of any kind. Never sampled pure undiluted 35-year-old Oliphant for ages.' We thought we'd recognised him earlier, chuffing among a steaming train of schoolchildren, acting as porter, guard, stoker and driver up and down the line.

He appeared in great distress. Had any fallen off? The Doctor pursed lips as Sandy panted nearer. 'Ridiculous, taking kids along a rotten ridge like this, with such exposure and no escape. Kids depend on us adults absolutely. We should be more careful. Sandy tends to overdo things.' We doubted if any single sprog would have been adept enough to push out of such a press, and fall. Probably a whole string had gone. Dreadful.

But no. Nobody had fallen. One, however, had decided to go home, his own way – 'home' being a camp down in the glen. He was sick of the queue. To Sandy's horror this independent youth had airily waved, jumped and slid down to that horrible loose south face. Despite entreaties he would not – probably could not – climb back up. When last visible, he was squatting on the edge of a gully, giving thumbs-up to his hand-wringing conductor – who, having noticed us a little way back, had tethered the others by a firm injunction to some rock, and then bolted here for help.

No, no, he didn't want official Rescue Teams just yet. The boy was intelligent ('Certainly is, getting out of this lot,' remarked the Apprentice) and would surely be waiting for assistance. 'You are the only competent climbers I've seen here,' gasped Sandy, 'You could nip over and get him up – or safely down – without any fuss. I daren't risk fuss, it would upset the others, scare the parents – and we've been that careful all weekend.... People talk so....' Sandy is totally without guile, and we were touched more than flattered. We bounded along behind him, towards his bereft and quivering flock.

'You know,' hissed the Doctor, 'he should have got the M.R.T. right away. Lord knows what that boy'll get up – or down – to. I don't like these private arrangements to save face, where kids are concerned – they're more important than anyone's pride.'

Of course, we had no rope or pegs. Not for a walk like this (it is indeed classified – by some – *as* a Walk....). Only a short nylon line – for emergency. We peered down. In the dusk a small figure crouched above the network of dilapidating overhanging gullies. Still there. Poor kid.

'Fine, we'll pop down and collect him. If we see a good way out, we'll take it. And signal by torch. Then you get the rest home and drive to the bottom and pick us up. Otherwise we'll have to try and climb back up this awful stuff.' Thus the Doctor.

A most unpleasant descent. The Doctor, skilled in horticultural psychology, led us through the less neurotic vegetation. My fingernails gathered *Graminaceae* and *Ericaceae*, the Apprentice no longer enjoyed what had promised to be the only interesting part of the day. 'All right, laddie, we're here!' cried the Doctor encouragingly, as he slithered down an invisible herbaceous thread among the unstrung and highly volatile vertical debris.

'So *you're* going this way, too?' the boy called up.

He was not shocked. Not alarmed. Rather, he seemed impatient. He finished what appeared to be sandwiches, rolled the paper into a ball and tossed it into horrifying black depths. Then, waving cheerily, he vanished after it into the gloom. 'Come on, then, it's easy enough below!'

'Lord, the boy's a madman!' wailed the Doctor, and literally shinned down the ghastly slope. 'He can certainly climb – downwards, anyway.'

We caught him up, at the top of another gut-rocking gully. 'I think this'll go all right', he was saying. The Doctor clutched him, none too gently. 'Careful!' exclaimed the boy, with annoyance, 'If you're going to slip, tell me first. Don't grab!'

We tried to instil some sense of guilt. 'Don't you know we've been called out to rescue you? Don't you realise your selfishness has caused us to risk our lives? We should really have had the M.R.T. out by this time, to do it properly – with more people risking their lives – and all in the papers tomorrow!'

The Doctor's exhortations fell unheeded. The boy – he must have been eleven or twelve – was pointing out his choice of route to the Apprentice, who appeared to agree. It seemed possible: with the Apprentice for the rock, the Doctor for the botany, and our 50-foot nylon line for any Emergency. Preferable to returning up that wall of short-fuse shingle, all triggered to go off downhill. We signalled back with our (only) headlamp, and then laced the vociferously protesting youth into the line.

To soothe him, we explained he was now our Leader. He demanded, if so, to wear the headlamp. No, the last man needed it, and *he* was not going to be the last man: he was Leader. Together, we quickly developed a technique. We dangled him down stretch after stretch, until he would call up 'O.K. – you fellers can come now, I've sorted it.' Then one by one we would slither down to him. And off he went again, raring to go. It resembled sounding the lead, as we repeatedly cast him overboard to find bottom.

And it worked very well. Too well. Until the last pitch.

This appeared, in the by-now darkness, to be a dungeon. We had lowered ourselves optimistically – and apparently irreversibly – into it. Sheer walls, left, right, and – now – up in front of us. Our feeble headlamp (it was really only for Emergency...) scraped unhappily on the wet rocks, and on the impending vegetation behind us, most of which had been swept off beneath feet, shins, backsides and shoulderblades. Damn.

'Looks like some fun, here,' remarked the boy. He offered us a Polo mint each. 'Sorry I've no more to spare: didn't reckon on company, like. We might need the rest later,' he further informed us, sucking composedly. 'Now, shine a light, Doc; just let's have a look down there....' and wriggled off. Our expressions were fortunately blacked out. Minutes. Badger-rattlings beneath; pebbles echoing away below. Then a shout.

'Fine. Just right. Come on, I've got you.... Quite safe.' However, we proceeded cautiously. Everything was rotten, undoubtedly irreversible. The boy had been astonishingly lightfooted. Only his (the boy's) presumed innocence prevented the accustomed string of maledictions from the insecure and disapproving Apprentice.

We found ourselves in a wet pit at the bottom of the dungeon, where some 1500 feet of trickle congregated before agreeing to run out beside

our feet through a large narrow slot like a letter box. Out to freedom. We knelt in the gurgles and peered. The boy took our headlamp and demonstrated a flash of easy screes down to the road beyond this otherwise seemingly impossible chockstone.

'Terrific, eh?' He was pleased at having guided us to so elegant an exit. 'O.K.? I'll go on....' And he slipped through, tied to his line, wearing the headlamp. 'Now you fellers.'

In the blinding flash-back beam, the Apprentice tried first. Then myself. Then the Doctor, that usually infinitely extensible assemblage of limbs and stratagems. Groan. Curse. Rip.

The boy was most helpful and patient. 'Try breathing *out*, it reduces your chest,' he advised the Doctor, speechless within the Tertiary.

No. We all stuck. We could not get through. And because we had no other torch, and had forgotten crowbar and Semtex, there we would stay until it was light or until someone could climb up the outside tonight and toss us a rope from the top of the chockstone. We could hardly ask our Charge to do that – now that we had successfully brought him to safety....

'Ah; and I thought you'd be able to do it. Too bad,' sympathised the lad. 'After coming down so well, all that way.' A pause. 'Do you want me to arrange a Rescue, like?'

'He is mature for his years,' gritted the embittered Doctor, with professional self-control. 'No!' he shouted, 'just tell Sandy about it. He's coming up the road. He'll know what to do. Don't make a fuss, under any circumstances. No need to disturb people at this time of night.'

The lad came back and hissed through the slot. His beam danced on our feet, wickedly.

'No, we don't want any more people risking their lives. Just selfish. And it'd be in the papers, tomorrow, like. Though the M.R.T. *would* do it properly....' He stopped. The Apprentice had partially blown a safety valve. 'O.K.' he resumed, 'I'll no rescue you, then: if you'll no rescue me – see? Fair do's, eh?'

'Fair do's,' replied the Doctor slowly. It was checkmate. 'Be careful, now,' he added feebly, as the boy whistled off and darkness became total, our line – still tied to the brat – slipping through nerveless hands. 'Let him keep it – it'll be safer, with him going down alone....' The Doctor sighed. A private arrangement, not the M.R.T. thank heaven.

For, this time, children were not *really* concerned.

Our child certainly wasn't. We heard him whooping away in sprays of scree. A most competent youth. He would be Minister of Sport yet. And at least he had given us a mint each.

Agonies of hunger, cold and wetness were nothing to the thought of the headlines and our colleagues' mirth if that urchin failed to keep his word. 'Boy Aged 11 Brings Three Experienced Climbers Down Safely.' 'Young Child Rescues His Instructors in Glencoe Mountain Drama.' 'Wee Hero....' Lord, they would pay him thousands....

Twice the Apprentice tried, twice he fell back, accompanied by his holds. Useless in the dark. Better to walk down in shame than be carried.

We must have dozed, for a light woke us. A voice. Sandy's, thank the Lord. Beside us.

'How did you get in here?' we asked, seeing no rope.

'Through the little keyhole up there on the left....' and Sandy pointed his beam. 'You can really only see it from outside. The boy described it to me. He left cairns to guide us, the whole way up.' So he did know of an easy way out, all the time.... our respect for the creature grew even greater.

As we stumbled to the road, munching chocolate bars, Sandy and his friend, a lean sardonic schoolteacher who, it appeared later, had suffered much from pontificating mountaineers, explained that the boy had stopped their car and told them.

'Has he... has he told anyone else?' we mumbled.

The schoolteacher whistled an unpleasing tune and kicked the odd stone.

'Don't think so. He went straight to bed,' said Sandy.

'Probably had a pint first,' scowled the Apprentice, all of an inch high.

'I didn't scold him,' explained Sandy. 'From what he told me, I gathered you wouldn't have liked us to.' Gulp. 'He's a curious child', Sandy continued, 'unexpectedly adult in so many ways. But unpredictable, quite unpredictable.' We shivered. 'I don't think I shall bring him again. He puts a great strain on everybody, you know.' We knew.

Our own great strain lasted more than a fortnight. We avoided radio bulletins and newspapers. We escaped possible journalists. Eventually we breathed. And now – now – we can even recount it; or much of it.

'A most extraordinarily well-balanced young person – in every sense,' summed up the Doctor, admiringly – also, thankfully. 'And, remarkable, isn't it – we never asked – we don't even know his name!'

The Apprentice put it more truthfully.

'Don't want to know his bloody name....'

POSTSCRIPT: But we nearly found out his name. Some Thursdays later, the *Journal* New Climbs Editor strode into the back bar of Daddy McKay's and flung a piece of paper down in front of us. 'What's all this nonsense?' he cried, 'here's a fellow done a quite unnecessary route off the Aonach Eagach, and says he led *you* down it, and *you* will vouch for it being a fine lead, a fine route, and well worth publishing....' We paled, and read. Yes, we recognised the pitches; the last one 'goes through a horizontal cleft to easy screes and the main road; the corpulent, aged or stiff avoid it by a traverse up and left....' 'Of course, I'll not publish it. The fellow has the cheek to say if I don't he'll send a much fuller version elsewhere. Good luck to him, then!'

We froze.

'Er, well, it's – er – after all quite an *interesting* way off', mumbled the Doctor, 'unforgettable, in fact. Do be a good chap, and put it in, this once....'

It took a great deal of Glen Droolie to convince the editor, but finally we breathed again. Before he left, we glanced hurriedly at the name of the climb; but never dared – then or later in the *Journal* – to read the name of our leader.

'I see he calls it *A Gentle Squeeze*....' mused the Doctor.

'His letter says it could be called *Blackmail*, but he thinks you'd agree that *A Gentle Squeeze* would look better, if it were printed in the *Journal*.'

When we were on our own again, we swore long and softly.

'Unexpectedly adult in so many ways,' sighed the Doctor. And drowned the whole juvenile episode in a truly mature Glen Droolie.

# B GULLY

We shall leave it as B Gully, and not name the hill it defaces. To say more would endanger the innocently curious; few people would otherwise find it, and only the Doctor would look for it. What it does in summer I don't know, and don't care. It probably breeds rabbits. In winter it drives one to theosophy or astrophysics.

That New Year the Apprentice, the Doctor and I had gathered some excellent high grades in the Western Cairngorms. The Apprentice found them relaxing after two days with the Weasels, wintering summer VS's on the Ben. The Doctor, no mean performer on ice, had led several hard pitches and was high for the last day. However, the night before, it blew and snowed so arctically that we resolved to go home. But the morning radio reported no road at Dalnaspidal or anywhere else; so we resigned ourselves agreeably to an extra day's climbing. But where?

The southeast wind had filled all the northerly gullies and they lay together in the cold morning sun hatching powder-snow avalanches, joining wicked hands and waiting for us. We turned to the less intelligent hills opposite, a huddle of bent and balding brows.

'That wind should have cleaned out Beinn X', pronounced the Doctor (naming the unmentionable hill) '*and* both its gullies. I read somewhere that B Gully is an easy snow walk with fine views south. We could have a gentlemanly stroll up it and watch for the ploughs coming through.'

We were not enthusiastic. But he had been robbed of a final good lead; so we assented. Beinn X was blunt bad-tempered scree, a dreadful slagheap of windblasted icy detritus; yet its two distant gullies blinked harmlessly enough. We headed for B Gully, through snow-dispensing Sitka spruce. 'Still,' remarked the Doctor, when we thankfully broke clear, 'they add a touch of difficulty to an otherwise easy day' – his usual, and usually accepted, invitation to Fate. We wiped our necks dry and followed a welcome path past a shepherd's cottage to the hill itself.

The gully began mildly enough. Its snow was hard and its angle slight. The jaundiced eye did note, a little way up, the whiter whiteness of deep new snow. The Doctor disagreed. 'Never, in a wind like last night's. All the loose stuff's been blown to Lochaber. Look how there's none on the scree.' He was still enlarging upon this certainty when he began to diminish. He was progressively entering his footsteps. We waded after, cursing his bobbing head. We were climbing into, not up, the gully.

'Don't worry. A softish patch. A mere aeolian aberration – due to that big rock – ' and he waved his axe towards the uniform scree slope on our right, which faced the equally uniform one on our left. 'We'll soon strike bottom again.'

And he ploughed on, treadmilling determinedly. No bottom could we strike. It was wrapped in eiderdown. We climbed through an endless sleeping bag. The floor could be stamped to some quiver of stability; front and sides fled from our grasp, and fell in again behind. Loyally, we underwent an hour or so of this. The Doctor, ahead in the burrow, kept promising an eventual excellent view of the snowploughs; an inducement we considered insufficient and, increasingly, improbable.

Then a mist came up from the strath; and our floundering lost any trace of relevance. We were isolated in space, each performing a private inexplicable penance. Up, down; up, down. Down, up; down, up. _Om mane padme hum._

Nothing could we see but occasional toiling pieces of ourselves. The environment had abdicated. Its ghost hung around in a thick flannel of expectancy. No doubt some Beatitude was preparing. Sensory deprivation is, however, unsuited to the impure, and our unemployed reflexes became restive. We spoke to them severely. But they prevailed. Nirvana would have to wait.

'I've had enough of this bloody place,' roared the head, shoulders and one arm of the Apprentice. Another arm, ectoplasmically dim, floated above him in vague Blavatskian deprecation; it repeated the Doctor's familiar assurances that rock would soon appear and that the view would be good. It withdrew and faded, exorcised by pulverising oaths from a demi-head sable, couped at the neck, issuant from an infinite field of argent.

Beinn X is only two and a half thousand feet at the worst, but to continue would disperse ourselves further into a dubiously-heraldic spirit world. B Gully under these conditions – probably under any conditions – is not the Eightfold Noble Path. It was not any sort of path; and to descend proved as baffling as trying to go up. Merely to stand still in such a whiteout entails much geometric unhappiness; the dimensions crowd round and leer unpredictably. They push back from in front and shove from behind. You inevitably fall. Our drunken progress down a thousand odd feet of this non-Euclidian picketing may be imagined.

We tried occasionally to escape from the side. During one of these time-consuming excursions the Doctor sang triumphantly 'A rock! A rock! At last! We're there!' And he carefully stepped on a small black triangle and pushed himself upwards. Then we knelt and pulled him out. He had stood on his own glove, dropped the moment before. The glove had, of course, vanished for ever into nether whiteness. We spat out snow and continued. B Gully had no sides any more; they had slipped, like the rest of our once so solid and Newtonian Beinn X, into a boundless continuum of uncertainty.

It was, in fact, impossible to measure advance in any direction. We began to sympathise with Einstein. The compass, and the Doctor's much-consulted but equally equivocal clinometer, tended to believe we were going down: yet small objects (borrowed from one's companion), when thrown ahead to prove this, would stick in mid-air; or annihilate themselves suddenly and permanently despite apologies. The Doctor aimed bearings from behind; but they never reached us. He blamed the Heisenberg principle. We suffered, in fact, most of the New Cosmology. Only a Black Hole was missing. It came later.

We swore we *were* going down. The air felt more still, and last night's snow-meringues loomed increasingly confectious. We became convinced we were descending a steep, sheltered and previously unseen branch of B Gully. Such unexpected fluvio-glacial gorges ferret these lower hills. We roped up and followed the Apprentice's erratic thread through piled hallucinations. The Doctor, at times disconcertingly below us, acted as anchor; he was our longest peg. But no steep pitch fell away beneath; whenever we imagined one, the Apprentice's torso would surmount it into space, a rising kite tight in our fingers.

It grew dark; but still no communication from Scotland. We leant against each other. We were light-headed from weltering in abstraction; our hemispheres had drifted up. We argued about the existence of torches; each assumed somebody else had brought one (only a gentle-manly stroll...). We would have to bivouac until this hopeless mist cleared up. The Apprentice, cursing dully, plunged his fist into the wall of snow before him to test its howff-forming potentiality.

His howls and fragmentary dance testified the negative. Solid. Obvi-ously ice. We had struck it at last. We *were* in a gorge. At a steep part. The ice appeared to rise above us; therefore it presumably stretched below. We collected ourselves. We smelt avalanches. I gathered the rope, and the Doctor, hovering beyond my shoulder, divested himself of legs and dug in. The Apprentice leant forward, sniffing cautiously, tapping with the point of his axe. Suddenly there was a thump and a dull crack, and a black line appeared across part of the wall; a fringe of dislodged snow trickled down it. Windslab! Windslab and powder snow.... This, then, was it.

'She's going!' croaked the Apprentice, snatching back his axe. The Doctor drove himself in, together with his comment, up to the hilt, and vanished from sight. I hauled on the rope and fell back into feathers, feet plunging. The Apprentice, as he later described it, was plucked from his steps and flung outwards and upwards....

We wrestled, clutching the rope, our only reality. It clutched back. Blows demolished my breath – we were over the wall – or was it the Doctor's boots? A rush of silence.... I imagined myself falling, falling, in the caress of a powder-snow avalanche, towards rocks or suffocation.

Then it seemed as if I awoke.

'Good Lord,' said the Doctor, just above my ear.

I clawed away snow. I felt myself carefully. Surprisingly, I could sit up, though it was painful.

We must have stopped; but we might never have moved. In front was an apparently identical ice wall, again with a black split across it. But the creaking and tearing was louder this time, and the split wid-ened, jerk after jerk. We heard tinkling, as of ice, into the abyss beyond. We were about to be swept down the next step of this appalling stair-way. We grabbed the rope again; and waited.

But the split grew wider, until it was almost a regular square. A black square. Our long-bleached eyes drank it with fascination. Black. Square. Hypnotised, we wrapped the rope round our arms.

And then, incredibly, the square slowly filled itself; and presented us

– with a Human Head. A large human – hairy and whiskered – head gazed at us from the square. Its eyes glittered in the half-light.

I groaned. This was Concussion; or worse. Maybe, The Other Side. Letting go the rope with one hand, I rubbed snow round my eyes. It was still there. 'Good Lord....' repeated the Doctor, perhaps appropriately.

The head spoke. With deliberation.

'Ye'll be the fellies: that went up the hill the day?'

Silence. 'Aah,' replied the Doctor, the only one with a biddable larynx.

'Well, then: jist ye come roon to the door: an I'll let ye in. It's awfy deep-like: oot there at the back. Wait now: till I pit on the licht.'

The head withdrew, and almost at once the square blazed forth. *Fiat lux*. It was not St. Peter. It was not The Gate. It was not even a Black Hole. It was somebody in a cottage. The cottage was snowed up at the back, it was whitewashed and, as the Apprentice had painfully demonstrated, it was built of sound local granite. There had been no avalanche, and we had fallen only in our own estimation.

We rose and followed the rope to the Apprentice, who had been buried and half strangled by our earlier presence of mind; pulled him up, brushed him down, stifled his questions and propelled him towards the approaching torch.

'Come awa in: come awa in. I jist couldna get yon windy open: an noo the gless is creckit. Pieces aa owre the flair. Michty: where hae ye been? Aa snaw? Ye've come doon the burn: that's what ye've done: richt aff the hill. But: ye'd like no *see* the road.'

We dripped beside a roaring fire, clutching hot sweet tea and new-made bread. Frying hissed wonderfully behind us. We gathered that there were only two places on the hill where snow always collected, B Gully and the burn that ran down from it directly to the shepherd's cottage, the cottage we had passed that morning. The burn, it seemed, was the usual place to find the more stupid sheep in weather like this.

'But: I've niver had three o them: at ma back windy afore!' exclaimed the shepherd, genially enough, pouring out drams for each of us.

We thought it best not to comment. Later, perhaps, the Doctor might describe how he had steered us straight to supper. Just now, he studied his whisky. We had begun hesitantly to discuss the hazards of lambing, when the shepherd's wife called us to table. Plates steamed, chips stretched themselves expansively on top of bacon, sausage and egg. 'And so it's Mr McPhedran you're knowing,' she said, naming the shepherd who had been our host on the Craggie expedition. 'He marches with us. A great man, Erchie, a great man.'

'Remarkable, remarkable, *mmm*, his fiddle has, *mmm*, exceptional bite and drive,' agreed the Doctor, munching affably, wielding his fork; and conversation was launched down the channel so tactfully provided.

# ONE HITCH AFTER ANOTHER

'Nearly there!' shouted up the Doctor, with relief.

We were on a newish line of the Apprentice's, threading the west (worst) side of central Buttress in Coire Mhic Fhearchair. Not really new – it owed much to the Nisbetry sprinkled around; we had urged, cajoled and threatened our leader away from his original extremist aspirations. Especially as the weather had suddenly turned bad.

Very bad. Just as we reached the quartzite. Hellish, for July and July clothing. Long waves of hail, liquid and solid, howled from the north and broke against our cliff, numbing fingers and necks. We were soaked and cold. Below, wet glaciers slid off the Doctor's hat down each side of his nose. The Apprentice, invisible above, spat high-calorie expletives into the roaring freeze-for-all.

Jerk on the rope. My move. I grabbed and sliddered on rock uncooperative as ice. Sleet lubricated hailstone-bearings. This last pitch was just Severe technically but Extreme climatically....

It had been a superb lead. When we finally hauled in the long lobster legs of the Doctor through the top surf, we crouched shipwrecked on a bouldery summit shore.

'Too much windchill to face this lot back to the car,' gasped our Medical Adviser, wiping a streaming blue beak. 'Let's go over the ridge and down to the Glen Torridon road. Easily get a lift this time of year.'

The old Merc reposed due north at the foot of Glen Grudie. We peered that way. Sleet.... Howl.... Drench.... Visibility – nil. No question – due south over the ridge! Easily get a lift.... Up Glen Torridon, turn left at Kinlochewe and down to Glen Grudie. It was the way to Inverewe, taken by all the National Trusters – even in this weather, for it would be fine at the coast.

Out of the wind we became merely wet. Above us screamed horizontal plates of meteorology. We slid and spattered down to the innocent wet ribbon of road. We shook ourselves. We looked guilty and disreputable. So, as Front Man, we chose the more amiable Doctor, who – on a drippingly close examination – seemed to boast a clean shirt. He stationed himself, rucksack carefully minimised, by the sodden verge, sucking a drowned pipe, thumb poised as if to confer some imperial favour. We lower orders tried our luck downstream, ready to dash back – with armfuls of rope and pitons – to gaff whatever the Doctor had hooked. Three or four vessels splashed past every minute, bolted and shuttered as submarines, windscreen wipers in nervous frenzy. None stopped.

'It's not all that bloody far; better walk it than freeze here....' The Apprentice's opinion had barely been launched into the flood before a small one took the Doctor's bait. The near door opened. Rubbish was ejected. The Doctor inserted his beak.

We galloped down. A packed and steaming interior. Large elderly beaming occupants, eating. The driver leaned across ample Lancastrian bosoms and pastry.

'Ee, but you're wet!' We were. (Chew, chew).

'There's only room for one of you.' There was. (Chew).

But the Doctor could whizz up with them, collect the Merc and then collect us. He wiped his cascading neb once more and was about to squeeze in among the festal boards, when the Apprentice's ever-casting thumb caught a large empty BMW object.

Much better (we thought). We thanked the masticators and leapt to luxury and the proprietorial Apprentice – 'Just put the luggage in the boot.'

*Brrrmm... Brrrmm...* The driver, Billy, a large blue-eyed optimist, threw a fag-end out of his window. He wasn't going down Glen Grudie way, but Kinlochewe would do for starters, eh? Yes, yes. We could get a lift to Glen Grudie from there.

Yes. We crouched in horror at the take-off. He certainly thought he could drive. Radar is a wonderful thing – without it we could only see through eighteen inches of the wiper's arc; tourists – both ways – were devoured unseen. The infamous BMW back-end swivelled excitedly at every yank of the wheel. We clutched our belays.

Then a mate of his in some other thunderous aquatic monster (probably a Cosworth Ford) beat on our tail. Billy smirked and pushed his foot further down. 'Poor old Chairlie. He'll no get past, eh? Eh?'

Above the neurone-quelling CD six-speaker stereo-pop, Billy queried the sanity of our late sport. As for him, he was up here on a construction job. That made sense. But climbing – 'Jist no bliddy safe, thae hills. An in this weather, plain daft. Ach, ye ―― !!' (A Metro or suchlike had ventured too far from the gutter and fled back crying). 'Na, na. No me,' he bellowed cheerfully, eyes feeding on the rear mirror, 'Ah'll stay put. Terror bliddy firmer fer me! Eh?' He burst into loud song as we skidded the next bend, and lit another fag.

We were too stricken to peer through the gale-splashed glass. Another shuddering power-slide and we swung right, the great baying brute that had tried to overtake us having to brake hard alongside and vanish backwards to tuneful blasts of a seven-fold trumpet. We belted along, unchallenged.

'That was Chairlie. Cannae corner. Nae use. Ye have tae DRIVE on these roads: eh?'

The Apprentice took courage and rubbed his fist on the glass. He peered through. He yelled. That had not only been Chairlie, but Kinlochewe and our turn left.... We were almost halfway up Glen Docherty already, heading for Inverness, swinging furiously curve to curve, Chairlie way behind.

Eventually, with extremely bad grace, Billy slowed down to let us out. We leapt away as all gears gathered themselves and rear wheels sprayed.

It was off, leaving a creamy wake – with our kit still in the boot!

We roared in fury. The Doctor, perspicacious as ever, jumped into the road and flagged down Chairlie. We tumbled in, and urged him on. Faster, faster....

Nae use. Chairlie couldnae corner. We bumped from verge to verge in a frenzy of pursuit, cursing ditherers. Ye hae tae DRIVE on these roads.

Then, wonderfully, a queue ahead: sheep blocking the way. We slithered up to the savagely-revving·BM, leapt out, beat the boot, tore it open and grabbed our things as – once more – wheels showered us and it stormed off. Chairlie trumpeted his derision, Billy shook a friendly fist out of the window and they roared away, foam to foam, overtaking joyously.

We collapsed, exhausted. We were so shaken we stopped the next car going up to Inverness, instead of down to Kinlochewe, and became lengthily entangled in broken European with the French occupants, who took us for Germans forgetfully signalling on the wrong side of the road....

We wearily waded to the opposite bank, and resumed supplication. A top-heavy launch-like campavan teetered unsteadily to stop beside us, stalling the engine.

A door slid back. Dozens of heads, mostly infantile, peered out.

'I can only take one,' warned a voice from way back. 'I'm not really used to driving this thing. We're full enough – we've had some near squeaks already.'

Despite this uninviting invitation the Doctor, a man of steel, stepped forward, cast a last glance at us and pulled up on the handle.

A muffled cry within, a horrid gurgle and splash, and he retreated hastily, slapping himself down. More cries.

'Ally's been sick again, Dad!' Rags were brandished from the doorway, showering us.

We staggered back, rinsed by the rain. No, we wouldn't inconvenience them further. We thanked them for the opportunity, and hoped Ally would get well. We ploughed on. We sighed for Central Buttress again. Elemental simplicity. Do or die. We could cope with that. But here – what were we doing here, sponging off everything we climbed away from each weekend? Were we really no better than anyone else? We were depressed. We were suffering from Severe Social Exposure.

Fortunately, another vehicle stopped beside us. (The weather was so dreadful, the stoniest heart would dissolve). Fortunately? It was a bulbous bluebottle-like Japanese pickup, with rusty cowcatchers, stone-guards, aerials, swivelling lights and a few canisters of – apparently creosote – in the open back.

The cabin was thick with joviality and fag smoke. Its window wound down and fresh air fled terrified.

'Aye, we're gaun to the Gairloch. That's your way. Chust chump in!'

We clambered into the back as it chuffed off in clouds of carbon. I grabbed the Apprentice – his hold had come loose; it clattered on the road behind us.

The Doctor lay on cold wet steel, feet outstretched against a canister. The Apprentice jammed his barrel into the small of his back. I embraced mine.

To little effect. All of them bounced and rolled and spat vile oily liquid at every bend. Black bilge sluiced our backsides.

But not far to go....

Hell once more! They turned back to Glen Torridon at Kinlochewe! They were *not* going down to Grudie! This was the same damned road we'd started off from....

We beat fists on the cabin roof, kicked it, wept and swore. The Apprentice sawed his canister to and fro across the cabin's back window bars. But they were too intent on some tattered tabloid inside, driver included.

At length they suspected something. They stopped suddenly and bashed open a door. (The Doctor, who was attempting a traverse along it to shout through a window, was dislodged instantly into the ditch).

Puzzled faces looked out, down, and up.

'You boys not well or something, is it? You'll be having the Car Sickness maybe?' (We certainly were, by now).

We spluttered that this was not the way to Gairloch, still less to Glen Grudie.

'Och, that's all it is, is it? Och, we've chust to pick something up at Inveralligin – a few drums of oil and stuff. It'll no take long, an hour or so. Inveralligin's a great place. Grand views in good weather. Then we'll chust come back and hit straight for Glen Grudie; you'll be home in no time, boys!'

Despite the risk of wounding their feelings, we stiffly dropped down to the Doctor in the rushes. They billowed off, genially distributing hydrocarbons.

The Apprentice swore he'd walk. WALK. We were a few hundred yards further *down* the road than when we started. We were not even holding our own.

So we splashed on, soaked, clapped out, smelly.

Then just before the Ling hut a big shiny car stopped beside us. And offered a lift. Opened doors and urged us in, despite our understandable hesitation. It was so warm, dry and clean. Hospitable old Yorkshire couple. The wifie leaned back as we melted into the rear seat.

'My, you *are* wet. It's all that *rain*, that's what it is!'

Yes, the driver said yes, they were going to, to Inverewe.

'Inver, Inversomething, isn't it, Doris, we're making for?' Much fumbling about a road atlas, and ultimate agreement. Direct to Glen Grudie at last....

'We'll not get to Inver, Inverwhatsitsname today, but you say it's on your way, so just tell us when you want to get off.'

We sighed and relaxed. It was warm, dry and soft. And slow.

Lord, it was slow. The driver, Ernest, was excessively careful. These dreadful roads were so dangerous. This dreadful weather was so dangerous. And these drivers were so dreadful, so dangerous. So fast, so rude, so thoughtless of Other People – always wanting to Overtake.

Ernest swivelled round – slowly and alarmingly – in his (driving...) seat and addressed us severely:

'I never let... 'em Overtake. I teach 'em... Manners.'

Yes, yes, we agreed agitatedly. Only turn round again, for the Lord's sake. We thought of Billy heading back for something he'd forgotten.

Ernest resumed his righteous peering through the flung monsoon. Hooters shrieked behind us incessantly. He veered out and kept 'em back. He checked his speedometer – 25 miles per hour. Fast enough in this weather. He taught 'em Manners.

Our ears burnt. Doris kept on knitting.

Surely we should have been warned, by this time. But it was warm, dry, and we daren't look out of the streaming windows with half a mile of accumulated fury behind us. Bellowings, bleatings, roars; like the dawn chorus at Perth Mart. And he was so slow.

'Listen to 'em. Mad. Always hootin. Always RACIN. They should enjoy the... Country. That's what it's for. It's not a... Speed Track. Is it, Doris?'

An evil dream. Unending. But warm. Then, in a brief comparative lull, we looked more closely out of the window.

No.... No! Glen Docherty! AGAIN! We had passed Kinlochewe and not turned left!

We were rude. We shouted. We pounded the back of the front seats.

Ernest appeared upset. 'But you did say... Inver, Inver, Inver... didn't you? That's where we're going, we turned right, at the sign.'

Doris put away her knitting slowly, and consulted navigational aids. She looked up, round-eyed, at Ernest.

'You know, I think it's Inver*ness* that we mean.' She turned worried lenses on us. 'Is it Inver*ness* you're going to, then?'

No! We continued to shout, shake and stamp. We continued to be assisted up Glen Docherty. Finally, on a blind corner, they stopped and let us out, shaking their heads. A cavalcade of blaring open-window-cursing vehicles ground past. We choked in the smoke of at-last-released exhausts.

'A bloody yo-yo!' screamed the Apprentice. He foamed. He was no longer depressed, but manic. He would much have preferred a decent honest death in Glen Grudie.

We shambled on down again. We were such poor drookit craiturs by then that a car stopped within two minutes. Gold specs, grey costumes. Three old ladies. National Trust, of course. Inverewe. Room for one. The Doctor hopped in. 'This is it! Soon be back! *Keep richt on Tae the end o the road...,*' he sang.   And vanished.

We two splashed on. A long pause. Then hot dieselly breath on our necks. A silver Range Rover, Edinburgh registration. An inviting door. We hauled ourselves in. Behind us wire mesh and two slobbering wolfhounds; in front, a tweedy lady and a kilted driver, Balmoral bonnet and all. The latter burbled forth.

'Jolly good! We're going along your way to Little Loch Broom. Delighted to help. So glad you're enjoying yourselves out here. Wonderful country. I like it best in this kind of... wildish weather, don't you? Sort of wind and rain on your face. Rather splendid for tramping about. Love to come up for a month or so in the summer. Kind of ancestral home, you know.' We recognised Ancient MacKenzie tartan and the plastic sprig of holly. The fruity R.P. vowels cantered on.

'My great grandfather sold his place up here and came to Surrey. And my grandmother was a Cameron – from Henley. So it's rather in the blood, you know. *Still the Heart is Highland* – even at Haslemere, hah!' We remarked on his number plate. 'Ah, I always have my cars registered in Scotland... keeps up the link, don't you see?' He blethered on compulsively. 'Now we're going to our daughter's – nice little place where she can paint and her husband can fish, watch birds and shoot 'em, and try to breed oysters. Of course he has his Fax to Lombard Street, keeps in touch with the necessary.'

His wife swivelled round and flashed a toothy explanation – 'Diana married a Bradbury-Hutton!'

We badly missed the Doctor, who would certainly have appeared to know all about Bradbury-Huttons and breeding oysters. Our monosyllabic answers were not only due to the Apprentice's black thoughts about White Settlers, but to our anxious watch for the old Merc pounding back up; we could easily miss it – on a day like this.... We were also melting like ice cream under the wolfhounds' plushy tongues, the netting being permeable to canine affection.

The Mhic Choinnich prattled on. He skilfully missed a beached cyclist baling out, and nearly ran over the legs of some poor subaquatic sod changing a wheel. Otherwise, an uneventful trip to the foot of Glen Grudie. As we climbed down, Himself reached under the steering wheel and his lady passed on to us a hip flask.

We were taken aback. Haslemere Hospitality. Embarrassed, I thought it appropriate to toast our nostalgic native with the MacKenzie war-cry: '*Tulach ard!*'

He appeared equally taken aback. 'Er, no, actually,' he said. 'Chevas Regal.'

Freed at last from our prolonged battle with the Knights of the Road, we strolled through fresh wet grass to the old Merc – still there, thank goodness. A few other cars, too. But no Doctor.

'He'll be in Inveralligin, admiring the view,' suggested the Apprentice. 'We'll leave a note on the seat and collect dry things for the tent.' (Tent – blessed secret sanctuary! There, snug at last from wind, hail, sleet,

Billys, Ernest and Lombard Street, we could celebrate again the warm sandstone and gleaming quartzite of our Central Buttress in the sun.)

We possessed no key. But my companion is suspiciously skilled at entering locked vehicles within the prescribed 12 seconds, and I admired the way he dismantled, with wire and a plastic card, the Doctor's ingenious booby-traps.

'Dead easy,' he proclaimed, loudly.

And then the roadside blossomed with figures.

'Hi! hi! You there!' 'Stop thief, stop thie-e-e-ef!'

We blinked. Many waterproofs, Barbour jackets and severe expressions closed in on us from their ambush. We were not yet done with our fellow men.

'Got you at last, you rats!' bellowed an unpleasantly large and powerful cove. 'Filthy swine!' screamed an emotional lady. 'You took my camera yesterday,' cried another. 'And my *best* binoculars,' squeaked a portly professional gentleman rotating a *Daily Telegraph* umbrella, 'the ones I brought for the Great Crested Grebe!' .

'The police will be here DIRECTLY!' triumphed the first lady. 'George has a phone in his car!'

The three largest characters attempted to clutch us. We had no intention of being clutched, and the Apprentice unslung ironmongery for this unexpected pitch. They halted, but all hope of a brawl faded when a white car purred to a halt on the road above and a lithe figure leapt out, saluted the occupants and strode down to us.

Our assailants, hopeful of police, gazed expectantly.

'Ah, got back before me after all,' cackled the Doctor benignly. 'We had a puncture. Damned wet job – and some fool nearly ran me over. But lucky I was there: the three old dears were quite helpless. But most generous' – he extended a large box of fine chocolates through the bucketing rain –

'Your friends like some, too?'

# A SPONSORED WALK

I suppose we did ask for it. The previous day we had forced a rather extempore new line on Sgòran Dubh, between Bachelors' Buttress and Married Men's Buttress, which the Doctor wished to call Unwedded Bliss and the Apprentice, Birth Control. An unsavoury argument early next morning was resolved by the Doctor suddenly exclaiming:

'Lord! I promised to meet Sandy at Corrour Bothy this afternoon... He's there with his family: wife, and baby twins. You know', he added apologetically, 'they all go out together. He *does* that kind of thing....'

We were tied to the Doctor's transport at Derry Lodge that night, and Sandy Oliphant – though somewhat tiresome about birds, beasties, kiddie-widdies and other good causes – offered what then seemed a wholesome change of subject. We had reservations about babies – and sprogs generally – and Sandy Oliphant displayed a weakness for organising Young Folks' Festivals, Bairns' Bus-trips and so forth. His house rocked to merry cries over Hallowe'en and most of the year it clapped and cheered with Parties. We shuddered. 'But he won't have much scope at Corrour', the Doctor pointed out, 'and he'll be extra careful, with the babies: it's their first trip.' So we meekly followed him out of Glen Einich. It was our last day, anyhow.

In the hot sun we foolishly preferred to grind round the north end of the Lairig rather than grill over the tops.

We struck the track quite low down, above what had evidently been a vast recent encampment. Despite a memorably dry summer, the place was flattened in mud and the path a quagmire. Huge clarty holes; hundreds, thousands of scampering footprints.

We had long been wary of popular solitudes and the Lairig seemed as trampled as a Serengeti overspill. We gaily identified deep prints of wildebeest and striped ones of zebras. 'Migration,' explained the Doctor. 'Lots of people use it now; camping each end, and in the middle at Corrour. Those in Braemar want to get to Aviemore; those in Aviemore have a passion for Braemar. Perfectly natural. Other side of the fence. Like the three Tailors that New Year's Eve.' (They had danced a reel in Rothiemurchus and went on to dance one in Braemar; a stone on the hillside, *Clach nan Taillear*, marks their final set....)

More than three tailors made this mess. We pictured the hapless conservationists and path-restorers sweating with shovels, crowbars, creosoted beams and plastic netting, while helicopters sprayed hundredweights of Ecological Seed about them.

'Natural erosion,' averred the Doctor. 'Should be left to take its course. If it discourages people, so much the better; negative feedback. Dynamic ecosystem.'

'Positive bloody feedback,' objected the Apprentice, clambering out of one particularly unsavoury pothole, filled with the droppings of what seemed a hundred deer. We were argumentative that day, even in so peaceful a scene; which, after the flinty obliquities of the Buttress, appeared an oasis – a morass – of Innocence.

'Strangely quiet,' unwisely observed the Doctor.

A subdued twittering ahead grew louder. Then the Apprentice leapt back from the next hole, just at the summit. Three – not tailors but – little girls, climbed out the other side and waved him on.

'That's a bad one; but the next's *much* worse!' they informed him happily, plastered in mud. They wore summer shoes and dresses. Huge fun.

When we struggled out and joined them we could see far down the Lairig. 'My God!' exploded the Doctor, as near Aghast as I have know him.

There appeared an endless string of small children, smaller children, large ones, bobbing and dipping all the way down the astonished defile. Gesticulating taller figures galloped alongside, endeavouring to exhort, extract or admonish their charges. A bright bubbling of sound, as from a moorland burn, punctuated by agitated whaup-like whistles. Hundreds of 'em. Thousands.

'I told you we should have called it Birth Control,' said the Apprentice bitterly. 'I expect they're all going to see your Mr Oliphant....'

'Yes, we *are*! Are *you*?' cried one of the trio now trotting and jumping beside us, fuelled inexhaustibly by pocketfuls of Mars Bars and the like.

'*You're* going to see Sandy?' asked the Doctor in disbelief. 'Sandy Oliphant?'

'Oh, is that his name? What a lovely name! Maggie, Mr Oliphant's name's Sandy! Mister, what's Mrs Oliphant's name?'

'And the Baby Oliphants' names?' squeaked up the smallest and grubbiest, yanked along by Maggie. 'What's the Baby Oliphants' names?'

'Er, Betty... is his wife's; and... I don't remember those of the children....' stuttered the Doctor helplessly. He indicated the vociferous files in front: 'Are you *all* going to see the Oliphants?'

'Oh, yes, Oh yes, ALL of us! That's why we're here.'

'Gey popular family,' muttered the Apprentice. 'Do *we* have to go? I don't think they'd miss us,' he added.

Further enquiry elicited the whereabouts of the Oliphants, who acted as a communal Pied Piper for all the bunch. They were assembled down at the front, at a Camp, the second of three along the route. Yes, the whole family – the babies had curly hair, they were twins, it was their first trip. They'd brought everything with them – big, big sacks of food, buckets to wash with, trunks to carry things in.

'A bit overdoing it,' mused the Doctor. 'Even with two sprogs a couple of extra rucksacks should be enough. But Sandy never does things by halves. And there's all this mob. It'll be Corrour, as he said. I expect this is one of his Sponsored Walks. Good job the weather's fine.'

But *what* a mess. What a smell. They had churned up years of Cervid sewerage. 'Like a monkey house,' sniffed the Apprentice. We took to the braes above for easier going, and overtook rapidly.

An astonishing sight – as far as you could see, milling, billowing, bouncing heads. Around, above them, fluttering in the gentle July breeze, a myriad butterflies of sweetie papers.

The braes got rougher, so we ran alongside and pushed our way through. Scouts, Rovers, Guides, Boys' Brigadiers, all the Responsibles, barked up and down the plowtering lines, keeping everyone safe.

'There's three away at the very back: Maggie and pals,' the Doctor informed one hyper-active young citizen, who thanked him profusely and cantered rearward, dispersing the corries with his three-tone whistle.

We were now jammed, moving desperately slowly; they had overflowed both banks. Then we spied, perspiring past, be-ribboned with whistles and compasses, maps, first-aid and a walkie-talkie, none other than Evergreen Smith – it was, after all, his kind of circus. We heard Doggie encouraging him above even this racket, with frantic mud-entangled yapping somewhere among the feet.

The Doctor roared, and grabbed Evergreen – or, rather, slightly delayed him *en route*.

'Sandy Oliphant, Sandy Oliphant, is he at Corrour?'

Evergreen pulled free, trotting backwards at great hazard, patting small erratic heads and reassembling his cords and cables, sadly deranged by the Doctorial clutch. Before plunging away again he gasped out:

'Sandy? No, he's not here, the kids have got chicken-pox. They've *all* got chicken-pox....'

Not here. Chicken-pox. What the, how the...

'The Oliphants have got chicken-pox!' repeated the incredulous Doctor loudly, stopping dead and being pushed on again from behind. 'Did you hear that – the Oliphants have got *chicken-pox!*'

A long officious individual did hear this. He in turn grabbed the Doctor. His spectacles flashed alarm.

'Chicken-pox? Chicken-pox?'

'Yes, they've got chicken-pox. Just found out. Most unfortunate for the kids.'

The officious one's mouth opened. Then it clamped firmly on to a whistle, a really LOUD whistle, for he was an important man.

*Blast! Blast!* said the whistle.

Pandemonium. Some officials were still urging the procession on, others trying to hold it back, crying 'Chicken-pox, chicken-pox, the Oliphants have got chicken-pox! Everybody stand back, everybody stand back!'

We scrambled ashore and sat on a large stone to eat our pieces. The tide about us rose and fell. Flotsam was flung out, reabsorbed. Screams and tears. Fighting. Clawing. Most distressing – and quite, quite incomprehensible. Why the panic about chicken-pox when Sandy's crew wasn't even there? When it was lying bespotted somewhere in Edinburgh?

The sea had fallen to a sullen murmur and we elbowed, chewing the last crust, through its weeping mass – a damp distasteful progress – towards Corrour. At least *there* someone ought to know. More holes. Worse smells. Great lumps of deer dung. This was – or had been – Corrour meadow.

We peered through heads and arguments at the distant Bothy. Beside it were pitched four large igloo tents, two of them huge. Obviously for the Committee. They were festooned with guys and with things hung over them to dry. People milled about them. Someone actually scrambled up the largest one and sat unsteadily on its top. He waved his arms. Everybody waved their arms. Cheers above the lamentations.

A tremendous trumpet call. Another. Flags were brandished. Wild cheers.

As bad as the Queen's Birthday; a sort of Corrour Gathering.

Trumpets again. Paper streamers.

The tents shuggled.

Then they moved, and began walking away.

Walking away....

It dawned.

Elephants....

Not Oliphants.

Elephants. In the Lairig Ghru. I suppose we should have guessed. The Doctor was with us that day. Elephants in the . . . .

Of course, it took time. But eventually all were reassured. The elephants had not got chicken-pox. Everybody was safe. Maggie, Tottie & Co. met Sandy. Had a ride on him and on a baby with curly hair. It took time, and was very late, midsummer dark, before the mob was counted, fed and put into their tents; and before the elephants, feet bathed and now unbound from miles of safety bandage, had peace to pack helicopters-worth of hay into their trunks. But it was all for a Good Thing, this 'Operation Hannibal' (as the organisers christened it); for the R.S.P.C.A., P.D.S.A., Dogs' Homes, Cats' Homes, Birds' Homes. And they were tolerant, kindly beasts.

Not so the Apprentice, faced with a long dark walk to Derry Lodge, demanding in righteous rage who would pay for repairing the paths, who would pick up all the paper, who would thank heaven – most devoutly – that the weather had stayed fine, who the devil – he appealed to the very place where Auld Nick had made his point – had dreamed up such an earth-destroying, sprog-endangering, elephantastically crack-pated scheme...?

The Doctor sighed, and handed another snoring brat to an official.

'Sandy Oliphant, I expect. He does that kind of thing.'

# CLIMBING AGAINST TIME

One by one we heaved ourselves over that most satisfying sun-warmed dolerite, and relaxed upon dry gravel and wet spring snow. We had made our own way to the top of a fine broken buttress; no particular route, just moderate mixed May mountaineering, ropeless and relaxed.

'You can't beat a simple off-piste line,' yawned the Doctor, stretching luxuriously before the wet seeped through, and ostentatiously pushing back the shingle with clinkered heels and gleaming tricounis. And certainly, on a climb like this, those nails (as the Apprentice and I had demonstrated every few cursing minutes) were much superior to our vibrams; we had left front-pointers in the car, for such a route in such weather would have meant either expensively blunting them or infuriatingly wooing them on and off our boots every couple of yards. 'A delightfully unconstrained few hours of exploration,' he purred, shifting to a dry patch and unwrapping the pieces, 'Just what the Old Boys did, in those gone-for-ever take-it-easy uncomplicated Golden Days. Wish we could join them for a bit. Too late now.'

We indulged him, for today was indeed a contrast. Our last meeting, two weekends before, had been in England, watching the Apprentice – as one of a team of Weasels – sweating through a highly-publicised highly-prized Sport-Climbing Competition in the Galactoramic All-Star Sports Hall at Grabsworth. He had done such things before, even at Bercy, but had kept his secret, as others hide their loot of Munros. Now, however, being expert (flashing a 5.12d) he had shyly asked us down to cheer him on. Which we did; though finding the whole performance somewhat odd. Through floodlights, spotlights, TV harnesses and an amplified rockfall from some incessantly detonated Group, we watched competitor after competitor assault the craftily-contrived wall. Its successive pitches billowed upwards in different colours, each one heliotropically advertising its own commercial sponsor. At the very top, above the overhang, it surged to silver, then gold.

A loud bell proclaimed the conquest of every crux, rising to electronic whoopee at the (very rare) final victorious few metres. Applause roared continuously, the commentator bellowed incoherently, figure after bronzed figure clad in lurid pants or imaginatively-stretched bikini sleuthed its way up by unbelievable exudations of strength, gymnastics and willpower. The Doctor especially enjoyed cheering the speed-climbing event – 'a kind of uphill slalom' – in which our companion, normally so deliberate, to his own surprise came as high as second, behind a greasy-haired barefooted young streaker in a purple nylon jockstrap.

But today, far from the smoke, sweat and financial sledgehammers, we could breathe again, in peace. We crushed cool sugary snow in our fingers and drank hot sun through half-closed eyes.

'Yes, this is a Sport. That was a Game. Fun, but just a Game.'

He handed round the pieces and beamed at us. While we chewed, he twirled his ridiculous waist-high axe, his only accessory that blissful day. He always liked to rub in the fact that he had climbed a few years nearer Raeburn than we had. 'A Wall has only two dimensions, a mountain has three; but mountaineering, you know, has *four*.' Twirl.

The Apprentice, like myself, had brought a little hammer-pick, just in case, and eyed the Doctorial weapon distastefully. 'No harm, I suppose, on a scramble like this,' he conceded, 'but bloody murder in a modern gully,' and jerked his head at one beneath us on our left. The Doctor, about to estimate – to the nearest millennium – the age of that particular geomorph, suddenly held up his hand.

'There's somebody coming up it!' We crawled and peered over.

It was not a very fierce gully. Nor modern. Just messy. Frozen mossy chock-stones, a descending gloom of aged snow and a few testy wrinkles of fairly senile ice. Its cornice, though, was of good classical architecture. We saw no one; but voices, and apparently a song, floated up from below. A grimy hole. Certainly not worth singing about.

We followed the ridge round until we could see into the gully. Yes, people were there. Four of them, roped nose-to-tail. Even at this distance we noticed the leader brandishing a long Doctorial axe. The others were gravely moving up, a step at a time. They had reached the last, icy, pitch below the cornice. They assembled there, and appeared to tie to a half-buried axe (even the Doctor was astonished – 'Damned primeval technique, no Dead Men, no ice peg!'). Then, to our complete amazement (the Doctor passed his binoculars round excitedly) one of them knelt down, another stood on his back, and a third – somehow –

clambered over them both and was raised aloft, one foot on an axe held by the second and one foot scraping on to another axe he had driven into some icy fissure. Striking up with his own axe he surmounted the crux by knees and a wriggle ('Must be tweeds', whistled the Doctor, 'otherwise he'd slide off.'), rapidly cut steps up the slope above, and crouched beneath the cornice. Another axe was passed to him by rope, he drove it in as a belay, flogged the cornice on to his companions (we heard their gusts of laughter...), then he stuck it horizontally into the now merely-vertical cornice, hauled himself up and, using it as a step and his own axe as a hook – just walked out of the gully. He lay flat on the top, recovered the second axe, tied it on, sent it down to his companions, marched well away from the edge, belayed, and brought the rest up. They emerged one by one on a tight rope some 20 feet apart.

It resembled a comic strip, a sick TV show, or an early Club photograph. 'Bloody acrobats!', declared the Apprentice, 'must have forgotten all their gear: pegs, runners, everything. What a shambles!'

But it had not looked a shambles. It had looked oddly business-like. They stood together at the top, unroping and dusting themselves. Their leader fished out a bottle and passed it round. Another pulled out a flask, and handed that round. Then – they shook hands. Shook hands.... And, mercifully, trooped away out of sight.

'Certainly,' concluded the Doctor, 'not a Modern Gully, if you can climb it that aboriginal way – 1880's, I should say.' But the climbing had appeared so simple; no primitive gropings or scrabblings. The Apprentice repeated that it had been a shambles. 'Serve 'em right if they get caught out some day, bashing on without proper equipment. Just lucky.'

Enough.... We had our own day to continue. We took in a sharp little knob to the north, above a long not very steep slope to the road, moving fast, as the weather had deteriorated. At the top, winter returned with a violent north wind, freezing us off quickly enough. Almost too quickly; for we found our descent to the road suddenly solid. It bared occasional black teeth amongst its now fish-blue iron-hard *névé*. Our vibrams were most unhappy; they shook and slithered alarmingly; would not kick steps or even scratch.

Then the blizzard hit us, driving Arctic particles about our unseen uncontrollable boots. The Apprentice and I pecked ineffectively at the slope with our baby axes; as we bent down to its gentle angle, our feet prepared to levitate. We clung. We swore. We would have to descend fifteen hundred feet sideways in socks or suchlike, it seemed, a metre a minute.

Fortunately, we had the Doctor with his despised axe. He darted about beneath us, trikes biting, and poked the pick around, winkling, slicing, carving, chopping, hacking, *willing* steps for our independently-sprung footwear. At times he fielded our feet and planted them in.

We knew we had sinned. That we should at least have brought our usual emergency line. But it was the month of May (with, alas, weather as eponymously uncertain) and a gentle slope (when we were, alas again, equipped for a steep one). So, holding each other's hand touchingly, with many a bitter oath the Apprentice and I side-stepped down, the Doctor beneath us active as some lightning conductor of the Fifth.

Of course we were bound to reach the road safely. Had not the Apprentice flashed to 5.12d? Had not he shone at Grabsworth? Were not his disengaged hand and mine clutching hammer-picks that would (if they could reach it) hook irresistibly into this next hour of glass and iron? But it would take so long. And we were so slow, and so cursed cold.

Then out of the whiteness behind us sped four figures. Skiing! No; glissading.... almost as improbably. Four tall, erect figures, their breeches and stockings unbent, their long axes – longer than the Doctor's – flicking expertly behind them.

They swung in beside us with hearty greetings. They must be the gully-climbers.

'Ha, deuced foul weather, what?' They paused, surprised, summing up our embarrassing predicament.

'I'm afraid', confessed the Doctor, gallantly sharing our blame, 'we're not really properly equipped for it....'

They looked at each other. 'No matter, no matter! We'll put you right directly!' cried the beardiest one. They all displayed white-encrusted balaclava-beards. They all looked perfectly at ease. They all wore massively-clinkered Brenva-demolishing boots.

We had little time to gape, for a rope was rapidly produced and tied – tied – round the two of us with expert knots. No jangling. We gripped it thankfully; it felt rough and hairy, stiff as a cable. We were joined to the massive anchorman behind us by a slender flexible shining one:

nylon presumably, ages old no doubt.

The Doctor turned and gazed at it with fascination as we continued jerkily down. 'Lord, it's silk... *silk*! Haven't seen one outside the Alpine Club rooooms....' He shot off downwards, having been butted by a backside-sliding Apprentice who had also, foolishly, turned to look. I followed.

With separate twangs, the Apprentice and I were arrested, amid joviality. 'Those little hammery things could be useful in some tiny gully, no doubt, but jolly old death on a big slope like this!' boomed our anchorman as he tugged us up. After that, we were lent two of their axes.

Mercifully soon, we reached the road. The sky cleared. The four, sheathed in frozen snow reinforced by a mattress of tweed, wool and whiskers, skilfully unroped us, passed round a silver-mounted hip flask, patted us paternally on the back and began to stalk off, coiling their creaking rope.

We tried to thank them and the Doctor, pointing to his car, offered a lift. Not at all, it had been Capital Fun; and their own transport lay just up the road. They vanished, with deep laughter, in which we did not join.

The Doctor shook off plaques of ice against the car and breathed on his key to thaw it. His passengers needed a strong drink for reassurance, so we drove to the nearby small hotel. We hoped to find another subject for conversation at the bar.

As soon as we stopped, one presented itself.

Bicycles. A gleaming heap by the door.

Mountain bicycles? No. 'Lord, what extraordinary contraptions!' The Doctor prodded them. Solid black monsters, with huge frames and long heads. The Apprentice, glad to shine on a day like this, polished his cycling lore and pronounced them of very old pattern – 'Late 1880's, early 1890's – and that one's just like an original Rover Safety.' We marvelled. Two of them sprouted brackets on the forks – these were fixed-wheelers, the Apprentice explained; you rested your feet there, going downhill. And look at that saddle!

We perceived that our marvellings were under scrutiny. A youngish fellow, tankard in one hand, pipe in the other. With a racing-handlebar moustache and knickerbockers of immaculate brown tweed – as were his tightly-buttoned Norfolk jacket and his cap. His ebony brogues dazzled us.

Apologies. 'Not at all. Delighted you find them of interest.' A fruity southern voice, with a firm background of stocks and shares. He quaffed, and puffed, and continued to regard us.

The Doctor hazarded: 'A cycling meet, eh?'

Puff. 'No.' Quaff.

Then, just within the door, we noticed a pile of ice axes – long, long handles and small heads. And coils of rope – hairy manila; and silk – again.

We stood and stared. Most rudely.

Our acquaintance removed his pipe and revealed a smile.

'Excuse our curiosity,' apologised the Doctor once more, indicating the axes and ropes – and boots, huge boots, far out-clinkering his own. 'but, unfortunately, you don't see many of those things today....' He then recalled that we had – indeed fortunately – seen several of those things less than an hour ago.

'Oh? I suppose it depends on who you happen to be.' A tone of amiable hauteur; and after a prolonged swig, the pipe was replaced. Still a direct gaze.

We realised what was lacking, and introduced ourselves. We shook hands. We learnt his name; familiar, but we couldn't place it. He explained that this was, in fact, a climbing meet. A meet, indeed, of the V.M.G.

V.M.G. The Doctor guessed. 'The Vintage Mountaineering Group! Excellent idea!'

'No, not quite. Almost correct, my dear fellow: but 30 years out. Not Vintage; I'd suggest that you' – he pointed his pipe-stem at the Doctor – 'you yourself are about Vintage.' He surveyed the Doctor's tweed hat, jacket, breeches, and nailed boots. 'Tricouni.... Ah, tricouni have not yet been invented, I'm glad to say. They are rather *contrived*, wouldn't you admit? Almost as much as that Eckenstein Spike. Not really Sporting – not sufficiently what you'd call in-communion-with-the-rock to be *satisfying*, don't you think?'

The pipe was replaced, alongside the smile.

('Communion with the rock,' muttered the Doctor, 'what does he want – bare feet?') However, the Apprentice, now geared to the motoring wavelength, took over from his extinguished companion. 'The Veteran Mountaineering Group!' he cried.

Our acquaintance winced a little. 'We don't in fact *approve* of that as a description,' he admitted ruefully, shaking his pipe free of emotion, 'Indeed, yesterday some of us cycled 20 miles each way to our mountain....' Certainly, he looked young and damnably fit, his hair and handle-bar glossily black. 'We prefer to be known as The Victorian Mountaineering Group.'

Just then, the gravel behind us scritched frighteningly, as four more great bicycles arrived. Their riders leapt off, swathed in ropes and rucksacks; they unwrapped long axes from the cross bars. Our rescuers, no less. Their own transport.

More people emerged from the hotel, in clouds of pipe and cigar smoke, billows of whisker and tweed, giving forth gruff and hearty welcome. With that, and further cries behind us of 'Capital, capital! My word, a fine little gully, to be sure!' it was like reading an old club journal, or an article by Campbell. Bemused, we tried to push through for our drink, now more necessary than ever.

'Ah, excuse me – the *public* bar is round at the side,' demurred our first acquaintance, directing us with his pipe. 'I fear the saloon is booked for the Group.'

Disconsolate, we were preparing to advance a hundred-odd years to the left, when one of the rescuers spotted us.

'Oh, but you must come in and celebrate our joint mountain; a first-rate Descent like that deserves something special, I do declare!'

This was a great honour. The V.M.G. were highly exclusive. Understandably so, for our torn and garish terylene and brassy zips appeared uncommonly vulgar (as they would have termed it) among the rich steamy heather- and deer-dung-textured tweediness that milled about us inside, guffawing, puffing and swallowing, shouting and singing, great feet stamping continual approbation. Only the Doctor – in a thin minor machine-stitched key – was passable, at an uneducated glance.

But our rescuers continued to bring us down safely to the Nineteenth Century. We sat at a table with them, feeling like small children who had done wrong, been forgiven, and were being allowed to stay up late with the grown-ups.

They answered our questions frankly enough. Oh they were all able to climb modern routes, if they wanted to. Some of the younger members had been international celebrities. But on their own meets, they aimed for the simple excitement of the old days, when climbing was unusual and those few who visited the hills were Gentlemen and obeyed the Rules, and dressed decently and unobtrusively. We became itchingly naked again. The Apprentice, irritated beyond endurance, unwisely pointed out that modern clothing is sooner spotted by Rescue Teams. Ah, but Rescue Teams – they smiled disarmingly – would not be needed if the Rules of the Sport were observed... (We felt too crushed to enquire if those Rules permitted three people combining tactics on an ice-pitch with one axe as belay.) No, the V.M.G. spared no effort to recapture the antique joy, they wore specially-made clothes, used specially-made equipment, rode specially-made bicycles, sported specially-grown or specially-stuck-on beards and moustaches, spoke a specially-learnt language. We thought it most tedious; Ham, in fact. But they swore that once you mastered the technique, then the enchantment and exhilaration surpassed anything you'd known on the hills before. Such Freedom, such Certainty. There was no going forward after that! Modern routes were just boring. Might as well be in a Sports Hall and do it for – money!

They met difficulties, of course. Mixing with the Contemporary Rabble eroded their own environment and provoked unseemly reactions from others. And so many things had changed for the worse. Trains no longer stopped at Highland stations, they did not accept bicycles any more, there were no Station Masters, hotels hardly ever gave decent service. Not that the V.M.G. journeyed often to North Britain, but it was the only part of Her Majesty's present dominions where they could frolic reasonably undisturbed. 'Imagine us at Harrison's or Cloggy, Langdale or Froggatt....' It had to be midweek, and out of season; today was a weekend, and see what had happened.... We drank deeper. Yes, they were mostly English, the true Romantics, but 'a few of your own club are with us, they keep it very dark of course; you'll recognise them, I'll be bound, because they won't *look* at you'; no, we had no heart to penetrate bashful and poorly-belayed beards.

North Norway was another venue. In that outback you could still do a Slingsby; but no wine, no whisky. The V.M.G. preferred the Alps, at secret vinous places with understanding inns, whence they would ascend remote and unlikely summits; the more skilful could climb right back to the 1850's, tackling peaks, passes and glaciers from goat-infested and herbicide-free *gîtes*. No, they did not use alpenstocks or ladders; nothing *silly*. And guides? Today's *führer* was most uncooperative, but porters, you could still hire porters, they were still very droll; why, only last season, old Josef...

We interrupted hastily. 'Guidebooks, anyway, are sufficient these days.' But no, they never read guidebooks, not even the latest John Ball: they *explored*. They perused little in the *Alpine Journal*, either, certainly

not after volume IX, when the rot was clearly setting in – that American, Coolidge; that dog, Tschingel; that bounder, Mummery. . . . 'But what about Harold Porter?' put in the Doctor, anxious not to appear too illiterate a Modern, 'He possessed the old spirit!' 'Precisely – and had to steam off every year to New Zealand to enjoy it. He was just greasy-poling in Europe; New Zealand in the twenties was fortunately even more backward than your Scotland.'

Fortunately, too, a gong called. 'Dinner, Gentlemen, is served.' We rose, thanked our rescuers again. Shook hands, bowed. As we sought the door, our first acquaintance reappeared, whisky and soda in grasp. He addressed the Apprentice.

'I could have sworn I'd met you before, laddie. Now I remember. You came right behind me, did you not?'

The Apprentice stared, shook his head.

Our friend glanced over his shoulder, then quickly unclipped his moustache.

'O.K.?' Grin, greasy black hair.

'It's you – Davey Baker! Of all the...'

Davey Baker, the crack speed-climb merchant in a nylon jockstrap who had beaten the Apprentice at Grabsworth by ten whole seconds two weekends ago.

The moustache replaced, David Clayton-Baker, C.A., gravely shook hands with the Apprentice, bowed to us, turned about and rejoined the other gentlemen making their way with quiet satisfaction to the Dining Room.

'Humbugs, humbugs, pretentious and doctrinaire humbugs!' exploded the Doctor, safe in the driving seat. His pride had been as much injured as ours. 'More damnably devious mock-up and make-believe in that two-faced shower than ever at Grabsworth! Just a game, a Game. Pure Egoism. No feeling for the sport at all....'

We kept hard at it, restoring our self-conceit, until the traffic and fug outside Edinburgh. Never had the three of us so agreed. They were just to be pitied, they just couldn't face Modern Life.

'Sheer bloody escapism!' pronounced the Apprentice, in conclusion. 'Pathetic. Now, where shall we go, next weekend?'

# A RAVISHING WEEKEND

Well, this was D-day. We gazed across the waves. They snarled agreeably beneath our keen and thrusting prows. It was wonderful; and yet – so improbable. We were on a Seaborne Assault. A preemptive Strike. At dawn.

We were in canoes, approaching Rhum.

That weekend the Doctor and I had agreed to accompany the Apprentice to Eigg; a theoretical line up a photograph of the Sgùrr had tormented him too long. I was there to offer advice and assistance; the Doctor, to peer at fossilised pre-Tertiary landscapes and drop a top rope if necessary. We hired a motor boat from Mallaig to take us there Saturday morning, and return us too early on the Monday. The weather – necessarily – was idyllic: a long-established summer anticyclone, with no wind.

Alas, we found the Sgùrr draped with anti-idyllic Glaswegian hammerers. The Apprentice's route had long been trodden over, and even more fearsome Extremes were in screaming birth.

Sickening. We mooched over to the west coast and booted, from the singing sands of Laig, a musical feast which – meagre enough – was preferable to the one the Doctor threatened; for he had brought his pipes, and would mobilise three hundred vertical feet of basalt behind him to act as sounding board, and the whole western ocean to field his wandering grace-notes.

But Fate had intervened. We saw five splendidly fierce shark-like sea canoes drawn up on the sands, their crewmen lying alongside. Better still, the Apprentice knew one canoeist well, and the Doctor hailed another as nephew. While we prodded their beautiful beasts, they explained they had just circumnavigated Skye and were resting a couple of days – three of them in fact being unable to sit in a canoe again until Dame Nature had darned their backsides.

It was the Doctor, as usual, who inspired us. Just across the glittering sea rose the great war-peaks of Rhum – Askival, Allival, Ainshval, Barkeval, Trallval: marvellous Norwegian, Lochlanner, axe-clashing names.

We would storm them on a Viking raid. Collect all the big tops in one *fjell* swoop. We had longed to tread them, but the tiresome grovelling for permits and references had repelled us. Climbing was about Freedom, we assured ourselves. Of course, Rhum had long been attractively *Verboten*; the Doctor possessed an uncle who had lawlessly ravaged the peaks, paraded the village and bonfired the driftwood years ago in some dim Bulloughian past. But now, as a tight little island Nature Reserve, its smug monkish insularity appeared even less tolerable. Our few scruples vanished with the sun setting behind its blood-red six miles or so of defenceless water. Our fingers itched for a hilt. We would wrest the summits from those sanctimonious clerics, send them fleeing with their precious apparatus and manuscripts; we would bring Battle, Fire and Rapine. The pomp and panoply of State-Supported Science offered rich booty to Pirate Enterprise, more satisfying than the nineteenth-century leavings of some Lancashire cotton-bobbiner. It would be Nae Bother At Aa. Sure Thing. Thor would Rule O.K.

We were well qualified for Assault. The Apprentice had slalomed canoelets through Tay, Spey and Findhorn. I had paddled among detergents in the Firth of Froth. The Doctor, reputedly an expert with the Canadian variety, had (he said) descended the Mackenzie, even been in one of Vaillancourt's birch-barks; and, more relevantly, claimed to have out-kayaked a triple-rolling Sir Hector Macassar off Angmagssalik. No problem there.

Fortunately, the owners were equally enthusiastic. The two who could still turn another cheek to the job would accompany us as off-shore escorts – for safety. (Safety! On a Viking Raid...) We would start at dawn, be back victorious by evening.

We practised each in his own canoe, learning about tetchety rudders, about wave-slicing, and how to keep on continuous terms with 17-odd feet of mind-of-its-own thoroughbred. Hunters they were, not hacks; killer whales, to vary the necessary macho metaphor.

So here we were, then, the following morning, approaching Rhum. Cold, wet, with raw backsides; but our deadly dragon-headed galleys snaked purposefully, mercilessly, in. We avoided the bays of Papadil and Dibidil and chose a less conspicuous and more appropriate sandy inlet by the cliffs at Rudha nam Meirleach, Cape of the Thieves. Our escort tactfully dropped back, to paddle about a bit and meet us here later.

Our keels grated in an authentically sinister fashion. We sprang ashore, the Doctor catching his paddle between his legs and executing a vigorous and oath-splashing somersault, a display of virtuosity which terrified the natives, for not one was to be seen. We dragged our steeds up the turf and lashed them to old driftwood, in case of a great wave being engendered by the curse of some bathymetrically-minded cleric; and hid the paddles among the many boulders nearby.

We raced across welcome grass to Beinn an Stac, as exhilarated after our voyage as Leif Ericsson himself. Then up and along the wonderful spear-brandishing ridge from Askival to Ainshval, its gendarme falling swiftly to our arms. Below us, a super-Aegean blue of sea, and the emerald aircraft-carrier of Eigg. And right beneath our feet – the proper place – Kinloch Castle and all its accoutrements, clearly in a state of panic.

We roared and stamped and projected runic V-signs in victory, but did not work ourselves up – or down – sufficiently to descend in fury upon the prostrate inhabitants. We really had not time to go berserk if we were to get back to Eigg that night for the motorboat next morning. Still, we managed to bear off the nine prize peaks of the ridge, and ravished a few of the better-looking pitches on Ruinsival. No one else to be seen. The island had been ours. Our only near casualty was the Doctor's Low G finger, just missed by a stone from above, which the Apprentice denied came from him but was an Act of Odin – besides, bagpipes were instruments unworthy of a Viking; and anyway, why should the Doctor complain, what was a finger or two to a piper like himself?

Battle, Fire and Rapine – all except the Fire for, despite the beckoning accumulation of driftwood in the western cliffs, our only matches had been in the Doctor's back breeches pocket and he had sat for too long in too much water on the way across.

Regretfully law-abiding to that extent, we bounded down from above Papadil in the lengthening light. And then right in our path we saw a group of people gathered on the cliff edge, peering over. Around them lay instruments of various sorts and they were jabbering together angrily. Obviously monks. There were too many of them to kill effectively at the end of a tiring day; and, having pushed attack and foray so successfully all those hours, we did not welcome the indignity of being seized as trespassers. We would, Vikings though we indubitably were, prefer any confrontation to be delayed until we got between them and our – now agonizingly naked – vessels beneath.

We wrapped our rope in an anorak and skipped round behind them, bog to bog, until well below.

Then the Apprentice fell over a stone, and it echoed along the cliffs. Sixteen eyes swivelled upon us. More furious jabbering; shouts; and they plunged down.

They met us at the boats. They carried sticks and telescopic metal rods. They shook with emotion.

While they were getting their breath back, the Doctor seized his opportunity.

'Can we help you?' he enquired, sweetly. 'You seemed worried about something up there....'

They nodded. Their leader, no doubt some Abbot or other, broke out: 'You could be most useful.'

'We thought we might be,' flashed in our crafty companion, 'We were just off-shore.'

Outraged ghosts of Thorfinn Bloody-Fist, Magnus Bareleg, Harald War-Tooth, Ivar-of-the-Long-Reach, disowned us, turned away. Bargaining with, creeping before, vermin like that. Next thing, we should all be Converted. Christened B.Sc. or something.

'Have you, by any chance, a *rope*?' the worthy one enquired, clasping his hands together in appeal.

We sniffed a trap, to lure us into Confession. We fingered swords belligerently. The ghosts looked back, and brightened. But the Doctor cut in.

'We have our sea-line, if that'd be any use – we thought it might, you know, that's why we brought it ashore....' True; and he undid the camouflage.

Relief on both sides. Amicable chatter. It seemed there was a nest of the white-tailed eagle (*Halliaeetus albicilla,* no less) on these cliffs, not far indeed from Sròn na h-Iolaire, Eagle Point; one of Rhum's very own brood, the second generation of Norwegian colonists invited here by these same clerics we had just refrained from massacring. Two nests, in fact, side by side, extremely precious – the Abbot rolled up his eyes – but both at this minute endangered by a huge teetering lump of turf dislodged by some lay-brother in their party who had been erecting a tripod.

The Abbot implored us to lend him the rope and to tie a good sailor's knot in it so that he could be lowered to the impending turf. He was no climber but… his faith demanded any sacrifice.

We all of course jumped in: O but we were not much of climbers either but we did understand knots and ropes – seafarers, voyagers on great waters, needed to.

All this resulted in the Apprentice leading a quite fine upward traverse and, at its end, kicking the offending clod into the sea, just starboard of our returning escort. A pendulum back, and an abseil down.

Uplifted hands from the brethren (and a sister). Blessings and apologies showered upon us; although one (maybe the laybrother) had regarded the Apprentice's climbing skill with an unpleasingly knowing smile.

'They are so valuable, the little eaglets,' sighed the Abbot. 'We have suffered raiders here, too, you know.' We shifted uncomfortably, avoiding the laybrother's (squint) eye. 'Raiders, egg-thieves, who came by powerboat and ransacked our only three nests last spring…. So selfish – years of devoted work gone for nothing' – and he dropped his hands piteously.

'Shocking, shocking,' murmured our chief Viking, 'no decency whatever; can't understand it.' 'Vandals,' put in the Apprentice, still reeking of recent gore, 'bloody vandals.' 'Mean sods, do anything for loot,' we agreed.

Beside us, our longships turned on their keels in disgust, they began to slither back to the rising tide, would no longer bear such cowards, lily-lips, turncoats. We grabbed their prows; the dragons' heads had already vanished.

Worse was to come. We were invited back in Land Rovers to the Castle Canteen. And to a slide show on the Smaller Mammals of South East Asia.

We came to our senses. This was no right end to a Viking Raid. We demurred.

'O but of course you can stay at the Castle. We could take you over to Eigg, canoes and all, in the morning.' Etc., etc.

'Are you quite sure?' We were quite sure.

Handshakes – handshakes! – all round. We sauntered down as insolently heroic as we could, ground the pebbles beneath our heels, and strapped on a bravado of golden lifejackets. Then we began to launch our steeds: and remembered about the damned paddles. The Apprentice and I dashed back among the boulders where we had hidden them – but there were dozens of boulders.... The Doctor, struggling with three very restive half-floating charges – which had entangled their leads and now jumped up and down like excitable and enormously elongated Afghan hounds - shouted useless advice and splashed unhappily. All of which detracted from our former magnificence of departure. With curses and bruised knees the Apprentice and I leapt from slimy rock to slimy rock. The clerics looked on, bewildered. Then that unpleasantly-grinning laybrother detached himself, ambled to a further group of boulders, and reappeared with our paddles. They were behind a stone, he said. We thanked him (he should have been the first one slaughtered).

When we had unwound the various leads from each other, we stepped into our craft – which felt decidedly cool towards us – and thrust out over the winking Atlantic. We heard grateful prayers behind us, but never looked back. We warmed once more to self-respect and forged through the blood-boltered sun-setting surf towards our piratical lair, boasting to admiring escorts of the violent deeds done. We would feast that night to wild music, on sausages roasted black by a flaming primus, and drain whisky and McEwan's from polished skulls.

Which we more or less did. We lay – we avoided sitting – beside a blaze of driftwood after our feast, and swore that henceforth we should wield axe and pick with renewed vigour, hammer without mercy; that Haston was right, that there was nothing like freedom, absolute freedom from bourgeois values, to bring out the best in climbing.

Next spring we would be back for eggs.

# DROPPING IN

A classical early spring day. Blue sky, marble snow. And a classical early route – Y-Gully of Cruach Ardrain. The Apprentice, cured of boils on the backside (a relic of last year's Rhum trip) by a potently patent prescription of the Doctor's, agreed that the least we could do was to join our nostalgic friend on such a comfortably old-fashioned and uneventful climb; anyway, he preferred not to risk his newly-repaired upholstery just yet by any abrasive high-Grade contortions. A nice walk like this would do fine.

So we had ambled up in crampons, drinking in the clear air, and the Doctor had skipped along behind – not all that far behind – with axe and tricounis, whistling execrably. He was strapped into a huge rucksack – which carried skis – so his performance was the more commendable. But we had to rope him when it got steep.

Why the huge rucksack? Mystery. Why skis? Mystery... he surely did not intend to ski down Y-Gully! Not enough snow elsewhere. In Kandahar bindings – and he had brought no sticks.... Mystery, also, why our companion kept stopping – on bulges of verglas we carefully avoided – apparently to sniff the air and study the few (but increasing) white clouds that sailed above. Taking omens, we judged. Up to something.

The cornice was a large Edwardian mantelpiece, safe as in houses. We hauled up the damned skis, their purpose still darkly unexplained; if he wanted to ski the gully, we would just tie him up.

At the cairn the Apprentice and I dismissed the thought, and prepared for the usual Doctorial summit lounge. But no, he was hopping about, still sniffing, wetting his forefinger and holding it up; and casting paper from our jammy pieces into the air. We gently remonstrated, puzzled. And turned our attention to the great white distances of Black Mount, the vast sweep of Beinn Dòrain, and the piebald heads of Glencoe, Nevis and the Mamores above the haze.

Much rustling behind. We looked over our shoulders.

Heavens, what was this? He had disembowelled his rucksack and was shaking out an enormous multicoloured sleeping-bag affair, with strings like spiders' legs – a parachute-harness sort of thing.'

'Could you chaps stand and hold me down – on these ropes here – while I strap it tight? Got to be jolly careful to do the right thing, you know – can't abseil off an up-current....'

We paled. No, it was not a collapsible hang-glider. Nor a parachute for that Extreme Ski descent of Y-Gully. But a little of both, in fact: the Doctor was preparing to Paraglide....

We had watched practitioners of this hybrid craft the previous summer; and concluded that – as rain could collapse the para part – any gliding with such an assemblage in the Scottish hills would be rapidly down the vertical component. As for wearing skis as well.... Easy enough on Everest; but here....

The Doctor had secretly practised on expensive evenings through the unusually dry autumn. And now modestly claimed he would, 'Just nip off the top here, and see you down in the glen there – as near as the end of the snow and the start of the trees as possible. Of course, I could land sooner if I wanted to – just pull on these strings and close the tubes. But I'd like to make a record of it – the wind's dead right.' And, as he strapped and buckled and patted his harness ('doesn't come undone easily, I can tell you; this is a new type, won't let you out in a hurry – absolutely safe!'), he threw at us observations on thrusts, thermals, downdraughts, updraughts... and the rest of the airy fancies of his vaporous trade.

'The very thing for a *quick* descent. Better than simply skis, you don't need snow, you're quite independent of terrain. So restful. You just sit up there; all too briefly, I'm afraid. Marvellous if you could dangle for hours above a distant earth....' He prattled on.

It sounded convincing enough, but the immense vacuum in front of us and below did not appear to bear the weight of enquiry. We drew back.

'You chaps carry my sack and axe and things for me, will you? I'll wait for you down there, or walk up and meet you; don't be too long.'

He shuffled into his long Neanderthal skis. We two looked at each other.

The Doctor gathered the various strands we had been anchoring. 'Now, keep out of my way. I'll start from the cairn.'

We watched his improbable figure, ballooning in crinoline skirt and

Bedouin cloak, as it billowed about the cairn. Then, engines roaring, it turned into the slipstream from the cornice and began to slide towards the edge.

Unfortunately, some string or other caught on a boulder, and progress was dramatically halted.

Unravelled again, and oblivious of our by-now almost frantic pleas for him to give it up, be sensible, think of the rocks, think of the ice, he taxied rapidly past us once more.

As the air, miraculously, puffed into his counterpaning robes, his skating strides grew longer and more dreamlike; so that at the last of the Apprentice's admonitions – appropriately enough 'For Heaven's sake, come off it!' – he toed delicately from the cornice, fluttered alarmingly, and disappeared, like an inflatable double bed, into the abyss.

Then he reappeared to our aghast eyes, bumpiting upwards on a surge, spinning wildly like a long-legged frog in his harness. We ran to the edge. He was floating down again, perilously near the rock, his canopy plucking out loose stones, showers of them; then the hickory kicked a crag and he pushed off at last, alarmingly detached from Scotland.

Happily airborne. The fresh wind, now clearly north, caught him and he soared away, legs flailing like an excited heron, away into a wavering kaleidoscopic dot growing fainter and fainter. He went a hell of a distance, bundled along like litter. It seemed, too, as if one ski had come loose, dangling by a safety-strap.

A passing cloud engulfed us; the weather was deteriorating. When it cleared, he was out of sight. Well, he had passed airborne over the roughest part; and appeared to be safely delivered between Grey Heights and Stob Coire Bhuidhe, towards the snowy grass and green forests below. He might even have broken his record; though skis, legs or neck seemed likelier casualties.

The Apprentice and I picked up the luggage and jerked away down, almost in envy. We enjoyed a good stiff glissade, thigh-burning and tooth-loosening. Then, galumphing down slushy rushes and heather, we scanned the upcoming hectares for him or his heliotropic marquee – which should have been visible for miles, however tattered.

No sign. He must have landed, packed up, and walked down the

forestry tracks. We marched about them, hallooing. No answer. It was growing dark. We dropped to the car; nothing. To the hostel: nobody had seen a... parachutist – one with skis.... They stared at us strangely. We combed the rides again, shouting and cursing. Some hostellers, intrigued, joined us.

Darkness proved a blessing. We heard a cry and raced to it; it was a hosteller who had seen a light, up in the sky, moving. Not a star, not a comet – he studied astronomy, he knew. *There.* It glittered above a few vigorous hectares of 50-foot Sitka spruce. Was it the Doctor? Lord, was he *still* gliding?

We pushed closer. It was clearly waving; high up; far in the wood. Near the point of a leading shoot – or a leading ski. Stationary; he was anchored to something.

We sent down for billhooks, axes, long poles. All kinds of medieval Bannockburnian instruments trooped up; Crianlarich was agog. Plus a couple of incredulous forestry workers, power-sawed for snedding branches. We set to work – after filling in a form with name, rank and number of the astronaut, in case of injury to Commission employees.

He was amongst the upper whorls of a very aggressively-unshaven *Picea sitchensis*. He appeared inextricably entangled, skis, ski-bindings, great primary branches and infinite needles embracing his integument. It took two hours – and much of the tree – to get him down. By now a large torch-wielding crowd had assembled, and the lop-and-top was speedily cleared. The bird-watchers were particularly interested, all binoculars raised; but not a nest could be seen.

Considering he had achieved both his desires – a quick descent, and dangling for hours above a distant earth – the Doctor seemed subdued as he climbed stiffly down the last few branch-stubs, still in harness. The Apprentice had gathered up most of the arboreal knitting, and roped down through the flicker of torch-beams engulfed in it like a drifting jelly-fish, a midnight *Medusa*. The skis had been pushed down earlier, scraping through the Velcro of a million needles. Apparently the one dangling board had caught in the tree on the way over – 'Just as I was going so well, could easily have made the main road,' the Doctor had informed us from his eyrie, above the smoke and roar of power-saws.

Most of the delay stemmed from our companion's tiresome insistence on preserving as much of the costly integrity of his fabric as possible. Moreover, his extra-specially-secure buckles had jammed immovably shut with bits of twig and sliced needle; and the Doctor firmly opposed prising them open or cutting harness or cords – 'We rely absolutely on these things!' Wrapping his committee-sized toga about him, he strode off along the aisles of the forest through a cheering gallery of torches, like a wounded archangel, his trailing wings carried behind him by eager acolytes. The Apprentice, bearing aloft crossed skis, solemnly completed this hierarchical procession.

Disdaining emotional invitations to the hostel, where local theatricals were to be performed that night, we made for the car, after thanking our bushwackers and gilding the much-soured foresters. The Doctor was as embarrassed as we have seen him. He had particular reason that weekend to avoid Publicity. A colleague of his had, a few days earlier, been celebrated in the press and ridiculed by his profession for unseemly exhibitionist conduct – 'Daredevil Medical Flies Own Helicopter to Snowed-In Patient'; apparently all the patient had needed was a packet of paracetamol, and his doctor a set of winter tyres. Our companion was unusually scathing; we suspected he had himself been reminded about some of our own unhappily-reported misadventures in the past.

Anyway, he refused to drive, cocooned as he was, even if we draped his chrysalis over the seat behind him. 'Suppose some fool skidded into us – the roads are hellish slippery tonight.... bound to get in the papers.' He crawled into the back to pupate, until we had driven him to a fellow-enthusiast at Killin who had experience and tools for the job. I was picked to drive, for the north wind had brought quite a blizzard, and the Apprentice disliked the huge old Merc, even on good roads.

I disliked it on these roads. Despite hoarse encouragement from the shrouds behind, I manoeuvred its dour slithering Teutonicity with uneasy tenderness.

A few miles further, lights waved, and we slid to a halt. Accident. The Doctor groaned. We two clambered out. Apparently an ambulance coming up had met a skiing-bus going down, and both now reclined across the road, heads irretrievably in the ditch. No casualties fortunately, except the two ambulance men – shocked – and a doctor in his car following the ambulance, who biffed it heartily; and had already been despatched southwards dazed, nursing a broken arm, followed by the equally bemused ambulance men.

So... the road would be blocked a long long time. The Doctor was well wrapped up, but we all suffered hunger and rage. Curse, curse. Then, an anguished head appeared at the window. 'Nobody here a doctor?' It seemed very worried. 'Kitty's in bad trouble....' We recalled a previous discomfiture with a damned cat, and were about to explode with a further oath, when the unwilling and mummified Hippocrates in the back hushed us and asked for details.

Harrowing ones. Kitty, who lived in a cottage on the big estate opposite, was having trouble delivering her fourth bairn two weeks early. I shall spare the details, but clearly the half-asphyxiated semi-infant had to be freed; the local wise women could not disentangle it, and the phoned-for Rescue Party – doctor and ambulance – had been effectively wiped out by the Denny, Dennyloanheid and Dunipace Cooperative Wholesale Society Rambling and Ski Club bus on its way to an evening ceilidh at Killin. Speed was vital.

I wearily urged the bucketing beast up the track to the cottage. We stuck halfway, and the Doctor – good soul – staggered out in his acreage of nighties into the blast; then – O most excellent soul and to the wonder of the milling crowd of locals (it was a flourishing estate, for once) – he flashed out a knife and cut his own cords....

The – I suppose – afterbirth billowed into the throng, whose smaller fry seized it joyfully. 'Look after it, now! I need it again!' – and we three trudged to the cottage.

No need to describe further. Our companion is proficient at obstetrics (as he needs to be, with his kind of mountain tent) and soon had the little stranger out of his predicament and into the steaming basin-slopping back bedroom. A loud howl announced success to us outside the door. Fine boy. We two were then regaled most alcoholically by delirious father, uncles and other thirsty next-of-kin; while the Doctor dilated within to assembled amateur midwives. Mr Bruce was so hospitable that the Apprentice soon could scarcely converse coherently, certainly not stand.

So that when the inevitable happened an hour or so later – after a splendid meal cooked by multiple aunts – and a pack of police and journalists flooded in, the Apprentice was seized for interview: the Doctor, horrified, had locked himself up, and I was being harangued by some hugely protective neighbour – 'Jist you be keeping yerself awaay from those kind o fellies, now... they're aall lies!'

The reporters had met crowds of sprogs parading about under the moon (all snow had ceased) with a Parachute. It was the one the New Doctor had come in! He was going to use it again! He always came in it! The journalists had photographed the held-up contraption from all angles, and now desired words from the intrepid aviator. They were baying with delight.

Even they could not mistake the boozed Apprentice for our worthy companion, but – hungry for bread – they took, alas, their Story from his grievously disconnected discourse.

Under such circumstances it is possibly understandable, almost excusable, if Kitty Bruce becomes confused with Sitka spruce. And that the graphic description of our friend's inextricable landing from 2000 feet on top of the latter, grows irresolvably entangled with his dramatic release of the former.

So much so, that – while the less mendacious newspapers next day carried the story of how gallant Doctor ____ (full name) had parachuted down through a blizzard to deliver a baby – their more imaginative fellows described how Dr ____ had not only parachuted down to deliver a baby (a feat he performed throughout the Highland winter) but had delivered it at the top of a 50-foot conifer.

And how did his name get out? Ask, maybe, the forestry workers, who had howked and hacked about him long enough: for – maybe again – insufficient reward.

Anyway, he has not yet been back to measure his long-distance Record. The other one scaled 8½lbs.

# A KINDRED CLUB

We hadn't climbed together for some time. The Apprentice had taken to collecting ('knocking off' was his injudicious term) frozen waterfalls; I, preferring ice cooked a little longer, joined some friends to gather as many Nevis gullies as we could in 24 hours; the Doctor – on his only patient-free weekend – streaked across a dissolving last stage of the *Haute Route Ecossaise* (version No. 6) between one thaw and the next, completing at last that very fluid itinerary. So we all felt sufficiently well-fed and self-satisfied to enjoy together a simple unclimbed Grade II up one of the few subsidiary Tops still unbitten by Doctorial tricounis. A final snack, a mere Munro mint, after those more demanding statistical orgies.

On the way down we passed a loch, frozen and snow-covered.

'Good Lord, there's a tent on it.' So there was. 'Damned fools. I suppose they *know* it's a loch....'

We went over. The Doctor shook his head. 'They'd get a shock if a thaw came. Or a Water-Horse.' (It was the winter after our West Highland haunting, and he was still somewhat sensitive to the paranormal).

The flaps were open. We looked in. Heavens!

There was a great hole in the floor. Flakes of ice lay round it; and, in it, black water licked thirstily.

The evidence was horrifyingly clear: a sleeping bag crumpled beside it, a primus that cooked the last meal beyond it, a rucksack spilled in the corner; and an ice axe, glazed with ice, overhanging the edge.

'Fallen through! He'd tried to climb out with the axe, but just broke off more of the edge. Soon chilled in this water....'

Dreadful. Nothing we could do now. The Apprentice poked his axe down; but met only welcoming gurgles. We straightened, and looked about helplessly. There were footprints all round: presumably his companions – we had noticed tents further down the hill – had tried to assist. Maybe they had pulled him out, here or elsewhere.

Then we saw a figure approaching through the dusk. 'One of the rescue team!' His walkie-talkie aerial bobbed importantly as he plowtered across.

He was a cheery cove, considering. His red face beamed from an eiderdown of jackets. Perhaps they *had* been successful.

'Any luck?' the Doctor asked him, suitably serious.

'Nane at aa. I've been round the shore, breakin it up' – here he brandished a kind of alpenstock – 'not a sign. So I'll just awa into the tent and drum up; and wait. There's always hope. There's always tonight and tomorrow.'

We gaped. The Doctor was shocked. 'He'd need to be a *fish* for you to get him out alive by then,' he exclaimed severely, but humouring the fellow's levity.

'He would so. Or back he goes in!'

This was too much, even for Survival Euphoria. The Doctor, biting his lip – after all it was his trade, or would have been had we got there earlier – asked if others beside our rather too equable acquaintance were on the lookout: 'for a bite,' he added, as further reproof.

'Aye, there's Andy down at the big loch, and Chairlie on the wee lochan up top. Nae luck yet, any o 'em.'

We swayed. Three people looking for three different campers fallen through three different lochs. No....

Then we saw the aerial was a fishing rod.

Things became clearer, though scarcely more probable.

Inside the tent, carefully round the hole, down which our friend – Boab – had now slipped his line for the night, we snuggled together, drank scalding tea laced with some breath-stopping rum-like liquor, and were regaled with the story of the S.M.A.C. – the The Scottish Mountain Angling Club.

Its members fished lochs – only lochs, mind, rivers and burns were a different thing altogether – lochs, as high as they could. The higher, the better. For the higher the loch, the more difficult it became: less fish, and more crafty – 'No so easy taken in.' But they had to be fish. Other things, you threw back.

They possessed a list – Topwater's Tables, they called them, after some probably legendary map-scouring old member – of all the separate mountain lochs over 1000 feet in Scotland; and a subsidiary list of the wee lochans ('aye, an some o *them*'s the best'). The joy lay not only in catching your fish – trout, char, eel or whatever – but in ticking off the lochs, the Topwaters, you caught them in. *That* made it really popular –

'gave you something to bite on.' The experts could go very high, with special equipment; alloy gaffs and landing nets, high altitude lines and baits – high-flies in fact: not the low-country Hecham Pechams, not the Black and Blae, but the latest Goretex ones, Neviscast, K2-Killer, Mustagh Toorie, Messner's Indispensable, Bonington's Glory, McInnes' Raised Hackle.... Some people would try anything to catch higher.

For it wasn't the weight or the length of the fish that counted for the S.M.A.C. – it was the height. And very few exceeded 2500 feet, Boab told us. But Andy, Andy had catched a fine little 3721-footer that very summer in Lochan Buidhe above Loch Avon. They measured in feet because feet seemed higher than metres – the idea of 'Bathymetros' was nonsense. Or fathoms – fathoms went down, not up. Feet was the logical thing. It was great, collecting Topwaters. They had another list, of who had done what lochs. They were starting furth of Scotland, too.

There seemed no end to this piscatorial puerility.

'But surely,' argued the Doctor, aware of Sin, 'surely you'll get some characters taking up fish specially to stock a high loch previously uncli-, uncaught-in?'

'Ah, that's Artificials. That's no fair. You've to fish free, or with a proper aid. Anyway, if you cheat once, you never feel the same again. All the fun's out of it.' No, that's why they never had false entries. Every loch they had caught a fish in, they had caught a fish in. If you couldna – that was Sport, eh? You might be lucky next time; or you might really have reached the altitudinal limit.

What was the limit? No one knew. That's what made it hook you, so to speak. It depended, too, how far east or west you were – climatic, like with plants. Every month, every week, someone would report a new loch they'd caught a fish in, a First Landing. They dug a wee puddle beside it, to let others know. So the Tables grew and grew, and the altitudes were pushed higher and higher....

We felt envious. The Golden Age. Robertson, Munro, Phillip and Corner, Gall Inglis, all over again. Everests piled upon Everests, on our doorstep. And what about Winter Fishing?

'A-ha-ha, yon's the thing, now. More skill, more challenge. Fish dinna want to feed in winter. You have to make 'em interested, really hungry, like.' There existed a whole range of Winter Mountain Angling techniques and tackle. Casting by compass in a whiteout; ice-screws for making a hole. And bait: only the top men used Ice Flies, the rest dangled flexible kernmantel worms; or a contraption called a Mountain-Fisherman's Friend – an alloy device whose glitter attracted window-shopping fish and, when they came close enough, snapped two metal jaws across them – 'Clap! Just like that!' Friends were expensive: bottoms of lochs were scoured for other people's lost Friends, and Friends tended to go missing at Meets, even at those of so respectable a club as the S.M.A.C.

The Doctor, though no great fisherman ('Look what happened to Collie!'), had fished through holes in ice abroad. Boab shook his head. 'Aye, but Scottish Winter Mountain Angling is a thing on its own, ken. The ice here is *different*. Humidity, the Gulf Stream. And the fish is more intelligent. People come from all over the world to fish these mountain lochs, lads.'

Of course they had a Club Song, Guidebooks, Annual Dinners, Journal.... We became increasingly uncomfortable. Did they have women members? asked the Apprentice sourly. 'Ah, yon's a great question with some kind o folk. Ye see, there *is* a women's club – the Scottish Ladies' Mountain Fishing Association of Edinburgh, Aberdeen and Glasgow: but that's too bloody exclusive, ken – what about aa those fra Dundee, Stirling, Ayr, Kirrie, Inverness, Dalbeattie and suchlike places? Eh?'

It seemed Boab might not rise to the direct question. The Doctor therefore cast, to windward, a more carefully-tied remark: 'So, quite a few women fish Topwaters?' 'Och, women catch fish as well as men, man. But, masel, I wouldna go as far as thae Mixed Rods, sharin the same bait, like. An there's an awfy lot o blether, wi wifies up an down your loch; nae Serious Talk. Mind you, they tie the flies no bad. The young lads likes the idea, nae wonder, but na, na, no for me.' He spat into the hole. After a reassuring swig, he continued more confidently into Bairns' Clubs (the 'High Fry' led there, it seemed) and decried the increasing number of mountain fishers ('the banks is trampled awa, lochs is fillin up'), commercialism and competition tactics everywhere. More spits. We rose to go.

Boab pressed toffee upon us. 'And what are you lads doing here anyway? Climbing, eh? Just gaun up to come down? Seems a daft-like kind o a ploy – beggin yer pardon, o course. Nae time for Reflection. An awfy *waste* o a day.' We feebly inferred the delights and heroics, the Spiritual Fulfilment, of winter cliffs, gullies, ridges, slabs. Scenery, and that.

'But ye dinna get *fish* out o them? There's nae *Rationality* behind it? Canna see the sense, masel. But let everybiddy tak his ain line – that's the Club Motto.'

Here Boab's particular one registered communication with Beneath. We backed out, avoiding the edge, so he could conquer undistracted.

'Aye, aye, boys, cheero. Look in on Andy on the way down. He'll tell you some fine tales, some gey queer-like gauns-on in these lochs. Ach, ye ____ ! Ye ____ !'

He had not ticked off that loch, at any rate.

We did not look in on Andy on the way down. The Doctor several times began to question the existence of such people. 'Imagine grown men (and women!) behaving like that! Going through all those complications of discomfort and – let's face it – danger for the sake of a wretched ego-trip! Dreaming up fake ethics, grotesque regulations, to excuse it! Among this magnificent landscape.... What a waste of good mountains! Why....' He checked himself repeatedly. He found he could say very little.

In fact, none of us could say very much. Beinn Fhada looked down sympathetically.

'I'll get a copy of the Club Song, anyway,' he remarked at the car. 'We'll sing it at the next Dinner. Should go down well, after the Soup.'

# THE RISKS OF EXPOSURE

The Doctor brings tiresome habits to the hill. Photography, for example. Recently, attacks of the click have become more pernicious, because less predictable. Before, symptoms were obvious; we could avoid him. His outline swelled, he swayed as in advanced pregnancy. We fled. The unperceptive were caught, forced to nurse a litter of satchels – 'So I can keep my hands free for a quick shot....'; to dandle them for hours while he delivered himself of various lenses; or to descend wearily on some Mercy Mission for the odd dropped adaptor – 'It's a small ring, silvery, you'll easily see it in the heather; about half a mile back....'

Zooms have changed all that. Even two zooms – an infinity of lenses – can lurk in a small rucksack. The mania incubates unseen. Especially as the Doctor no longer carries a tripod. His collapsible Litewate Tripod, a detestable appendage contrived by some surrealist Manxman, collapsed expensively a year or so back. He used it for a delayed action picture of an Easter Meet. The first time, he set the camera off before he rushed over to join us; the next time, he rushed over to join us but forgot to let go of the cable release; the third time, he let go of the cable release and rushed over and joined us but the thing got spasms and took a photograph backwards. The fourth time it stared straight at us and didn't go off at all, and the Doctor marched back to reset it and got a blast of Ektachrome bang in the stomach. In those days we could watch, and keep away. Zooms are hidden and treacherous. They can be pulled on you like a gun.

Because of this, we were badly caught last summer. We went to Ardgour, to do something on Garbh Bheinn next day. In the tent the Doctor sprung on us a Great Photographic Competition, sponsored, appropriately enough, by the then Highlands and Islands Development Board. Prizes were in four categories: The Beauties of Nature; Landscape; Action; and Humorous (Funnies). The Doctor was determined to enter all four, and zoomed and unzoomed beside the roaring primus.

'This lens is damned good: 35 to 105, macro setting, splendid resolution, no flare, no distortion.... Should do the whole lot tomorrow no bother; just bought a new film. We'll start with the Beauties of Nature!'

Zoom. Zoom.

We groaned. But the Apprentice fingered his Compact – usually reserved for his second's disasters. 'Might try an action shot....' he mused above blue smoke and ebony sausages.

Next day's good weather therefore had drawbacks. We were first delayed by prolonged breathing on, and polishing of, the zoom. Then the Doctor had to blow and brush out his Canon's body cavity with surgical deliberation before inserting the new film. He was thrilled by a long golden hair he extracted. 'How *could* it have got in? And where from?' Impatiently we attributed it to some previous Beauty of Nature and ushered him, still trichophilic, on to the hill. It may well have been his wife's, when she was younger.

Once there, we buckled down to Nature. Nature was doing a big thing that morning. It hummed, whistled, bloomed and seeded no end. We pointed out to the Doctor pretty blossoms and jolly tweets. We were doubtless irritating. But the real dig for button-smackers is always Carnivorous Plants, and the Doctor ensconced himself appreciatively beside a Greater Sundew, screwing its gullet into focus. This talented vegetable had recently taken on board a fairly fat bluebottle which was now, alas, a mere eviscerated hulk. It raised a salivating gob hopefully towards its admirer. Begging for more.

And just then another large buzz of bluebottle did plop into his sundew and began, with inaudible bellowings, to become enmeshed. The Doctor, swithering too long between Beauties of Nature and Common Humanity, could only retrieve an irremediably digested *Callimorpha vomitoria*. Sentimental about flowers, he returned the plateful to its indignant owner. Not much there. What next?

We led him to various pleasing possibilities. A monumentally wide-spreading cowpat was carefully inspected, the Doctor insisting that such places held a large and varied population; the Apprentice assured him Glasgow Was Miles Better. After an exceptionally-dead sheep and several sardonic birds, the Doctor finally fell for a parasitic Lousewort which, despite name and habits, glowed pink in the sun. Several shots at that. Good.

Over to landscape. It filled the rest of the morning. If the Great Glen Fault had ambled a mile further on, the Doctor could have netted a superb perspective of Bidean; as it was, Sgòrr Dhònuill got in the way.

Lochaber remaining unmoved, we had to shift more amenable *décor*. Under direction, the Apprentice and I tore away interfering branches of native trees with a zeal worthy of the Forestry Commission. This done, the Apprentice was dismissed twenty-five yards down to Pose; he gazed sympathetically towards the site of execution of James Stewart of Appin.

'No; a little to the left – STAY *THERE* – *look* a little to the left; head up, chin in, don't scratch your backside – all right, scratch it once; *once*, dammit. Fine...!'

But the artist was not yet satisfied. ('Hmmm....') The Human Interest had to remove his own shirt ('Hopeless colour – doesn't go at all!') and put on mine; and re-enter his (now much trampled) Foreground. ('Hmm, aah; hmm.') I had to stand on the right and drape a careless spray of birch before the lens. 'Hmm, hmm – *and* on the left.' This was clearly impossible unless the Apprentice came up to help; when he would no longer be down there. So I drove in a piece of long-suffering willow on the left and held out my offering on the right.

'Splendid!' cried the Doctor, about to press. Whereupon the Apprentice, hearing and unhappily anticipating, turned with relief and climbed back towards us. He had to be driven down again and be fitted once more, minutely and with abuse, into the landscape.

Ready? But then People began to arrive, plugging inexorably across the field of view. First a cheery and apparently deaf couple collecting Corbetts. Then a man gathering beetles. Then some fellow with a ginger dog who desired the Doctor's opinion on The Depopulation of the Highlands. Then a lady needing a Ranger. Then a shepherd with a gun looking for some bloody fool with a ginger dog. Then the beetle man coming down. Through them all, the Apprentice stared stonily eastward; Appin and Lochaber, arms about each other's neck, beamed back. The Doctor grew pale and drawn.

Then who should appear but Geordie and Wull, on the same misguided mission as ourselves, Geordie lugging his great mahogany and brass contraption and trailing a tripod limbed with steel, Wull festooned with the expensive consequences of his usual duplicatory precautions – though having only two jobs he failed to extend to a hexapod.

We were not overpleased to see them thus arrayed. Twice before we had suffered from their photographic deliberations. Once during our

Freeze-in on The Dreepie, and more recently at Gunpowder Green when the Doctor, entering backwards in his socks, had overturned the primus and set the tent alight. That was a bad affair. We had escaped with most things except some hair, a dozen eggs and the tent, but as we raked the smouldering debris, weeping and cursing, the Apprentice frantic for his new Goretex breeks (which were in the car all the time), Geordie and Wull had sauntered affably by, cameras swinging. Two days later we saw ourselves in the *Scotsperson* as 'Climbers Enjoying Their Camp Fire in Glencoe'. They appeared coincident with disaster. Omens.

'Ay,' greeted Geordie.

'Ay, ay,' added Wull.

'We'll no get in yer way,' promised Geordie.

'Keep tae the side, like,' confirmed Wull, similarly stomping plumb up the middle.

On arrival, they piled arms, and Wull trod on the willow. He held out the bits, helpfully. We replaced it by another. Meanwhile Geordie had wandered down for a chat with the Apprentice.

Violent un-Doctorial oaths restored order, and silence reigned, broken only by sucking and grinding beside us as Geordie and Wull enjoyed their glacier mints. Unfortunately, a sweetie paper was spat across the foreground just as the Doctor clicked. 'It'll no be seen,' Geordie reassured us. 'Invisible,' agreed Wull.

Nevertheless the latter lumbered across to retrieve it, and coincided with the next click.

When the impossible had at last been partially achieved, we limped off exhausted. Below us, an artillery offensive traversed the panorama: Wull's rapid staccato – two from each camera, twice to make sure – and Geordie's occasional heavy clang. Angry words down at G.H.Q. indicated that they too were having trouble.

It was high time for a break. We unpacked pieces, but refreshment was diminished by the Doctor's desire to snap Mountaineers Eating and, when we were not paralysed in midbite or half-swallow, he kept crawling around us to snipe Unselfconscious Attitudes. We were almost glad to be ordered to the Great Ridge for the Action Shot.

Action Shot. I shall not recount the passionate *pas-de-deux* executed for the Action Shot. They were complex, for each of the *deux* – usually at the same time – wished to shoot the other. A sort of vertical duel.

My job was to boost the vertical bit. This entailed pulling the rope hard between them and ensuring that ironmongery did not dangle sideways or upwards. The uncooperative horizon was rigidly excluded. A hoped-for release, when the Doctor – wishing to include in his field all of pitch three – stepped backwards over the edge of pitch two, came to nothing; we hauled him back *camera intacta*. The Apprentice finally untied in a rage and stormed off, the zoom goggling to 105 in hot pursuit – 'Got him!' purred the Doctor, winding on.

Meanwhile, Geordie and Wull were busy. Geordie had his huge leather-jacketed telescopic lens – like an outsize stalker's glass – aimed at us, supported by groaning tripod and breathless Wull. He was taking an Action Shot of the Doctor taking an Action Shot of the Apprentice taking an Action Shot of the Doctor taking an Action Shot... an ever-diminishing vista easily disappearing into the maw of his monstrous monocular, a 1937 Trafalgar Mk. IV. Fortunately, its almost infinite accommodation stopped short of sound waves, which were breaking fairly blue about the Doctor's ears.

At the top he sought to mollify us. 'Can't see what you're complaining about', he sighed, 'you've taken it easy all day. I've done all the damned work....' Then he gloomily remembered he had a Funny to take, and we were allowed to descend.

At a boulder halfway down, our companion warily resurrected the subject of an Action Shot. His eyes gleamed sideways.

'Superb against that blue sky. You needn't rope up, it's only eight feet and the ground's quite soft.'

Reluctantly, the Apprentice arranged himself on a crux.

'Reach up with the right hand. Aah... *left* hand, reach *down*. Don't TOUCH anything – keep it like an *ongoing* movement: that's the impression we want. Left foot – raise it; now raise the *right* one....' Predictably, the Apprentice, following these instructions, found himself eventually quite free of the rock. It was, in fact, an off-coming movement.

He appeared in mid-air.

'Excellent! Hold it!' Click. 'Lord, I hope....'

We hurried over. No damage, only curses. A softer landing could not have been found. The Apprentice sat, stuck, in a black, amiably receptive, deer wallow. He had given one more desired impression.

'Marvellous. Stay there a moment.'

Click.

'Just the thing for the Funnies. Good man.'

Back beside the tent, apologies were still not accepted.

'... *And* the waste of an entire bloody day,' swore the Apprentice, wringing his peat-sodden doup. 'No, no; used the whole spool, all good – except for Wull and the bluebottle – some really terrific'; and the Doctor happily spun the rewinding lever.

He unclipped the back. Paused. And let out a dreadful cry.

There was nothing inside.

Empty.

The film had been left in the tent.

That distraction about the hair....

He brandished the camera, eyes and mouth at full aperture; an image of maximum aberration.

And of course just then Geordie and Wull padded by.

With ponderous agility Geordie levelled his mahogany and clanked.

His picture of our screaming group won Fourth Prize in the Funnies. It was entitled

'THE PHOTOGRAPHER:
*Who truly records with patient skill*
*Hours of delight upon the hill.'*   (1/30 sec., *f* 1.4).

# UP THE WALL

It was the Apprentice's fault, this time. Or rather, he shared it with the Himalayas. The two of them combined to bring us a fairly nerve-cracking Saturday afternoon in one of the grimier outskirts of Edinburgh.

Before the Monsoon that year he had scaled a knife-edged pinnacle among those excitable adolescent mountains. It was a fearsome affair, beside which the Mustagh Tower and companions could have slouched unnoticed into Glen Lyon. Previous to his ascent it had been the fortress of some vague but amiable warrior-god of the snows, a putative Being adored by the simpler natives, who called it after him by a name I have preferred to forget but which could be roughly translated as Mount Lord Bonington or suchlike. It was certainly very high and very smooth, and we were proud of our companion. Mind you, he had worked for it: devotional exercises every few hours, bends, grips, pull-ups, press-ups, middle E's each weekend, evenings spent eroding Meadowbank climbing wall.... The Way to the Highest is hard.

No wonder he suffered a Reaction when he returned. No wonder he sought relief on a friend's 750 Kamikaze, a ferociously willing beast which he had unwisely exercised on the Musselburgh by-pass (the Doctor, equally fond of the occasional canter, preferred to speed on minor roads – 'twisty ones where they'd never even try to trap'). One of the two constables who booked him was an old schoolmate; the other was not. The Apprentice succeeded, nevertheless, in reducing his recorded speed by a quarter, to just under the Ton; and trying his luck further (he was still suffering from Summit Fever) had opted for Court rather than Cash. His excuse of a Following Wind appeared less and less plausible as the Case drew nearer.

His happiness was yet more diminished by the matter of Seeds. Before Expediting, he had rashly agreed with the Doctor's wife (who was one of the Sponsors) to collect on the walk-in (or in some unscrupulous bazaar) seeds of a certain Asiatic Primula which flourished in that locality. As he had several other things to do, including Mount Lord Bonington, he had decided to leave behind, lose, or suffer the theft of – he never settled on which – the (imaginary) packet containing them.

The Doctor's wife did not choose to lay the blame squarely on some erring Dhotial, and her sceptical gaze further fuelled his embarrassment. She – well versed in reducing even tougher material than the Apprentice – requested, icily sweetly, an alternative Favour:

To perform the Opening Climb on a Children's Indoor Climbing Wall at some Interdenominational Youth Arts and Activity Centre in what she was pleased to term a Deprived Area, just outside Edinburgh. Deprived or not, Craigiescunner was certainly Tough, and its children notoriously Wee Hard Men (or Women). To compound the horror, her husband had been trapped (as penance for some unimaginable misdemeanour) into Opening the Wall itself – drawing back curtains and things. For the Doctor's wife was a Trustee of this Centre and determined to display both an Eminent Professional Man and a Distinguished Himalayan Mountaineer doing their stuff before the Deprived. A third exhibit was another Trustee, Sir Angus McFell, exemplifying the Successful Entrepreneur and Local Politician; who was to make the opening Speech, and really rub in the salt. Loyal as the Apprentice is, he might well have caught flu just before that Saturday, had not Sir Angus turned out to be the magistrate hearing his case the week after; the Following Wind might therefore pick up, a little.

My companions of so many difficult days implored me to see them through this one. So when it came, all three of us slipped in by a back door. The Trustees, local councillors, the odd minister and a battery of priests festered about the front entrance, awaiting Sir Angus. We knew him only by repute: he had sprung originally from some tourist trap at Taynuilt, and expanded deviously enough to become a well-known Contractor. One of his enterprises, Kruachan KonKrete-Krushers plc, had masticated much of the Old Towns of the Central Belt, and the products of another, Etive Slabs plc, were employed by flutterings of architects to pave square miles of New ones: at an ankle-wrenching and slippery gradient whose multiform cracks alone prevented pedestrians from gliding to destruction. Sir Angus distributed his gains skilfully enough for a grateful Government to award him a knighthood, and a struggling new University an Honorary Doctorate – which in pre-metric days would have been an L.S.D.

We awaited himself and his speech with interest, and meanwhile mooched about inside. The corridor leading to the main hall was lined with tables displaying the Arts – scrawls and daubs indicative of undoubted if unspecified *joie-de-vivre*, and a few hundredweight of much more particularised statuary, in some quick-set plastic substance. These arrested the wandering eye. Behind the Mickey Mice, Wally Dugs, St. Christophers, B.V.M.'s and Seven Dwarfs, some outstandingly virile Apollos raised themselves, partnered by topless – but certainly not bottomless – Aphrodites. Many outstripped the outrageous, and clearly had been smuggled in uncensored. The children of Craigiescunner were a worldly bunch. A collection of busts amused us too – of pop stars, the Pope, and well-hated (unidenominational) politicians; two of us being further diverted by a lifelike Head of the Doctor: who complained that the nose and chin, especially, 'verged on caricature'.... Still, it was Thoughtful of them.

In the Main Hall itself, normally devoted to various tiresome forms of Activity, sat serried rows of young and their putative progenitors. Through the industrious haze of tobacco fug we recognised the Dais – chairs, table, jug of water, glasses: behind that, a white sheet covering, presumably, the Children's Climbing Wall. Ropes, harnesses, No Smoking notices, hung from above; a huge mattress lay on the floor.

To deafening hoots, cheers and boos, the Entrance Party arrived and marched up to the Dais. Sir Angus led, bovine, redfaced, with a white-toothed and determined grin, wiping his gleaming brow from perspiration and a rain of wet pellets that had met him at the door. My companions edged in behind them. The Doctor's wife crystallised for us a granitic smile, and elegantly folded her intimidating stature up there at the back. I squatted in front of the audience, among fag-ends. .

Some nondenominational nonentity, the Chairman of the Trust, introduced Sir Angus; who charged at his speech without ado, bellowing his audience into silent admiration. His peanut-butter vowels and milk-pudding consonants – the Conceived Pronunciation of Lord Provosts on the Southern make – spattered forth with a vigour and velocity rare in such usually lip-lickingly uncertain linguists. Frequently he tugged at his collar to ease the strain.

This was a Claimbing Wall. To teach you to Claimb. Claimbers claimbed rocks and mountains, but they all began on a Claimbing Wall, laike this. (The Distinguished Himalayan Mountaineer choked, but was silenced by a deft kick from the Eminent Professional Man). They conquered the Haighest Mountains by skills learnt on a Wall-laike-this - care, *care*, planning and *making sure*. So that Nothing goes wrong. Thought Out. Planned. But also by Qualities brought out in you – YOU – by a Wall-laike-this: Courage, Will-Power, Determination to take a Risk. He thundered on, demolishing difficulties and logic like a well-serviced bulldozer. 'What you will learn from a Wall-like-this, is how to be a Success in Life. *Really* to Claimb. To claimb the Real Things. To Master. Not to graipe and grovel, but to be Men'; ('or Women,' he granted). The male parent among whose ash I sat, bent down and nudged me: 'Ah'd no like tae work fer yon bastard – eh?'; and spat meaningly. 'A Wall-laike-this...' and so on for five more minutes, by which time most of us – perhaps even my expectorant neighbour – became convinced that a spontaneously calculated, prudently daredevil Ascent of a Wall-laike-this must inevitably raise us to high executive altitude in concerns like Kruachan KonKrete-Krushers plc and Etive Slabs, plc.   Great.

He stopped suddenly, extended an arm to the startled Doctor, and roared: 'I declare this Children's Indoor Claimbing Wall at Craigiescunner Interdenominational Youth Arts and Activity Centre – OPEN!'

He swung towards the sheet. We all gaped, mesmerised. The Doctor jumped up, couped his chair (the Apprentice, in his best move that day, grabbed it), and marched to the dangling rope. He pulled.

Nothing happened. 'Not that one, ass!' hissed his spouse, 'the red one, with a tassel on it!'

He marched across, amid rapturous applause, and pulled that.

The curtain parted in the centre and drew back, jerkily, revealing the Wall-laike-this.

It much resembled the usual climbing wall, except that it was bright green, with pink holds, and on a smaller scale; and that in the middle was stuck a large white poster which announced:

*Bloody McFell*

*Done himself well*

followed by two quite unquotable lines, the whole a quatrain rhyming *a a b a* and evidently a product of the Post-Modern Literature class.

A Trustee rose hastily and tore it down, to further cheering. Now it was the Apprentice's turn. He pushed back his chair and approached the Wall. The Doctor buckled him into his harness (it was a tight fit), whispered 'Don't make it look too easy,' backed away, and held the

(correct) rope. Sir Angus, at a slightly higher pitch and with more spittle, broadcast his commentary on all this. It was wildly inaccurate, but went down well. Paper darts, plastic cups, old syringes, flew in a friendly manner towards him.

'Now on a Mountain if he fell, he would be dashed thousands of feet into thousands of pieces. Here he would land on this mattress,' (kicking it). 'But he won't fall, he can't fall, he has claimbed great Himalayan monsters, he has just come back, he is one of our Fainest Young Claimbers, *you* can be laike him, he goes up and up, *carefully* – see – but never hesitating, he is quaite safe, you will be quaite safe, look how the rope goes over the pulley and down to his Steady Companion, the Doctor here.' Sir Angus crossed to the Doctor, planted a large incorporating arm about him and beamed at the hooting and cheering throng, patting his beautifully-dressed iron-grey hair in satisfaction.

The Apprentice poised momentarily, and surveyed the top few feet. There seemed to be chalk on these last holds. Jug-handles; they didn't need chalk. Stung by shouts of 'Gerronupit, Jessie!' he seized them and heaved towards the ceiling.

But: the chalk was not chalk. It was that quick-setting modelling plastic. The jug-handles snapped off neatly, as presumably planned, and the Distinguished Himalayan Mountaineer plunged all of ten feet on to the mattress.

Bounce; bounce; roll.

His Steady Companion, engrossed in conversation within the circumference of Sir Angus and taken unawares, was shot upwards a couple of feet, his elbow on the way smiting that worthy in his (redeemable) City of London teeth; the rope which, alas, he had held so steadily, whipped around to wrap them both intimately together. It also dislodged Sir Angus' unsuspected iron-grey wig.

There was no doubt that the Opening was, for the Deprived at any rate, a huge success. Their long-sustained appreciation loosened quite a few ceiling tiles. Then, overwhelming the demoralised rabble on the Dais, everyone rushed to try and claimb the Wall. West Berlin might have twinkled the other side. A special route was cleared for the Doctor – no false handles, they assured him. He had difficulty shortening himself into the under-age holds, but thereafter swarmed up in some style until, at the final mantelshelf, he forgot it was a Children's Wall and his six feet two smote the ceiling, bringing down, appositely enough, part of a plastic cornice. Again immense applause; during which we delicately vanished through the side door again. I overtook my old neighbour. He coughed out a fag, back-handed his mouth and sputtered delightedly: 'Man, that was a grand do, eh? Bloody McFell, Done himsel well....' The rest dispersed itself into bursts of bronchial hilarity and generous spitting over open sights. We fled.

That evening, as we thrashed sweatily through steely Sitka spruce in the rain with rucksacks and tent on the way to a secluded upper corrie, the Doctor, detaching himself from some grinning coniferous entanglement, saw fit to observe that 'Some people, you know, develop a kind of passion for Climbing Walls. Sir Angus, for instance. But I don't envy them – they do everything indoors; you know, they just wouldn't enjoy this kind of thing, one little bit.'

# A WIDER VIEW

No, we are not really skiers. We agree with Unna that skiers regard a mountain as a thing to use skis on; self-righteous mountaineers like ourselves regard skis as just one more thing to use (or not use) on a mountain. The wider view.

And use not only by ski-touring over the backsides of sleeping beasties on a Haute Route, but also by climbing their rudely-awakened faces, with skis there to rub it in. A really wide view.

This last ideal of ski-mountaineering proved elusive. We had frequently skied up to a difficult winter climb; left them at the bottom; climbed it; roped down; and after searching frantically in the dark, never found our skis again and been forced to walk back for them next morning. Or, we had skied to an easy climb and hoped to crown it by skiing blissfully down from the summit, either through (a) climbing with skis on our backs or (b) towing them behind us; (a) effectively swept chimneys up to the first bend, (b) grievously eroded both skis and whatever steps we tried to descend after untangling them. Then we arranged for a Tame Friend with skins to drag our skis up to the summit by gentle slopes while we climbed by a decent route. But naturally if a Friend is as Tame as that he must also be stupid; and never did he find the summit or the top of our climb, even without the usual mist, but wandered around hallooing disconsolately for hours, causing us also to halloo and trail about, and eventually to plowter down on foot through cursing miles of breakable crust; arriving himself, exhausted and weeping, about midnight, with a claque of rebellious planks yelping and snapping at his ankles, loyally losing only an odd stick or bit of Tyrolia on the way.

Last weekend, though, everything had worked. We dumped skis below Raeburn's Gully on Lochnagar, climbed it by The Gutter, glissaded what was left of the left-hand branch of the Black Spout and skied back to the car. A gentlemanly excursion which even the Apprentice confessed was satisfying.

This weekend, conditions promised sterner stuff and we planned Parallel B, which the Doctor deemed worthy of his new front-pointers.

But Saturday blizzards blocked all roads in that direction. In any direction – Dalnaspidal, Glen Ogle, you name it. So, in outrageously fine Sunday weather we finished up on the main road between Crieff and Comrie, at a recently-cleared patch by some cottages, whose occupants let us park beside another skiers' vehicle, likewise snowed out from accustomed haunts. We enlarged the patch with the Doctor's shovel and calmed the old Merc – which had wallowed like a panic-stricken mastiff – with the tightest of chains. Then we set off simply to tour the foothills of Ben Chonzie, which were extremely proud of their dazzling new status. They swelled with ultra-violet. Moreover, in an easterly wind, the Doctor assured us, we should continually inhale Glen Turret, from its distillery over the shoulder.

We soon left the other tracks along the forestry road and struck bare slopes. Fine buxom-breasted snowy virgins they were, billowing into the azure. We skinned on, in delicious silky rhythm. Snow and silence stretched unbroken. Dream-like.

Then a faint chirrupy squeak.

'Hush!' from the Doctor. We all stopped.

We listened.

Silence.

'I bet that was a Snow Bunting,' he breathed, excitedly. We groaned, for he had suffered from ornithology already that season. So much so that the Apprentice and I had thoughts of subscribing to something like the Royal Society for the Prevention of Birds, or whatever. 'Hush!'

Silence.

'We've scared it. They're so suspicious. Don't like people, you know. It's the blizzard that's brought them so low.' Indeed. We moved off.

Squeak. Chirrup.

Halt again. 'Yes, a snow bunting – that curious hesitant modest little song. Delightful wee mites. And as you see, invisible against the snow....' Etc., etc. The serenade ceased abruptly when we stopped, resumed as we moved on ('Oho, they're *clever*!'). The Apprentice, of a cold logical mind, held me back with him as the Doctor pushed ahead. Chirrup, chirrup. It only sang when the Doctor moved, only stopped when he stopped.

We informed him it was not *Plectrophenax nivalis* but a once common, now much rarer, visitant to Scottish snowslopes – The Little Squeaking

Ski-Strap. A haunter of old-fashioned bindings.

The Doctor seemed hurt. He wrapped himself in his Extra Years. 'You young chaps are too narrow-minded, obsessive, selfish. You should make allowance for maturer people's naturally greater range of interests.' For the next hundred feet, he illustrated his thesis by dreadful examples of youthful prodigies like Wee Dander or That Boy who abandoned us below the Aonach Eagach. 'You should take a Wider View....'

Then we breasted a rise, and saw the owners of the roadside ski-tracks.

Two figures, short and tall, watching a small third one pirouetting high up.

We sighed. You can't avoid meeting people these days. Poor *Plectrophenax*.

We reached them. A large mournful-looking man with a grizzled moustache, and a small bright boy. They'd gone far enough. Just beginners. The lad had sprained his knee, anyway; he cursed his luck colourfully. 'Na, na, come awa doon, Wullie', said the man, 'it's a long way back.'

'Hey!' whistled Willie as the small figure above coruscated an untidy melodrama of turns. 'Braw, eh?'

'Pretty good for his age,' agreed the unwary Doctor. 'Wunnerful, considerin,' confirmed the elderly man, 'but bloody stupid all the same, never left off all day. An he smokes like a fish, tae.' 'Shouldn't smoke at *his* age,' warned the Doctor, stepping deeper into a mire, 'after thirty more years he'll be gey short of breath.' 'He will that,' said the man, 'noo, Wullie, awa doon an we'll wait for him at the car; ye can be playin yer new tapes, mind, there.'

The Doctor patted the small irate head benignly. 'Yes, you take your father's good advice.' We nodded.

The head looked up indignantly.

'He's no ma feyther.' Pointing to the figure above, now herring-boning determinedly back again: '*He's* ma feyther!'

We should have minded our own business. But worse was to come. The large man rubbed his sleeve across his nose, and turned to go. 'Aye, an he's *mine*, tae, begod,' he sourly observed. 'Awa doon wi ye, Wullie. Pap'll be back in his ain time, as per bluidy usual. Us weans dinnae count.'

They were about to shuffle down when the stricken Apprentice was further struck: 'That's no Peerie Bob Peterson, is it?' he demanded.

It was Peerie Bob Peterson. A legendary figure in the West, Peerie Bob had scrambled about the cliffs of his (so he said) native Shetland Lord knows how many years ago, then gone – or been ejected – to Glasgow and into uncountable jobs, pubs and horrendous climbing escapades, none exactly – or often even remotely – to his credit. His first wife – mother of our large dour acquaintance – fled to New York for a quiet life, and in his reputedly seventieth year he had reputedly married Willie's mother (a real flash cookie) and, between other V.S.s, begotten Willie. Now, beginning to feel his age, he had taken to skiing.

We said our farewells and plugged on, vastly intrigued. Peerie Bob swept down to us in a cloud of spray and tobacco smoke. He spat out a fag-end.

He reached our shoulders, the Doctor's waist-band. Beneath his bright orange balaclava, black rat-lively eyes sniffed us. A red morocco countenance, thin twitching shrew-nose, long white tucked-away baccy-stained whiskers (grown every winter for whatever resorts give free chair-lifts to O.A.P.s), and three or four well-distributed yellow teeth.

Hardly the typical Shetlander. His genes must have blown there on some strong southwesterly gale. His voice, too, had lost – if it ever possessed – those reassuringly rocksolid consonants and Muckle Flugga vowels. It exhibited a disarmingly Glaswegian agility.

'Whaurs youse boys gaun?'

We vaguely indicated up the corrie.

'I'll join youse. O.K.? I'm aye for company, ken.'

Fine. We all four continued, Peerie Bob herring-boning the steep bits. But no more silence. And an enveloping fug like the toilet outside a No Smoking compartment. We yearned for those promised whiffs of delicate distillery-emitted Glen Turret.

Peerie Bob recounted endlessly improbable yarns, well dosed with personal heroics ('If it hadna been fer me...'). And proudly bemoaned his advanced years. 'Eighty-five, ken!' Nonsense; but he was no chicken. Beside him, we two and the Doctor warmed into contemporaries.

He confessed he yearned for a climb. His old companions were 'aa deid' – few of them, we suspected, from their beds, if they'd climbed often with him; and the young yins nowadays too Academic (a fine catarrhal contempt) and Safety Conscious (a terminally bronchial dismissal). He rolled fag after fag during this with no slackening of rhythm, he plucked paper and tobacco from the surrounding air, rolled them, licked them and lit them, blethering all the while. He liked a good simple climb, with just that bit of Risk (eh?) that gave it Interest. Remembering the multitude of disasters Peerie Bob had thriven on, we shuddered and blessed our present innocent slopes. But not for long.

'Aye, just like yon!' A ski-stick pointed. Yon was a sudden small black defile soiling a spotless upper corrie on our left. 'Bet, noo, it's never been done! Too easy in summer. Jist dandy the day – a bit o Interest... eh?' He slowed and gazed at us appealingly, little ferret eyes suddenly round with liquid simplicity.

We were annoyed at the disturbance of our day; and for feeling annoyed. A lonely old man. Shame.

'Would you, would you like to, have a look at it with us?' hazarded the kindly Doctor, heedless of previous omens. 'Would I no!' Ah, he was, despite all slanders, a true enthusiast. Poor old sod. We thawed; we skinned up and planted skis firmly below this little gully, marking the site (from bitter experience) by a big snow cairn. Peerie Bob penguined further on his absurdly short skis and stashed them under a boulder.

Then he let fly a 'Hurroo!' and began to squirrel up the flour, wielding a ski-stick and a small terrordactyl plucked from his bulging rucksack. The latter aid we thought excessive for such an apparent Grade I. Ourselves, we possessed the Doctor's inevitable axe, his tricounis, 50 feet of line and two ski-sticks. Ample. We two wore dual-purpose double-priced ski-mountaineering boots, Peerie Bob something – from years of misuse – approaching them in unsuitability for either pursuit. 'We can tow the old goat down when he crashes out,' remarked the Apprentice charitably. 'Thing is, keep out of his way till then.'

We followed the blazed groove into steep hard steps. Above us a flailing of weapons and untunefully improper carolling. Peerie Bob was happy. 'Does you good to hear him busy again!' cooed the Doctor, whose knowledge of snow buntings and Bob seemed on a par.

Icicly rock closed in on us. The gully narrowed to a slit and steepened to a cornice. A glance downwards brought out our emergency line. Peerie Bob coughed scorn. 'A doddle!' he spat, contemptuously curling his smoke.

Doddle or not, the Apprentice swam up and tied him on. Whatever his real age, he was too old to keep at this pace and, small as he might be, we preferred him on a string when he eventually had to fall out. The Doctor, plus axe, became his solicitous second and kicked scrabbles into steps. Peerie Bob imperiously threw him down the ski-stick – 'Nae room!' Our youthful companion collected it obediently.

We were nearly at the top of this increasingly exacting slot when it narrowed to a mere chimney cleaving holdless white-ice walls. The terrordactyl and its owner sang in happy discord, between scrambling silences and blue exhaust smoke. We, of normal human stature, regarded this final pitch – a slot like a mini-Parallel B – with horror. At his age! On bald tyres!

Peerie Bob was deaf to entreaties. Slabbering, skiting, coughing and clutching, he wormed up to the very top of the rock slit – a wide crack as holdless as the ice all round – and there indulged in, of all things, a back-and-knee job....

We dug in our anguished axe and constructed a Forth Bridge erection with ski-sticks; and waited in terror.

A note of alarm above. We grabbed the thread of line – it would fillet our fingers, for sure.

Nothing, nobody, fell.

'I'm stuck!' he cried. 'Jammed! Canna move!'

He roared with most disconcerting laughter, a paroxysm which probably settled him in even more securely.

'It's ma heuks! It's ma heuks!' Chokes and guffaws.

We looked at each other. Heuks?! Sheer senility.... No place to laugh in, here. How could we get him down, or ourselves up? Humour the old fool. The strain had been too much.

The Doctor leant out and called comfortingly up the flue in his best chimneyside manner. He was genially rebuffed. Peerie Bob was rock-firm, and would haul us all up to him. After that –

'You jist climb on owre me. *I'm* the only holds here. I'm a right good chockiestane.'

Chockiestane, though perilous, sounded healthier than chuckiestane so one by one, reluctantly accepting well-pensioned assistance, we gingerly processed over a hilarious Peerie Bob, the Doctor leading and placing his tricounis with therapeutic exactitude in a kind of multiple acupuncture. The Apprentice trod as hard as he could; to press him in.

It certainly was an unusual pitch, exceedingly aromatic; Peerie Bob's attire being coeval with himself, and his baccy almost as strong.

These intimacies over, we three belayed under the cornice. The Apprentice hung down and persuaded our aged companion free of western Perthshire with his boot.

Wearily, we turned to the cornice. It impended unforgivingly. As Peerie Bob crawled stiffly up to us, we heard ominous cracks and grindings. The Doctor called out and leapt aside, searching for tell-tale fissures above. 'Hush!' he cried, ears cocked.

'It's only ma knees, lads. They get awfy bad in the cauld. But – it's a grand cornice. Nae bother at aa.' He crept crepitatingly past us. The Lesser Creaking Knee-Cap, we informed the unsmiling Doctor.

We held him on a tight rein and let him thresh with terrordactyl and ski-stick, dislodging it seemed acres of snowcake. Then propelled him up the funnel he'd excavated.

The sun shone through, and he was on top, capering and shouting more rude songs. A revolting old creature. He untied and disappeared, leaving us to struggle up on our own. We recalled a similar desertion by the boy prodigy. 'Only Climb With Those Of Your Own Age,' hissed the Doctor through snow.

But it was nice up there. Then we all set off down to the skis. For a good run back on boards.

We plunged away, rejoicing in limbs once more. Peerie Bob lagged behind. Our consciences again. Poor old devil; if we felt stiff, what about him, vile as he might be? Heavens, here he was, running down backwards, fast enough, taking quick looks into his left hand.

He explained that his knees always seized up on the descent, unless he faced backwards and fooled his arthritic joints into thinking they were still going uphill.

'I can bash on aa day uphill, mind. It's the doonhill that gets ye when ye're auld.' (The Doctor later admitted, uneasily, that this was indeed so). We were impressed; most of all by his little driving mirror. It was cracked – from the Apprentice's boot earlier – 'but the wife's plenty mair.'

The slope steepened to the corrie. A fine sitting glissade: but too deep and slow – we three, poling desperately, could only ooze downward.

Then a swish and a roar, and a triumphal cry. Peerie Bob shot past, at terrifying speed. He was light, did not sink, and skimmed on a plastic agricultural sack (N:15, P:15, K:21, with added Magnesium). Far too fast. There were boulders down there!

'Old fool! He's done it this time! Have to carry him back after all!' The Apprentice seemed cheered by the thought.

The geriatric dot below us, heading straight for disaster, leant backwards and disappeared in a cloud of snow. Which settled, revealing Peerie Bob sitting unscathed, grinning and rolling a fag a few feet from a vast glacial erratic, cheated of its prey.

When we arrived, he was inhaling complacently.

'Ma heuks, see? The verra thing when ye're an auld man. Davy Glen gave me them years ago.'

A harness, bristling behind with curved iron hooks. 'Ye lean back – an ye stop. Jist as good on grass. Grand on Suilven.... Saves ma knees no end.'

We'd heard of Davy Glen and his larks with the Dargies; the Doctor, of course, had even seen him. We regarded Bob with increasing respect. The Experience of Age. He certainly took a refreshingly wide view of things. Made us feel stodgy, safe, suburban; naive....

To hell with respect! Where were our skis? Our snow cairn had vanished, replaced by a mighty cone fed from Peerie Bob's wanton demolition of the cornice, and from all the loose snow it had swept down.... Buried, lost, lost till the spring!

Peerie Bob nodded in sympathy. 'That's terrible. Ye should always put them oot o the way o a gully slide, boys.' He extracted his own from under the boulder, and smartly clicked them on. 'Ye'll no have a shuffle, either?'

No, but there was one in the car. Och, he'd ski down and fetch it up. Och, his knees were fine on skis. It was the walking that did them in at the end of a good day; at his age, like. Skis was nae bother. 'Jist ye wait, lads. No lang.'

And he slipped off, rolling a fag expertly between linked turns.

Of course, he never did come back. This being predicted by the Apprentice, we grimly set about disinterring our transport. An hour of the Doctor's axe, plus his dissecting skills, uncovered all our skis and most of the sticks. Enough.

In the gathering dusk we hissed away, frozen and muttering. At the

road we met a large party, with lamps, ropes, stretchers. We guessed immediately, having been sustained all the way by the Apprentice's uncharitable stories of Peerie Bob. That old scoundrel had ordered a Rescue Party, and this very minute, a Hero, would be conducting Press Interviews – for Gold! Free drinks had already flowed through the whiskers.... Maturer people, the Doctor had warned us, possessed a naturally greater range of interests. A wider view.

We stormed into the throng, blazing. A cottage door opened and a small figure sped through into a car, which drove off hurriedly. A bottle was flung out. We glimpsed the morose Elder Brother at the wheel, Feyther crouched in cover beside him, and a cheerful brat at the back window.

The Doctor in righteous wrath is overwhelming, and his doubtless unethical descriptions of Senile Delusion mollified the rescue team and also – together with impressively legal jargon – rooted out whatever press contacts Peerie Bob had 'phoned from the cottage, and stunned those gentlemen to unaccustomed silence.

So that the whole episode was reduced to one small paragraph in an obscure Gallovidian evening paper, and the price of a half-day ticket for Peerie Bob on Aònach Mor the next weekend. When, we were glad to see, it rained heavily from Friday to Monday.

Of course, that kept us off Parallel B.

But we took a wider view.

# FAMILY MATTERS

'Families and climbing simply do not mix,' the Doctor had pronounced. 'It's bad enough managing ropes – without apron strings, umbilical cords and matrimonial chains. We come here to get away from all that.' The Apprentice had said he agreed thoroughly, and peered up at the next pitch. I myself felt a few reservations (we also came here so we could – eventually – get back to all that), but not many. Certainly, no one could approve of people like the Oliphants – who shamelessly displayed outbursts of babies all across the Highlands. 'Sandy's changed nappies in front of nearly every damned Club Hut,' the Doctor exclaimed indignantly. We felt uncomfortable beside such milk-bespattered exhibitionists.

Like most of those we met on the hill, we knew little, and cared less, about each other's domestic concerns. (Imagine a Mrs. Geordie, a Mrs. Wull – the latter presumably in duplicate....) The Apprentice and I had visited the Doctor's house a few times, and enjoyed wonderful banquets there; but his children were always away, and his wife – well, we have mentioned her elsewhere; kindly, indeed, but – for us – about as approachable as Nanda Devi, whose remote high-nebbit elegance she shared. Doubtless the Doctor enjoyed a warmer relationship – they sparred conversationally with mutual entertainment – but we preferred to keep a safe distance from that imposing Face, especially when presenting a Southern aspect. Of the Apprentice's family life, neither the Doctor nor I knew anything. He did exhibit an occasional passing weakness for girl-friends – or just girls; but apart from such pardonable peccadilloes in a lad less than half the Doctor's age, and a good four years younger than myself, we climbed happily among – and with – all four sexes, our mountains unperturbed by tornadoes from any domestic teapot. The Apprentice, indeed, boasted a tough unconcern for all family matters. He agreed thoroughly with the Doctor, and hauled himself over the crux.

Hence our astonishment when, after several weekends of his 'being too busy to join us', we came across him one evening at Traprain with what the Doctor nostalgically described as a 'a right wee smasher'. To our pointedly innocent remarks, he mumbled conventionally red-faced replies. He was teaching Jeanie to climb rock – not that she needed much tuition, she swarmed up: you could well say, beautifully. We – I certainly – envied him. Small, flashing-eyed, with a most attractive smile. The Doctor and I became maudlin, drinking lonely toasts in Daddy McKay's: for the Apprentice would spend even our Thursday evenings with her on some climbing wall. The Doctor dolefully predicted an outcome of Oliphantiasis.

Things did look serious. Not only for the peace of mind of our companion but, more importantly, for ourselves. Hills would not be the same without the Apprentice. Imagine our surprise, therefore, at his behaviour when we next saw him with Jeanie.

This was at Craig-y-Barns – the weather being too wet for further north. They were talking to a tall, handsome (I suppose) fairhaired guy; and then this guy pinched Jeanie's arm affectionately; and bolted up the rock after her, in the approved biological pursuit. And the Apprentice looked on, coolly; even with satisfaction.

He came shyly towards us. He pointed at his lost love, now two free pitches ahead of her admirer, and said: 'See that! I taught her no bad after all, eh?'

'Taught her to go off with somebody else?!' we exclaimed. 'Sure. Shug's been hot on her for months, and Jeanie on him. But it was nearly all over. She couldn't share his climbs at weekends. Now she can – and is she chuffed! Never look back any more.'

This unlikely philanthropy was rationally explained, it turned out, by Jeanie being the Apprentice's kid sister. Yet I felt puzzled, as well as sour, that his thoughtfulness extended to that yob Shug. But he had a good reason. It strolled up just then in the highly-powered form of another young lady. The Apprentice blushed and stammered. This was Cat, Catherine, the sister of Shug, and one of the top climbers of the year. The Apprentice was sweet on Cat. It was therefore politic to be sweet to Shug. Love my Cat, love me. That lady did not appear likely to be sweet on anyone; but had, it seems, climbed a few times with the Apprentice. She purred dangerously at him. Jaguar rather than Cat. We backed away from our perspiring companion, and left him to field her barely-suppressed energies.

Then the delightful Jeanie and the cursed Shug came down. 'Okay, Hughie?' grinned Cat, 'satisfied now?' A foursome was speedily arranged on a fairly Extending area of the crag. Shug and Jeanie set off, then Cat and her Apprentice.

Now the Apprentice is very good on extending rock. Very good indeed. But Cat stormed ahead, a ripple of tiger-skin; and so demoralised him he began to slow down and grab at things. Shug, really no bad climber at all, blast him, lost Jeanie in the slipstream of Cat. The two girls hooted, made rude signs, and raced off to the next Tier.

Shug and the Apprentice, one blown, the other disgruntled, slithered down to us.

'Hell, you've taught Jeanie a thing or two,' gasped Shug admiringly, mopping his brow. 'Cat's going to take her on a new route she's made.'

The Apprentice looked bitter. '*Womans' Lib*, I bet she'll call it,' he growled. He enjoyed an evidently stormy relationship with Her Felinity, and this was not one of the Good Days.

The Doctor tried to be helpful. 'You know, girls are likely to climb better than us on these balance routes, at that age; less frustration, less rage, they take it more smoothly.' He quailed under six hostile eyes. 'Up to a certain time that is,' he added. 'Until, in fact, they've had a baby. That slows 'em down – physically and mentally. Makes 'em more responsible. Good thing, too,' he whispered, glancing about him with understandable caution.

'Doesn't seem to have affected Cat,' remarked Shug, off-handedly.

The Apprentice stared at him, horror-struck.

Shug looked surprised at his concern, and added, 'Wee Jerry'll be a year in August. You havena seen him? Cat didna tell you? His Granny's fair daft on him, he aye stays with her. Cat's fond of him, like, sees him now and again. But it's the rocks she's after – an no the ones you give the cradle, eh?' He cackled at his stupid joke and scanned the cliff.

We waited for further information. The Apprentice licked dry lips. There might still be hope.

'She's no married? She never – .'

'Och no, of course not. What an idea. No yet, anyway. God, look at what they're doing – pheeeew....' Shug's mouth fell open.

The Apprentice ignored the climbing. He remained fixed on family matters.

'The... the... Father.... Is *he* interested?'

'In climbing?'

'No, for _____ sake! In the baby!'

'Interested? Oh aye. Jeeze, look at that. Jeanie, girl, Jeanie.... O aye. Sep's real delighted. Keeps sending presents for him near every week. What a move – did you see that? Jeeze....'

Sep? The name alarmed our bells. We suddenly recalled meeting, a year before at these very crags, Virginia Prusik – that small intensely knotted American rock-scorpion from Joshua Tree – and her amply-flowing pink companion, the genial Sep....

'Is he American?' The Apprentice sounded hoarse.

'American? O aye. Cat's likely gaun out there inside the year. She'll be havin to take the bairn along with her – Sep's as fond of it as she is of him. She'll be for Yosemite and yon places. But she'll have to pay her fare, ken: Sep's folks want an old-fashioned-like Ohio wedding. And Sep's a real soft family-man sort of a guy, he'll no disappoint them. You've met him?' he asked the by-now tragic Apprentice. 'Cat's not told you? Ah, she's a real hard case, Cat, no time for anything but climbing; don't think her family matters much to her nowadays. No ties. She keeps us all at arm's length. No like your Jeanie....'

Shrieks and whistles. The girls were coming down, and our informative conversation ended.

'It's no use,' explained the Doctor, peering into the mirror as we joined the A9, 'families and climbing simply don't mix.'

We two remained silent. The Apprentice's silence suggested he agreed – thoroughly. My own was occupied by imagining how perhaps I might call on him at his house some evening – Shug being away, of course; preferably in America, married to Sep's sister.

# AN ARTICLE OF FAITH

The Doctor is a persistent man, loyal to his beliefs. Two or three years ago he led us up a winter route on some vegetatious horror we encountered in the West, a loose and rambling sniff-about, which he followed remorselessly to its top end across a mutually disagreeing rubble of rock and slush. As route-finding, if not climbing, it was epic enough and he insisted that his peregrination be recorded for the benefit of whatever Posterity might visit that god-forsaken area. So he scribbled notes on 'The Solution', as he rashly christened it, in the tent that night. 'A good Grade III; must go in the next *Journal*!'

Things intervened and when he looked out his scribblings again he discovered one page – describing the final, crux, pitch – was missing. 'Dropped out of the file! Been shredded!'

He must go back and reinvestigate that pitch. Accuracy, he maintained, is essential in descriptions of new climbs: slovenliness betrays the faith of our successors. Each one of those bald stereotyped paragraphs defacing so many pages of so many journals is a Scientific Communication: inexorably boring to the casual reader, but of prodigious, obsessive, interest to any would-be explorer of those particular few square metres. 'It's Reporting an Experiment: you can prove it true or false by simply repeating the described process. Testable topographical research! Not like Munro-ticking – if you cheat there, only your Recording Angel suffers; but a New Climb is up for public adjudication. One just has to be Exact!'

We sympathised. It is a human weakness to like your name in print, at the head of a fine new route as much as at the foot of a list of Munroists. And not a selfish one – journal editors, guidebook compilers, publishers, printers, booksellers, depend on it for bread.

But we refused to waste a good winter on so scavenging an expedition. It was therefore some time before we took up The Solution again. Naturally, on a driech drizzly thawing weekend fit for nothing else.

We peered about below the cliff. According to those Doctorial notes still existing (though not to non-Doctorial recollections), *The route is unmistakable – a striking direct line immediately obvious on sighting the crag.*

Somewhere. Somewhere....

We identified the start of the climb only when the Apprentice recognised his old spare sock, left behind at our beginning the year before. Somewhat holey, faded and shrunk, fit only for a one-legged dwarf, but a topological certainty. Fresh pieces of fallen rock lay about it.

Above it, pitch one. *A clean corner bounding the lowest buttress on the E.* The buttress presumably being that part of the snowy gravel a little steeper than the angle of rest, the corner three sharpish stones in line above each other; and time, sheer time, must have grown that grimy beard of lichen all over them.

We kitted up. Small stones fell around us. A striking route, indeed... The Apprentice, as so often, offered the Doctor his spare helmet. The Doctor swore by his own thick fishing hat: 'Helmets are damned dangerous; with hats, you keep alert, hear more.' But he donned the dome to please us; and within a minute let fly an oath. A pebble pinged from his helmet. 'You see!' he cried, snatching it off and replacing the hat, 'damned dangerous: on only a minute, and hit by a stone!'

The experiment was irrefutable. Be faithful to your own beliefs. We began to go up, embarking on a long meander that did not end for weeks.

The Doctor led, notes round his neck. Once again we trod the watery glue of wet ice. 'Purely a winter climb,' its originator observed. He followed his Description as far as possible, though a few minor landmarks – the tilting flake, the uneasy block – had shifted downhill a bit, to left or right. The notes were eagerly readjusted, with no sense of scientific shame. 'A winter climb is, after all, constantly changing....'

Astonishingly, he did ferret out his approximately original route. The crux, though, remained in cloud above. We reached the pitch below it: *A large smooth slab, climbed by ice on its W.* No ice today; and the slab was split by a huge fresh crack. Yet this seemed the place: damn-all either side....

The Doctor scrawled another amendment, put away his notes and gallantly essayed the slab by its newly-inviting crack. As he grabbed its edges it quivered, wobbled wider; a horrid rumble underfoot....

'Weathering!' averred the Doctor, mounting it nimbly nevertheless.

He vanished beneath the hem of the cloud.

Then, a shout. As from the old Tay Bridge.

'It's gone...! Not here any more!'

The cloud was obligingly lifted higher by the Creator of the Problem whose Solution we had embarked upon.

Our companion then appeared, poised on the rim of an airy rip-off: a fearsome gash beneath him in front; and, overhanging above, far out of reach, a ghastly white scar glaring from the otherwise melancholy cliff.

There *was* no final pitch any more. Weathering. The carefully-described wall, like its documentation, had dropped out of the file; been shredded.

To proceed was Impossible, Unjustifiable. Everything shook, ourselves especially. We held him by pressed-in runners, but his feline skills sufficed, and we all scuttled down, the Apprentice, as anchorman, soothing an increasingly restive mountain.

At the bottom, a fresh heap of debris, burying the sock. The spare helmet had been dented. 'You see – these things *attract* stonefall! Damned dangerous.' Small bits still fell about us, remnants – or precursors. But he had to photograph the loss of his last pitch.

Then off to the car, followed by ruminations of rockery. We never looked back.

The Doctor took his bereavement manfully. But it did pose an ethical problem. You can't publish a description of a route that no longer exists. Science would be outraged; no re-run is possible. Yet that last pitch *had* been so exciting. People *would* be interested to read about it.

So he must redesign his communication as a Personal Account of the whole climb – before and after. Certainly the *Journal* Editor would publish an article of such unusual interest. 'A most discerning man, James Anderson. Prefers historical accounts. Detests the superficial and trivial. Very strict about facts. Should be more editors like that. Knew him, anyway, at school.' We two thought that Editor a self-important Pain: aye pontificating about the Spirit of Mountaineering. James Anderson. Nobody had ever called him Jim.

The Doctor read us his thriller, draft by draft. We recognised the enthusiasms, less so the route. But no worry – this was Art, not Science. An interpretation of the Truth.

When it was ready, only the climb's name bothered him. By his own creed, it could no longer be The Solution, for it lacked one. The Apprentice thought hard, leaned across:

'Call it Dissolution,' he said.

Excellent. The Doctor folded his masterpiece and licked the envelope, humming with anticipation. 'It's bound to get in. James Anderson loves this kind of thing. Brisk, factual.'

It did get in.

As a brief note at the end of MISCELLANEOUS:

*A correspondent reports a recent rockfall on the NE face of the crag below Meall nan Ceapairean in Coulin. The scar is clearly visible and the surrounding rock unstable. However as the cliff generally is loose, vegetatious and unrewarding at any season, possessing no attractions for climbers, the only danger would seem to be to anyone picnicking directly beneath it.*

We thought that shocking. So much for James Anderson. But the Doctor is persistent, faithful to his Faith. A few days later with the help of Evergreen Smith, an expert in these things, he sent his article to *Fresh Air (The HAPPY Outdoor Magazine)*, and the following Thursday told us that the Editor of that publication, passing through Edinburgh, would look him up here at Daddy McKay's (so near the station) between trains that very night.

Sure enough, a short dark-suited tight-moustached character, carrying a briefcase manufactured from the skin of a plastic crocodile and accompanied by a small round-eyed girl child, marched up to our table; shepherded by an anxious Daddy McKay, who endeavoured to hide the sprog behind chairs and the Doctor's raincoat. Introductions.

'Ha, Doctor, glad-to-meecher, name's Brimble, editor, this is Dorothea-me-youngest, up-here-to-see-her-auntie, yes a drink'd go down nice-like, very kind, no not whisky, stick to gin thanks, now' – a deep breath – 'this article is a good article, we'd like it, BUT.' He spread the MS on the table. 'The ending won't DO. Too sudden. Breaks off.'

Our companion protested. 'It's TRUE – that's just what happened; it broke off.' He searched our eyes for affirmation.

'Sorry, won't DO. *Fresh Air* runs Happy Endings to clean, complete, stories. Readers don't want to know what *happened*; they want Happy Endings to clean, complete, stories.' Mr Brimble, an agreeable Cockney-like individual, sipped his gin and lit a small slightly sinister cheroot.

The Doctor blustered. Mr Brimble continued his gin. An uneven battle; for that article had to get in, somewhere.

At this critical point, Dorothea expressed a sudden desire for the Toilet. She grabbed the startled Apprentice: '*You* take me,' she demanded, 'My Dad's busy.' Red-faced, he led her out, hand in hand.

The Doctor argued on. Mr Brimble sipped, understandingly. 'You only have to add a little bit to show you reached the top after all. Just go on from *there*....' He leant over and prodded the MS. A half-inch of ash fell from his cheroot into the Doctor's whisky: our stricken author cried aloud. 'Sorry, Doc, I'll get yer another – Johnny Walker? Black and White?' The Doctor waved an anguished arm at a hastily-summoned Daddy McKay – 'Macallan, Macallan,' he gasped; '16-year-old,' he added. He was becoming unnerved. Brimble was a skilled editor.

Then an irate and buxom wifie burst into the Back Bar, pushing Dorothea (who clutched a bag of crisps donated by the scandalised Daddy McKay) and a scarlet Apprentice before her: 'He's no *fit* to look efter a wee lassie, no fit, no fit!' Mirth from the Rugby tables near the door. To them, she poured out the offences: first, he had taken Dorothea absent-mindedly to the Gents', but had met a Gentleman emerging, adjusting his dress, who observed 'Ye cannae tak a lassie in *there*!'; and then, panicking, fled to the Ladies', whence he had been evicted with shrill maledictions by a posse of matrons. 'Tried tae shove himsel intae the Ladies', jist like thaaat...!' 'No fit, no fit at aa!' gleefully chorussed the Rugby tables, loyal to the Rules of the Game.

This was the final straw. Brimble, and his daughter, were skilled editors. Battered by the turmoil and faced with gin, cheroot, crisp-eating child and a choice so obviously Take-it-or-leave-it, the Doctor agreed to continue up the scar by a route neither ourselves nor Gravity had noticed, right to the summit (a feature not unarguably possessed by Meall nan Ceapairean), and then to gaze westward at the golden sun setting over the Magic Celtic Isles (west of Meall nan Ceapairean intervene the midge-breeding magic-denying buttocks of Beinn Damh). And then to Race Down to the lapping sea shore (several miles and two ranges away). 'They all love an ending that Races Down to the lapping sea shore,' confessed Mr Brimble, rising for his train, 'A fine finish to a clean healthy day out of doors.' He belched good-naturedly, and strapped up his plastic crocodile.

Dorothea inflated, and satisfactorily exploded, her crisp packet, showering us with fragments of fry and crystals of salt. We all rose. We all left, the Doctor hurriedly swilling back Macallan and pieces of floating crisp. Ah, well....

None of us mentioned the article again. Two months later it appeared. None of us read it, either (who would buy *Fresh Air*?) But the next Thursday night the Doctor spent the fee (shared with Evergreen Smith, an expert in these things) on several rounds of Knockando, an appropriately-labelled spirit for the climb.

But we shuddered, all the same. How could he, with *his* principles, put his name to an obviously untruthful, Posterity-betraying abomination like that?

'Didn't put my name to it. Used a pen-name.'

What pen-name?

'James Anderson,' he replied.

# BEYOND THE LAST BLUE MOUNTAIN

'Exploration is the very soul of the thing....' The Doctor lit his pipe, and stamped his fourth match decidedly after the others into wet heather. 'Even on your Extremes you have to' – puff – '*discover* there aren't any holds.' We were about to add our own contributions to the obvious when we heard a sudden altercation on the slopes below.

It had been a quiet solemn sun-lapped summer evening, the last of our long weekend in the far Northwest. We had fled there for a peace and freedom no longer known in the industrious South – in Lochaber, Mar, Badenoch and other overspoils of leisure, now organised down to the last microchip of bedrock and breakfast. We had come to Coigach simply to explore: hills, cliffs, achingly empty miles of gneiss and lochan – haunts of wild yellow waterlily and roaming sea-otter – beneath blue sky and sailing white cloud. We would enjoy once again the dignity of rarity, without needing to emigrate to that unpeopled paradise of Baffin Land the Doctor so often lectured us about. We carried no mechanical aids to navigation beyond a sealed emergency compass; certainly no Gutter Press of guidebooks; and not one map – we had escaped for three whole days from behind the National Grid.

Marvellous. Our pioneering faculties had been further exercised by continual rain, thick mist and implacable midgery. They registered some success. On the long walk putatively south we had discovered the summit of Cùl Mòr in five places, a recurring excitement only exceeded by our stumbling upon a displaced Atlantic, which – thanks to the cunning of the Apprentice – turned out to taste like Loch Sionnascaig. These delightful uncertainties lost their charm after two and a half days of wet groping, and therefore – as our chief (and eventually sole) enthusiast had tirelessly predicted – we were the more gratifyingly surprised when the weather suddenly turned fine over the last couple of hours.

A glorious prospect of sun, sea and mountain. And where might it be? That beercan glinting in the long low light suggested a popular enough Nature Reserve; that porcupine peak above must surely be Stac Pollaidh; and this tormented No-Man's-Land of a trench tunnelling desperately through the mud in front of us could only be the Tourist Route up it. We had blundered back into the welcoming arms of humanity, on a fine evening. We were content. You could keep your Baffin Land. And the Doctor was about to enjoy his pipe and enlarge upon the – yes, still possible – role of exploration in Scottish mountaineering.

Then this damnable noise below. A knot of struggling people. A fight? Unfortunately, no. They were running towards us, up this appalling morass, a flypaper so entangling them they seemed to be marking time. Fascinated, we watched the plunges forward and the slitherings back. Two-dimensional Purgatory.

The knot unwound into a couple of parties. The larger was led by a hairily-bony middle-aged man in peaty beard and mud-slavering shorts; followed by a diminishing gaggle of – yes – children similarly attired, though beardless. Alongside them, but exhausted and falling back into passive engulfment, wallowed two gesticulating flappers of paper.

The panting string reached us. It seemed unable to stop, and we could only satisfy its breathless entreaties by padding alongside. Most tiresome.

We confirmed species, sex and age, but the ethnic minority as Yorkshire only when the leader, staring devotedly ahead, announced himself as *Herbert*, he came from *Huddersfield*, and he Ran Up *High* Mountains – the aspirate adorning this not very illuminating information being blasted forth with every third pounding of his left foot; and those were his *Kids* behind him, real *Keen* they were. Nasty little bog-eyed horrors, showering us with mud. Nevertheless, to the point: Herbert swivelled egg-white eyes, gulped out:

'Is this... the way... upStacPollaidh?'

Yes. But it was gey late.

He brandished a wet roll of black paper, and with Olympic agility the Apprentice reached across and grabbed the baton.

We unravelled it and tried to jab out the position, but the juggling and the joggling and the tendency of the exasperated map to part repeatedly at its folds and cast pieces of itself into the morass did not help; though we caught most of them in the slips.

It would have been considerably more convenient to have stopped and discussed the route more soberly, but this was not possible. They must keep going. They were after a Record – a Family Record – and were now enjoying the last few miles of it. Quite possibly they had begun to run at Huddersfield. They were certainly programmed to stop only at the summit of Stac Pollaidh, where a Reception Party was gathered. Herbert should have been in radio communication with it – he waved another baton in his right hand – but mud had ditched the electronics. Yes, of course someone with a radiophone was to have been posted halfway up to guide them, but he had mistaken A837 for A835 and gone up Canisp instead ('Easy enough', gasped Herbert, 'in the mist; you can't *read* those road-signs').

We bellowed our instructions to Keep-On-Up-You-Cannae-Go-Wrong; and any faltering of the father as he cleaned out his nearest ear was greeted by shrieks from the earth-devouring young behind, indistinguishably welded together in each other's wake:

'Go on Dad – Dolly's Blister's Fine!'

Exhausted, we fell back, wiping off micaceous drift and small embedded pebbles that had not enjoyed such a strenuous day since the late Postglacial. We hoped we had imparted sufficient information to get the party up in long enough time for us to vanish before they tried to come down again. We turned in relief; we preferred our own obsessions.

Lord, then we were accosted, belaboured by the other two. Fortunately they had no objections to stopping. They collapsed, purple and stertorous. We hauled them out of the gurgling track on to the heather. We loosened their knotted cagoules and pulled off their bed-rolls and cup-dangling hundredweight of rucksacks; we administered glucose sweets. They resisted a little because we were taking them off the Path, people should stay on the Path....

But they were tough. Hardly had they coughed their breath free of the Pliocene than they were heaving at the octopoid cords of their rucksacks and gouging forth a library of peat-eared and bog-stained volumes. The maps, which we had prised from their hypoglycaemic clench, were shaken out and laid flat. They polished their spectacles and gazed up. Their question followed what by now we recognised as the local oral tradition.

'Is this the way up Stac Pollaidh?'

They explained they had tried to ask Herbert from Huddersfield, but he had been too busy shaking humus out of his stopwatch and they had no breath left to keep up with him. They were glad, really were glad, we had turned up.

'Because this Guidebook', expostulated one, Pete, shaking a coagulated sponge, 'is ALL WRONG....'

'They shouldn't *write* a Guidebook', scolded the other – Cyril – 'if it's ALL WRONG.'

'How could we ever find our way in this kind of place', they chorussed, indicating much of Wester Ross, 'with a Guidebook written ALL WRONG?'

Swift clinical examination by the Doctor diagnosed one specific cause of their complaint – the usual misreading of lefthand bank for true lefthand bank of a crafty little burn. But we agreed it was as difficult to find your way about that particular Guidebook, even when dry, as about a real mountain. At least you had a compass for the mountain.

'Ah, but our compasses have GONE FUNNY.'

The Doctor sighed, and continued his investigation. They possessed no fewer than three compasses (one better than Wull) and had kept them all together waterproof in a tin.... Presumably the consequent wrestle among the respective lines of force had resulted in a common declination to agree – each of the three avoided the others; each preferred its own North. We did not feel competent enough in Lower Physics to explain, still less rectify, this aberration; and advised Pete and Cyril to call it off, Go Down. It was too late, anyway.

Further search among the bookshelves. They extracted a limp and sweating *Hill-Walkers' Handbook*. Rather unnecessarily licking his index finger, Pete flicked for the relevant page. Here it was. Naismith's Formula.... (Ah, Willie, Willie, little did ye reck....)

Cyril produced a folding metre rule. Tongue protruding, he laid a curvilinear length of it across the map and declared the distance to the summit.

The Doctor leant across and moved the rule to the correct mountain. Cyril pointed out the distance was the same, anyway. Pete calculated with his thumb. 'One and a half hours. Easy do it.'

We winced. Although even they could hardly lose their way up a gutter, a gully, a veritable glen such as this path, near the top things opened out and grew teeth, and darkness would close in. It was already six-thirty.

They packed, and hummed to themselves. The Apprentice was all for leaving 'em. 'Plenty of grub, couldn't even climb out of the track, and there'll be a Reception Committee coming down, phones and all. Not our responsibility.' We all wished to flee from such guileless caricatures of our past – maybe indeed of our present – selves. Anyway, wasn't exploration the very soul of the thing?

But our medical companion flinched under the accusing eye of Hippocrates. He tried to resist our dragging him away, he tried to shout a warning over our cheery 'Good Luck, Have a Fine Night'; when two other figures hurtled down that gelatinous groove.

Swiftly as skiers. We leapt back. Cyril and Pete, kneeling at their luggage, stared in amazement.

*Squirrch...* to a stop. Beside us.

Two unrecognisable objects. Then the glue peeled away, slapped down flatly about them.

Two sodden black balaclavas were pulled off. Two broad muddy paws wiped two broad muddy faces. Two cackling and soil-distributing guffaws.

Geordie and Wull!

Talk of the devil.

'Aye,' said Geordie.

'Aye, aye,' confirmed Wull.

'Terrible day it's been,' declared Geordie.

'Fine the now, though,' pronounced Wull.

Yes, they had been after Bennets, scavenging the guidebook lists as ever. Doing them this time on Mountain Bicycles.

We wondered at such an impure approach from so devotedly conservative a pair.

'O but they're grand things,' said Geordie. 'Tak ye doon in nae time.'

'No so easy gaun up, though,' qualified Wull. Bravely, although draped in two extra tyres, he had only a single bicycle, not being able to carry – or ride – the spare one left behind in the van.

They had enjoyed their day despite this deprivation, and despite the earlier mist and the quite impossible path going up; they had to make, in fact, another track of their own ('Near as bad, mind: thae grippity tyres fair work it aboot....'). They left the bikes below the summit pinnacles, fearing a puncture.

The Doctor took them aside, whispering. These two self-confessed apostates should do our dirty work for us.

They muttered. And then sauntered across to Cyril and Pete, now lifting on each other's packs.

'Ye're no gaun up there the night, like?' growled Geordie, slapping grey alluvium off his lower breeks.

'Wh-why not?'

'Och, its *terrible* up there: aa mist. Ye'd niver get doon alive, that's for sure, lads,' declared Geordie.

'Ye'd be right deid,' acknowledged Wull.

Pete and Cyril complained they could see no mist.

'Of coorse not; no fra *here*. Ye're awfy low doon here; it's when ye get *up* ye see the mist.'

'It's over yon first top,' volunteered Wull.

'There's aye a mist on the true top of Stac Pollaidh, it's near the sea,' explained Geordie. 'Thae ither lads is havin a terrible time – they'll lose the record by hours, ken.'

'An they've freens up there tae help them,' pointed out Wull, 'wi flags an aa; hours an hours,' he added.

'But the map says this top is the summit,' protested Pete, pulling out that indispensable adjunct.

'Let's jist see it.' And Geordie spread it out carefully in the mud, and knelt on it. Wull trod helpfully about its edge.

'Now look – this yin's the *top*; the one ye're *seein* is doon here....' and his uncompromising finger wadged a permanent depression over a now completely unreadable area. 'Yon path, now, doesna go on efter *this*, ken' – another massive prod, with like result. 'An thae lads is stuck *here*' – still more obliteration.

'It's no easy tae find yer way, like, even on a map,' admitted Wull; 'an it gets dark, see, at night....' he further informed them.

'An what's aa this aboot nae compass?' demanded Geordie, rising, shaking most of his B Horizon into the map, folding it brutally up and handing it back to the petrified owners. 'Ye cannae dae things like this in a National Nature Reserve.... It's no like in *England*, ken,' he added, heavy with meaning. Hands on hips, he eyed them severely. Wull shook his head again and again.

Cyril tried to stand his semi-liquid ground. 'Are you the Ranger for here?' he quavered.

Geordie swelled further; his bristling – though mud-encumbered – moustache would have done credit to Inspector McHaig.

'Ah'm no sayin Ah am; Ah'm no sayin ah'm no. Jist *now* Ah'm gien yese Advice, no Orders. Jist awa doon, ma lads, sensible-like – or else... mebbe....' Swell. Bristle. Swell.

They looked at each other, picked up their rucksacks and, without a word, sloppered off down the trough. Silent, heads bent. And safe now from the very soul of the thing.

When they had gone far enough not to return, and we had been told all about gear ratios, tyres, saddles and front and rear suspensions, and about the shrill festivities cape-capering in Record Time about the embarrassed cairn above, Geordie and Wull donned balaclavas again; they thrust legs over their dripping steeds, stood up on the pedals, and squeezed off.

'We'll be doon afore ye!' Geordie bawled back.

'Get there first, like!' shouted Wull through orbiting spare tyres. 'Heh, heh, heh!'

We watched them gather speed until, when the wheels locked solid with glaur, they took off from the steep parts with a terrifying *schuss*, like toboggans; leaving behind twin ditches worthy of the Forestry Commission.

Far out of sight, with triumphant hoots and ringing of bells.

From equally far above came cheers and clapping, a sing-song, bangs of fireworks and thunderflashes.


We went down through the last of the glorious evening – sea, mountain and loch – blind to it all, heads together, planning our three weeks in Baffin Land.

The Doctor knew of a good guidebook to it.

# BEATING THE RECESSION

It was a fine late-October day, in the middle of well, either Gaick or the Monadhliaths, we are not supposed to say which. We strode over snow-freckled heather, across a plateau of bowed heads similarly dusted. Between them, huge declivities of black glens. Above us, the cold blue sky of early winter.

We always came here at this time, to breathe the change of air and tread freshly frosted earth. Soon all over Scotland the gullies would be in condition, the faces beckoning with ice. A glittering prospect. It should be a good winter. Why, there was even a fair stretch of snow already in the little corrie just below us.

We ran down to it. Just to get that hard slither beneath our heels again.

It was snow right enough, an inch or two on top of old hard stuff. Really old snow, dirty, scattered with bits of twig and spruce needles. Spruce needles! Here in the middle of the treeless plateau of – er – Gaick. 'Up-draughts,' explained the Doctor. But he could not explain the *depth* of old snow, at this time of year. Nor – look – the spoor of tracked vehicles across it. We kicked – hard as ice. The Doctor screwed in his axe (he'd brought one, to make things look wintry); but couldn't reach bottom. Last season's? Not possible, these warm years, at just under 3000 feet. But, still, the corrie faced north-east and could catch miles of blown snow from every direction on this table-land.

Then we saw snow fences, to gather drifts and encourage them into the corrie. And machinery – a snow-maker with its hose snaking into a plastic lochan, and a couple of piste-bashers, pistie-beasties. And coloured sticks marking the slalom course. Obviously a good snow reservoir like this had been taken over by the Ski Industry.

Yes, a track led up from below. With a truck, tractors and a bulldozer. And workmen. And buildings down there, and a cable over pylons – clearly, restaurants and chair-lifts....

We hurried over. The Doctor was astonished. 'No mention of skiing here in any plans I've seen. The main road, yes; not here. Must find out!'

The truck and bogeys were being loaded with great heaps of stuff cleared off the snow, and taking them down the roadway.

Heaps... of spruce branches! Spruce branches...?

Ecological snow fencing? Why taking them away,then? We went up to the gaffer and enquired. Pure nosiness, of course. He smiled slowly.

'We're jist makkin ready for the winter. Now the hard weather's settin in. Clearin awa the cover.' And would not be drawn further. 'Na, ye'll hae to ask Dr MacPherson. It's his affair.'

A bell rang under the Doctor's fishing hat. 'Archie MacPherson?' he asked.

'Some might call him Erchie,' was the experienced reply. 'But he's owre there,' pointing.

The Doctor peered. 'It is, it is old Archie. Lord, I knew he was back, what a coincidence. Fancy *him* starting a Ski Resort. In an Economic Recession, too. Let's go and ask him about it.'

On the way he explained that Archie, a fellow-student of his, though older and studying geology, had gone abroad and struck it lucky with oil in Alaska. Had made a fortune. A prudent man, hard-headed, very reserved. In fact, downright Mean, yet possessing a fairly mineralogical sense of humour. He'd retired early, come back a few years ago and bought an estate in the old MacPherson country. A sentimentalist, like all these self-made men. A hell of a lot of land, the Doctor recalled, here in (shall we say) Gaick. 'So that's what he's up to. Ski resorting – strange; he never used to *like* people.'

Archie MacPherson, a short powerful pipesmoking man in an old cap and filthy raincoat, did not seem to like us, at any rate. He grimly surveyed the Doctor, and ignored the Apprentice and myself. But we overheard.

Yes, this was his estate. Then a pipe-smoking silence.

The Doctor, avoiding the main question, chose to ask: 'Spruce branches...?'

'From my woods in the glen.'

Yes, but why moving 'em down again?

'Because I brought them up here in the summer.' Stare, puff.

The Doctor, pipeless and thus at a disadvantage, could only venture further in pure nosiness. 'Why bring them up in the first place?'

MacPherson looked him over, then examined us carefully. We stepped back. The Doctor began to re-introduce us but the pipe waved him down. We had, however, passed scrutiny. The pipe answered.

'To preserve the snow. I am building up snow here, year after year. This corrie collects a great amount, I bring in a lot more, and it's sheltered from any warm wind. The branches keep off the sun. Give insulation. We get very little thaw even in a hot summer; even after a poor winter.'

So things became clearer. It *was* for skiing. Year after year, and we'd never heard of it. Archie had bad P.R. But a wonderful idea, trying to keep last season's snow to gain an early start to this one. We asked the direct question, indirectly:

'You're certainly making a fine place here for skiing in the winter. It should become very popular.'

He withered us. Skiing? Skiing!

'Do you think I've nothing better to think about than... Skiing! Nothing better to spend my time and money on than a childish self-indulgence like that?' He put away his pipe. His eyes became dreamy. 'I suppose you've heard how they've managed to bring back ospreys? And sea eagles? And reindeer? And how some people – good luck to them – want to bring back bears and wolves? A kind of palaeo-conservation mania, for reintroducing the Post-Glacial fauna?' We nodded, quite at sea (was he going to suggest Polar Bears?).

'Well, *I* am bringing back – a GLACIER. I am reintroducing a Late-Glacial inhabitant. I *have* brought back a glacier, the beginnings of one, and here I am *conserving* it. I know something about glaciers, I worked with them long enough in Canada and Alaska. *This*', he stamped vigorously on the snow, 'is a glacier. Now' – he stared fixedly at us – 'I am being confidential, I don't want it blabbed around, encouraging' – he stared at us one by one – 'fools here to poke and prod and break up the surface. The first few years of a glacier's life are critical. Disturbed, it never develops, fades away. Mind you, once settled in, it makes its own climate, doesn't need cosseting like this' – he waved at truck and tractors – 'keeps on growing, cooling things down. Positive feedback.' He took out his pipe again, a little warmed by our astonishment. He struck matches, the flames quivered.

He was fiercely possessive of his glacier. Any suggestion that it might merely be an occasionally perennial snowfield like that in Garbh Choire Mòr provoked wrath. He flung the last match away.

'I've piled enough depth now for the bottom to be pressed to ice. It's begun to FLOW. A whole metre forward this last year – look how those sticks have moved. Internal strains developing too – subsurface cracks and incipient crevasses – found 'em by sonics and lasers. Yes, it's a glacier right enough – though for Final Popular Proof', he added scornfully, 'we'll need OPEN crevasses, I suppose.' He glared at us.

Alas, we failed to disguise our doubts sufficiently. He plucked out his pipe, spun round, waved dismissively and marched off to a rusty Land Rover. So much for the hospitality of an old friend.

'A hard man, Archie, a difficult man,' observed the Doctor, lighting up now the competition had gone. 'But a wonderful depth of cold compressed motivation. He'd wear down any opposition. Just keeps pressing on.'

We strolled over his acre or so of proto-glacier. If only it *were* a glacier; the first for 8000-odd years. We began to thrill. One man alone, fighting Global Warming. Reconstituting his own glacier. A world-wide recession of them, but not here. Private enterprise indeed.

We inspected the outfall, a mini-snout, its progress being measured weekly with the latest apparatus by that dour-faced Archie, kneeling in the patched-up breeks of a visionary millionaire. Soon, perhaps it would spill over and down the burnside, through the old gap its predecessor had made, re-enter its rightful glen, grunting and shoving aside with piggy delight turf and trees, piling up boulders, heaving itself into great blue and white icefalls between scoured cliffs – making wonderful climbing.... It would chill all its fellows into resurrection: the A9 would run a gauntlet, fanged and grinning above you. And here we were at the *start* of all this!

We sighed and gazed around at the resolutely unglaciated landscape.

Ah, well. Then – a *crack*. The Apprentice had disappeared. He was not there when we turned in alarm. Just a hole. And a furious voice from below.

He had fallen through the crust. Was jammed about five feet down in a baby dimple that hugged him lovingly – and our rucksack and spare line.

'A real crev...' gasped the Doctor, stepping back: and vanishing likewise.

I made for the side and sank slowly; my last view was of a couple of grinning tractor men and a grimly complacent pipe.

We were cold down there in the pale blue; damnably cold. But we needn't do a Joe Simpson: it was an infant catastrophe, the glacier was just learning: not deep – we were all unhurt and loudly demanding a rope.

Archie took his time. He needed photographic proof, he explained, and samples of the failed crust before it was messed up by things like rescue operations. Great probes and instruments with winking lights purred about us unfeelingly, intent on their personal business. Things like huge dentists' drills – quite on their own – operated small toothy saws, trepanning the ice alarmingly near our immobilised heads. We supposed it was really very necessary – after all, this glacier was on a Life Support System.

Eventually, all was completed and they decided to haul us out – by floodlight. We stood grey, frozen and shivering on the heather as the men jovially slapped back our circulation. We stared at the equipment still trundling up and down the cables from the laboratories twinkling below. Like a dream. We were speechless. And Archie?

Archie was as pleased as ever he allowed himself to be. As pleased as if he'd reintroduced bears and they'd eaten someone. His glacier felt at home, had asserted its place in the Late-Glacial biosphere. He twinkled icily beneath the stars. He crackled orders. Cameras still flashed: holes, footsteps and broken-up surface were recorded.

Archie in fact exuded a kind of Polar bonhomie. Although we had messed up his – Scotland's – glacier inexcusably, we *had* provided Final Popular Proof, and our hungry (and thirsty) expectations rose, not to mention hopes of a roaring wood fire.

Yes, he had thawed; he took us down in the Land Rover, the gaffer driving, and remarked how cold and hungry we must be.

Ah! – we stopped at the Big House (dark and shuttered). Archie got out. 'You'll be mighty glad, I'm sure, of a good meal right now.' Splendid man! We agreed heartily and half-rose in our seats. 'Now they do a fine one at a little place in Dalwhinnie,' he went on, describing a ghastly refrigerator we'd suffered in before, 'It's rather late, but just mention my name and they'll likely open for you. It's quite cheap, too. Well; good to have met you. And thanks for the Subsurface Monitoring,' he added. 'Quite useful, in fact.' Slammed the door, waved, and went.

The gaffer dropped us at the car. He seemed damnably amused about something. We climbed stiffly into cold seats.

'A hard man, Archie,' the Doctor reaffirmed, as we drove off to pie, chips and a gas fire at Pitlochry, 'Mean as hell: but if anyone can encourage a glacier, it's him....'

# WITCH'S SABBATH

It was a most extraordinary chain of coincidences. It began, like much else, in the back bar of Daddy McKay's. After that first extraordinary coincidence, others followed, as the Doctor said, 'Exponentially, like Evolution.' Yet – like Evolution – no more (of course) than a series of quite random occurrences; born of climate, topography and our by then disordered imagination. No Malicious Intent behind it. None whatever. We are quite sure now. But we are still careful where we go at that time of year.

We had been studying the map at our table by the fire. We had settled Saturday's campsite high in Coire ____ : no, I shall not name it, nobody shall be lured there – and we sat back. The Doctor called for another round, put away his spectacles and lit his pipe. Peace. Puff. We gazed about us. The other end of the room was a scrummage of Rugby overflows from the front bar. Some kind of pre-season Border Sevens reunion. Thumpings and singing.

Our whiskies arrived, were set out, and the Doctor – as so often – had paid and was stuffing his wallet in the back of his breeks when a voice from above exclaimed:

'So ye're gaun tae Coire ____ ?'

A great square forefinger, of good eye-gouging elasticity, stubbed down on our map, bang on the campsite. We looked up, astonished.

The voice belonged – just – to a huge barn-shouldered, micro-eared, screw-nosed individual clutching unsteadily a fistful of foam. It continued, much awash.

'Ah've been there as well. Ah've climbed on thae cliffs. When Ah wis climbin, ken. KEN?'

We smiled indulgently; but had hoped for virgin ground....

'Niver again. Pit me aff climbin fer guid.'

We raised eyebrows. They rose still further when, with much elliptical swaying about us, our informant explained they tried one good line for two whole days.

' – An couldna make it!' His orbit was fairly regular and through a sort of Doppler effect we gathered that everything had gone wrong on that climb. Stonefall, stonefall – aye, *up* as well as down.

'Ah cannae tell ye the hauf o whit went on.' Anyway, they did not succeed. But they gave the climb a name, nevertheless.

'We did that. We caad it' – screwing his eyes – '...*Poltergeist!*'

This last, most unexpected, word was delivered with remarkable skill, considering his condition; though the sibilant bespattered our map. The Doctor hastily wiped and refolded it, but our visitor, relaxing his concentration, lurched heavily and drenched him with Eighty Shilling Ale or suchlike. Some contaminated the whisky, and a dollop landed in his pipe. Steam, bubbling, indignation.

Answering ribald summonses from his own table, our acquaintance staggered away, finding time and equilibrium to pause and bellow back:

'It's no a right place at aa!'

Though not as put out as the Doctor's pipe, we were taken aback.

'At least, they didn't climb anything – we should make some brand-new routes,' the Doctor reassured us, swabbing his bowl with a strip of *Evening News*. 'But what a remarkable coincidence his being here to-night.' The first, alas, of many, as I have suggested.

Before we managed up, several Saturdays had passed, and soothed apprehensions. The low sun gilded luminous late October colours; a good season for Coire _____ which, unusually, was neither stalked nor forested. We had glimpsed its unrecorded crags from a neighbouring hill that summer.

A grassy track led there, and we parked at its beginning, by an ancient cottage. We knocked at the door.

No answer.

Then an old woman appeared on the road behind, lugging a large black plastic bag.

'That'll be her – been out for messages,' cried the Doctor. The Apprentice ran to help with the bag. His knees buckled under it. We stepped aside.

She opened the door. The Apprentice relinquished his burden, like a ton of rocks. A cat emerged from within and rubbed against the old girl's rumpled black stockings. The Doctor offered a conciliatory finger; but hastily withdrew as the creature arched back and spat eyes.

The old lady cackled. Her own eyes were black diamonds, dramatically crossed. It was difficult to look at her. Occasionally both eyes agreed to stare at you together, and this was even more off-putting. A regular witch.

We hoped our car would not be in the way.

'Na, na.'

We explained where we were going, what we hoped to do.

She cackled again, booted the cat indoors, effortlessly lifted the bag and fixed us with sudden binocular vision.

'Yon's no a place to go campin in.'

Shook head, went inside, snibbed the door. That was that.

'Funny old girl. But to everyone here, mountains are dangerous,' smiled the Doctor, magnanimously.

We splashed up the track, the Apprentice rubbing his biceps – 'Almost half a bloody hundredweight, those messages. Tough old bird. Must have got a bus, or a hitch.' The nearest shop was unimaginable miles away, the last bus in 1953. 'Broomstick,' explained the Doctor.

We camped in the Coire, on its only bit of green, bisected by a burn and facing grey soaring cliffs. A perfect evening, long clear shadows, midgeless. After pitching the tent we wandered up to look. One line was immediately evident, a rib, the only unbroken route. Like all such crags, distance lent the sole enchantment (or so we thought...). The rib was hardly even sporting, but should at least be virgin.

Which reminded us of the curious episode at Daddy McKay's. We laughed, maybe over-heartily; for dusk was falling; and raced down to the tent.

The Doctor halted, puzzled.

'Lord, it's the other side of the burn. Don't remember crossing any water.'

None of us did. But there it stood, neatly pitched, primus outside, just as we'd left it. Both banks of the burn looked identical. Easy to mistake. But we *did* think.... No matter. These things happen.

The Apprentice and I laid out bags and the Doctor began cooking. The primus refused to light. Several times. Such a reliable one, too. Moreover, both prickers snapped their whiskers. Odd. He swore continuously, in frustration.

Rain arrived. But even inside, the stove withstood oaths and entreaties. We supped on bread and cold spam, drank cold burn water. Everything was cold. We pulled bags up to shoulders and sipped the Doctor's whisky, perhaps too often. (He had resisted offering it to the primus – 'One can go too far.')

But his pipe, even, would not light. The bowl was soaked, the water-proof pouch was soaked; and now the remaining matches had dissolved to paste. The Doctor's jaw dropped at this chain of disasters.

'Well, I'm damned!'

The response to this unwise assertion, or admission, was remarkably prompt. A fearsome flash through the fabric; and an emphatic disapprobation of thunder, rock to rock, summit to summit. Our headlamp went out. Rain pelted.

In the suitably Faustian silence and dark that followed, we remained speechless.

'Mains fused,' remarked the Doctor at last, wearily. He retired beneath his bag. We did likewise. Sometimes, ye cannae win.

We were physically uncomfortable, also. A sharp stone jabbed my shoulder-blades wherever I lay, although we had tooth-combed the turf before pitching. But we must have slept, for we were woken several times. Once by a thing, or things, trampling about outside. 'Sheep,' mumbled the Doctor. Guys twanged. Heavy breathing. Stomp, stomp, twang. The Apprentice, wroth, shone his torch through the door.

Nothing, of course, there. 'We've frightened it off, anyway.' Then *his* light went out. Just as well, for the sudden illumination of a horny head, however placidly ruminant, might have upset us by then. Trying to replace the bulb with a spare, the Apprentice lost both. He sank back, beyond care. Then yelped. Something was poking his back. I felt beneath me. He had got my stone. 'Continental drift,' yawned the Doctor, as he turned over.

At first rim of dawn I woke to distant music and singing. I crawled out: a cool clear half-light, untenanted. My disturbed companions were not enthralled by the serenade. 'That old wifie's radio', growled the Apprentice, 'coming up on the wind.' The Doctor favoured burn water across pebbles. 'Often heard it like that. Mass in D Major, MacGregor's Lament, Hibs *versus* Hearts. Or it could be some ramshammy in that fairy mound by the track.'

We did not sleep any more. While the Apprentice tried blowing the kiss of life into the primus, from matches dried in his hair, we re-told odd happenings we'd met elsewhere in the Magic West. The Doctor sucked his empty pipe and recounted the jumping about of tables and chairs in two houses in North Uist, and the minister's importing a Priest from the southern island to tranquillize them – Rome enjoying closer relations with the Devil; no, *he* hadn't been at that particular country dance, but his friend, his friend certainly had. Interruptedly – for my stone had returned – I described footsteps up and down the stairs at Steall Hut; which the Doctor explained as a tap dripping. The Apprentice remembered a fairy – 'fine-looking girl, a bit thin, but smashing legs' – he'd encountered by the loch at Quinag; when he'd grabbed his camera, she'd gone. 'Just as well for you,' remarked the Doctor, warned by the misadventures in 1692 of the Rev. Robert Kirk, M.A. 'Did she have wings? If so, she wasn't local; our fairies don't have wings. She'd be an English visitor, flown up.' The Apprentice confessed it wasn't wings he'd been thinking about just then.

After a cold breakfast we set off for the crag, meticulously checking rope and the little equipment we thought necessary. 'Bring a few pegs: they don't like iron,' advised the Doctor. His jocularity jarred at that hour.

We found no other excuse for pitons. The route was at most a V.D. and surprisingly sound. But mist thickened, and stones – as our beery prophet had foretold – began to trickle down the gullies either side; fortunately still obeying the laws of gravity.

Then, out of the mist above, a cackling; like the old wifie's, but harder, as of bones rattling. 'Tough old bird,' quoted the Doctor, with mirth, but notably studious of his holds. A fearful yell; followed by stones and earth, and a great beating of air. Mouths dried. Our leader paused.

A black shape above. Flat head, great beak. Huge wings. Flap, flap. Cackle. Rattle.

'A bloody raven,' gasped the relieved Apprentice, 'Gerrout, you ___!' He flung bits of mountain. 'Careful,' cried the Doctor....

Words were lost in a sudden wind that roared up – yes, up – the gullies, carrying grass, heather, sand and small stones. Anoraks billowed about our heads, we were belted hard on the backside by pebbles; they ricochetted about us – we drew hoods tight. Rain followed. The raven guffawed.

'Up-draught: atmospherics,' bellowed the Doctor above the din. 'We're near the top, anyway,' and he decamped hurriedly to the left. Still roped – no precautions seemed excessive that day – we scrambled towards the summit, the Apprentice clutching, I noticed, a piton with religious fervour.

We never found the top in the mist. Our compass shared the atmospheric excitement; it cavorted like Uist furniture. We gained a distinct impression of not being at all wanted; and descended the east rim of the corrie into comparative shelter and considerable relief. As we coiled our rope, the Doctor was explaining how the configuration of Coire ___ must inevitably provoke such Aeolian excesses. 'No wonder those chaps called it Pol....' We all stopped.

But the three great ghostly shapes now blooming in the mist evoked no more response.

'Brocken Spectres,' sighed the Doctor. He waved an exhausted arm.

A spectral arm was raised in reply. 'Of course, that's what the Grey Man of MacDhui is,' he added, restored by demonstration, 'Curious how both Collie *and* Kellas – a much more reliable chap – got all het up and fled. Just atmos...

At this point the third Spectre, which was myself, raised its arm. Unfortunately, I had both mine folded in front of me. Then they all, with waving limbs, billowed towards us.

'Atmos...pherics,' gasped the Doctor as we belted down, leaping rocks, galloping bogs. I glanced back. The three Spectres had been replaced by a large Dog bounding after us. It was gaining, we felt its breath, heard its thump of paws, a long howl.... I remember crying 'Help!' and the hoarse croaks of my companions were no less urgent.

Then suddenly we burst into sunlight, and into an astonished couple of walkers on the track.

They were elderly, respectable, tweed- and green-jacketed, and most taken aback. We stumbled to a halt, sobbing and gasping, the Apprentice mouthing 'Dog, dog,' as he tripped over a tussock and literally fell into the arms of the lady.

'There, there,' she said, holding him up, 'you shouldn't be so upset. He's quite harmless; a *dear*, really. Jeremy, Jeremy,' she called. A black Labrador panted up and jumped about and licked the unhappy purple-faced Apprentice. 'Look, he's making friends. Jeremy, what *have* you been doing to frighten this poor young man?'

They were very kind. We parted with thanks, and feeble explanations. To reassemble himself, the Doctor extolled to us the smart rainproof jacket of the pink old gentleman – who was the very picture of some retired General or Brigadier. 'Grenfell – the sort of cloth you could buy before the war; wears for ever, not like this terylene trash. Wonder how he gets it nowadays?' But we had been shaken.

During our limp back to camp, the Doctor valiantly attributed everything to Atmospherics: wind and mist. 'But a hell of a fright', he admitted, 'at the time.' We could no longer throw stones (throw stones!) at Collie and Kellas.

When we reached the site, no tent. But there it was – on the other side of the burn again. We said nothing. Atmospherics. Packing up, the Apprentice and I searched for our wandering stone. The turf proved innocent, everywhere. We decided to forget that, too.

Just before the car, a sudden owl terrified us. Then the Doctor knocked on the cottage door, to thank the old wifie. No reply. Utter desertion. 'Gone shopping for another half-hundredweight of porridge oats,' muttered the Apprentice, heaving his rucksack into the boot.

Coire ⸻ had not quite finished with us. The old Mercedes itself was bewitched. It would not start. The Doctor fumbled under the bonnet. Unwisely he had left the key switched on and the gear in, and must have touched some nerve, for with a roar the great beast leapt into the ditch.

The crofter who eventually – he lived two miles away and it was the Sabbath – tractored us out was not forthcoming about Coire ⸻ , and we did not press him. We asked him, though, to convey our thanks to the old lady who, we explained, was not in.

'Effie MacFarlane? The Cailleach Dhubh? She's no been in these three month, she's with her son ten mile this side o Inverness.' We blenched. 'But, yess, he has been visiting his daughter down there at the hotel some Saturdays, mebbe he wass giving her a lift up for the day.' We brightened. 'Or mebbe not: she's no very *communicative*; and mebbe jist as well....' he added, darkly.

The Doctor delicately proffered recompense for the tow-out. Our rescuer restarted his engine. 'No, no, I would not be doing it at *all* on a day such as this', (it was, you'll remember, the Sabbath) 'but for a traveller in distress.' He leant down and eyed us keenly. 'But what were you *doing* up there in the Coire, on a day such as this? It wass not for *pleesure?*'

'No, no,' we fervently assured him. 'Examining rocks,' volunteered the Doctor.

'Geologists, mebbe?'

We did not disagree. 'Business, well, business is no perhaps the same as pleesure on a day such as this: but, yess, it iss a dangerous place, Coire ———, a very dangerous place.'

'Oh, not if you're used to doing what we do,' laughed the Doctor. 'Geologising,' he added hastily.

The crofter stopped his engine, turned sideways in his seat, laid his hands on his knees and gazed down seriously upon us.

'It wass before the war, it wass this time of year, it wass this day of the week, there wass two people from the hotel went up this very track to the Coire, a colonel or general it wass, and his lady. And' – pause – 'they never came back.'

'Never came back?' We thought of hotel bills and Captain Rawlings' prudent decampment at Balqueenie.

'Never came back.' The crofter raised his head and stared into distance. 'There iss rocks and bogs up there, and there wass search parties for weeks but – nothing wass found.'

'So they've not been seen since,' said the Doctor, amused; 'Very sad.'

'Oh, they have been *seen* often enough.' The crofter laughed, and our flesh began to creep. 'That iss the trouble. All three of them.'

'Three?'

'Yess; they had a dog.' Our flesh crept further; as far, in fact, as it could.

'A... a black dog?'

'Very likely a black dog. People have heard it *howling*.'

'Did the gentleman have a white moustache?' croaked the Doctor.

'Very likely a white moustache, but: *I* do not know. *I* have not seen them myself. *I* do not go up there. It iss a dangerous place. Especially on a day such as this.'

He swung round and restarted the engine.

'What was the dog's name?' shouted the Doctor, hoarsely.

'I do not know.' He slipped into gear, he leant down to us as he

jerked off. It may have been a smile, or concentration on his clutch –
'But Effie would know. *She* would be knowing.'

He saluted gravely and puttered away in blue smoke.

No one wished to speak first. The Doctor, after thinking, no doubt,
about pre-war Grenfell cloth, announced briskly: 'We can't stand here,
it's getting dark. Jeremy and his friends may come back this way, they
may take the long way round to the hotel – or they may not come back.
It's no concern of ours. Dozens of generals at the hotel, I dare say. More
than enough to make up any – er – deficiency.' We saw his point, and
climbed in.

'Probably,' he declared, driving off and reaching out to wipe the last
of the ditch from the windscreen, 'in fact, certainly, it's all very simple.
A chain of coincidences; extraordinary, but nothing more – blast!!'

A cat, a black cat, *the* cat, had leapt from the dyke and under our
front wheels. There was a bang and a bump. We stopped and jumped
out. Of all the...

Yet, there was no cat. Or pieces of cat. Only the song of birds – not
owls – the gentle autumn breeze, the bliss of early evening about us.
Coire _____ smiled grimly in its shadow.

We were relieved. 'A wee innocent beastie,' burbled the Apprentice,
demoralised, or moralised, by the day. He was cut short by violent
oaths from the Doctor.

'Flat, bloody flat. The front tyre's burst. Burst. And a new one last
week. At *that* price....'

We arrived home very late. There had been a further coincidence or
two. Almost an hour later, just before Inverness, a crowd. Torches. We
stopped. Police. 'A doctor here?' He jumped out, disappeared. We ate
crisps.

Ambulance, lights flashing. Amid thanks and handclasps, he climbed
in again.

'What was it?'

He appeared lost in thought. 'An old lady. Knocked down by a car
about an hour ago – about when we ran over the cat.... Just found. Only
broke an ankle. She'll get over it.' He turned round to us – at 60 m.p.h.
on the Kessock bridge – and gleamed.

'She's a tough old bird.'

No, he did not ask Effie if she'd been up the day before. No, he did not ask the dog's name. No, he did not even ask if she *was* Effie. It was dark and we'd all had enough for one weekend. And no, we never enquired further. Corries can be dangerous places, and West Highlanders, particularly on the Sabbath, can display a black sense of humour. Let it remain a tale to be told by torchlight, like the Steall staircase, the mobile homes of Uist, the Apprentice's fairy. Or – wherever should we be?

However, one last coincidence. No bad thing to be late, the Doctor assured us. His wife had given the neighbours' children a Party the night before, it would have taken till now to clean up, it had been a 'Do you know,' (here he turned round again, at 80 m.p.h. on that dreadful Dalwhinnie straight) ' – a Hallowe'en Party'.

So there was a rational explanation, after all.

# JUST OVER 20

This tale is an Extra. Tagged on. Like what it describes.

Now, we are wary of Beginners. They usually End by embarrassing us. Especially the young ones, whom you can't curse satisfactorily. Previous examples will doubtless be recalled.

We therefore uncooperatively resist requests to Take Up Youngsters Who Are Interested. Having been so often Let Down.

However, last spring we were persuaded, by no less experienced a practitioner at the Bar than Daddy McKay, to take an example of new blood (as he put it) up with us the next Sunday on some easy snow-plod. The weather was forecast fine. Daddy himself was, of course, obliging a friend (they always are) and didn't know the applicant (they never do). We pointedly refused – even after so many Thursday nights of his discreet ethanolic dispensations – to oblige our Host, if the victim he allotted us was juvenile. So Daddy got on to the phone behind the bottles. Through a foam of clatter, gurgle and banging we were assured that no self-satisfied adolescent or infant prodigy was involved.

Indeed, Daddy called across to us: 'Seems to be 20 at least!' Then, to his phone, 'What, just over 20?'; to us again, '21 by Sunday, in fact! That's enough, eh? That should satisfy you!' 'What sex?' the Apprentice bawled back, becoming more interested. But the noise was frightful. Daddy waggled the phone, shook his head, and put it down. He forced his way over to us. 'Line's terrible. Can't tell you just now – you'll have to find out on Sunday....' A little joke; he smiled and rubbed his hands.

What could we do? Refusal would deeply disappoint. Just after his (or her) birthday, too. That weekend, then, we awaited our Fourth Person in the car park below Lochnagar. The name of this lamb who was to look out for us was – improbably – Smith. Francis (or -es) Smith. We kept to the outside of the burgeoning throng, and tried to look as like ourselves as we could.

Then a car drove up, perilously close, and a figure jumped out and clasped our hands damply. We flinched. Our fears were confirmed. Male, enthusiastic; but, at least, certainly over 20. 'Yes, Smith's the

name.' He blinked eagerly at us in turn. 'Francis Smith?' 'No, Freddie....'
Ah, some misunderstanding on the phone. That noise! No, no, Frankie
would be here in a moment....

Fr... Two of 'em? The other figure climbed out, a plump and accosting
character. Frankie Smith. We submitted, numbly.

Another car sloshed up. Five people, of both sexes – or, rather, of
either sex, or each sex – you know what I mean, leapt out, in eye-
splitting anoraks and – were introduced. 'So good of you.'

'But Mr McKay said.... We thought....' The Doctor spluttered;
helpless. The Smiths and others regarded us kindly. Then a minibus
drew alongside, tooted, and a whole mob tumbled out of its rustily
sliding doors....

An F. Smith began introductions. We cut him short. We began to
count. It began to dawn. Just over 20. Not years. People. Just over 20
*people*.... 21, in fact; this Sunday.

It was no use. We couldn't disappoint them. And, true, there were no
sprogs or suspicions of sprogs. It seemed (so far) good weather and
they were all so excited. Being assured no more would arrive, we
checked their boots and clothes – adequate. Axes... none. So we
shouldered all our full-lengths of rope and moved the expedition on to
the hill.

The snow was spring and the trail well broken. Axes not needed, for
once. The Doctor stalked in front, the Apprentice and I shepherded the
rear, for any byes. We answered questions. We smiled at jokes. We
were almost looking forward to remembering this trip. We were (almost)
remembering our own first mountain; almost remembering not
to be ashamed at having enjoyed that wonderful far-off day.

We reached the Top, as promised. Together with a few score others.
We identified, excusably rashly, all the peaks that became visible when
people chanced to move out of the way. But they (the peaks) were
vanishing one by one. Clouds had gathered and were lowering. *Splat;
splat.* The usual late spring blizzard was developing. A thrill ran through
our receptive charges. Real Excitement.

We acted promptly. Strung 'em all together on our combined ropes.
It was not easy, for similar garlands were being assembled around us.
Dozens of play groups. Like DNA.

Then the storm broke. We plunged off, the Doctor exuberantly gallant ahead, brandishing his axe, the Apprentice appropriately stern at the rear; myself, unroped, patrolling the flanks.

It was easy enough. The tracks were unmissable, even in the few metres' visibility. And all were tied on, nose to tail; no chance of any getting lost. I counted them several times, to make sure; the average came to 20.8 – statistically comforting. Someone, probably, was not quite all there; but several had looked that way, anyhow. The advantages of such a long string became evident: one end was always above, or below, any dubious stretch of topography, and could fairly accurately wag the rest of the dog back on to course. It was a doddle, and we felt rather pleased with ourselves. Our charges, naturally, were delighted, and kept stopping to tell me so, seriously discomposing those tied on to them before and behind. A shunting progress that frequently derailed the Doctor and finally uncoupled the Apprentice.

Just above the car park we left the cloud and, because bellies and backsides were understandably chafed by then, untied the kilometres of rope. We repeatedly counted the liberated: 23, 18, 26; but some had gambolled off, and so many passing goats had joined us, we hadn't the heart to persevere.

We shooed 'em down over simple slopes to the car park, and once there tried to sort them into the cars and the minibus. The motorists were easy enough in theory, for they were supposed to know each other, according to the Messrs Smith; but the minibus held a job lot of Rent-A-Ramble and Wish-A-Walk, who were too delighted with having gone up – and come down – to think about much else. So we had to try and line everybody up and count in real earnest.

This became difficult. Buses and cars roared and flashed, spun and smoked beside – between – us. Weather blasted across us. Other groups splashed through us, or adhered like glue; or bore away some of our own. Brownian Motion. We flew about and swore. The Doctor recalled (much later) the Magic Pigs of Cruachu, that no man could ever count – *when they were being numbered they would not stay; if anyone tried to number them, they would be gone....* We plunged as low as 14 at one time, and shook with apprehension; then the Apprentice pointed out that those from the cars were inside them, eating pieces. And once soared up to a giddy 36, when the Balloch and Dumbarton Girl Guides' Outdoor Activities included latching on to our left-hand end. One of the F.

Smiths gave us a list of names, but as the the top half had dissolved away, that was of little help (we did notice yet another Smith, F.).

Eventually the cars were satisfied and rolled off, bearing their seven. Now for the minibus. Every seat had to be occupied – the ultimate check. It was a hell of a job to get the jabbering sleet-dripping figures, vigorously changing clothes and shouting with mirth, to sit down for one moment; and then you usually included the driver or the anxiously bobbing Doctor by mistake. One old girl was lustily singing, with the voice of two, *The Back o Bennachie.* Fourteen. 14 plus 7 equals 21. At last.... We let them drive off. In the opposite direction to that much-serenaded mountain: home to Edinburgh.

Phew.... Never again, as so often said. Lucky this time, but.... Then: a long too-bright youth pushed up to us, wiping his sweaty prow.

'This Frankie Smith's lot? Fraid I'm late.'

We clutched him savagely. Where had he been? Been? Up Eagle Buttress, with some friends he'd seen as soon as he came off the bus that morning. Had a real good time. Fab. Was lent a pick, crampons, helmet an all. Better than a bloody snowplod, eh? And he laughed like granite and demanded his seat.

But we had counted (more or less) 21 on the rope and despatched 21 certainly off in the various vehicles....

Then a commotion behind us. Pitfoulie MRT; with its new fluorescently-plumaged (Discovery) Land Rover. Someone was missing. Had not come down. Couldn't be found at her bus.

Ignoring the indignation of our belated proselyte, we squeezed towards a bereaved minibus, stark with a vacant seat. Eck, the Pitfoulie leader, was thoughtfully sucking his pencil before a gesticulating driver; his radiophone squawked in the slush at his feet.

The Doctor sized things up. An Aberdeen minibus. Lots of real old weatherproof crumblies inside, aghast or asleep.

He grabbed the driver.

'Was she a big fat wifie in blue? Fond of singing?' ....